NUCLEAR GEOLOGY

NUCLEAR GEOLOGY

A Symposium on Nuclear Phenomena in the Earth Sciences

JOHN WILEY & SONS, INC., NEW YORK
CHAPMAN & HALL, LIMITED, LONDON

Library of Congress Catalog Card Number: 54–12809

Printed in the United States of America

CONTRIBUTORS

JOHN A. S. ADAMS *University of Wisconsin, Madison*
LOUIS H. AHRENS *The University, Oxford*
JAMES R. ARNOLD *University of Chicago*
KENNETH G. BELL *U. S. Geological Survey, Washington*
FRANCIS BIRCH *Harvard University, Cambridge*
S. H. U. BOWIE *Geological Survey of Great Britain, London*
FARRINGTON DANIELS *University of Wisconsin, Madison*
FRANCIS J. DAVIS *Oak Ridge National Laboratory*
HENRY FAUL *U. S. Geological Survey, Denver*
RICHARD FOSTER FLINT *Yale University, New Haven*
IRVING FRIEDMAN *U. S. Geological Survey, Washington*
HEINRICH D. HOLLAND *Princeton University*
PATRICK M. HURLEY *Massachusetts Institute of Technology, Cambridge*
DONALD HASKALL JOHNSON *U. S. Geological Survey, Denver*
FRIEDRICH F. KOCZY *Oceanografiska Institutet, Göteborg*
E. S. LARSEN, JR. *U. S. Geological Survey, Washington*
JOHN PUTNAM MARBLE *National Research Council, Washington*
HANS PETTERSSON *Oceanografiska Institutet, Göteborg*
GEORGE PHAIR *U. S. Geological Survey, Washington*
GEORGE R. TILTON *Carnegie Institution of Washington*
CHARLES WILLIAM TITTLE *Gulf Research and Development Company, Pittsburgh*
HARRY G. THODE *McMaster University, Hamilton*
HAROLD C. UREY *University of Chicago*
GERALD J. WASSERBURG *University of Chicago*
WALTER L. WHITEHEAD *Massachusetts Institute of Technology, Cambridge*
EDWARD J. ZELLER *University of Wisconsin, Madison*

Edited by HENRY FAUL

CONTENTS

This book is dedicated to people
who pick up rocks and stop to think

PREFACE

The volume in your hand is the result of an attempt to compile an authoritative text that would cover the rapidly expanding field of knowledge between nuclear physics and geology of the pick-and-hand-lens type. The principal purpose of this book is to introduce the graduate student and the practicing professional geologist to a new approach to some questions of the Earth. It is hoped that both will find information in these pages that will be of use to them in the solution of problems of their particular interest, perhaps by methods they have never tried before.

The book begins with a simple introduction to nuclear physics, actually little more than an animated glossary, followed by an outline of the more important techniques. The occurrence of radioactive elements in rocks and oceans is discussed, and thermal, physical, and chemical effects of radioactivity are considered. One chapter outlines the nuclear methods of geophysical exploration and well logging, and another, a fairly long one, delves in some detail into techniques and results of absolute age determination. The last chapter discusses the ultimate in geologic problems, the origin of the Earth.

The geology of stable isotopes is mentioned only in passing, not because the subject does not belong in the realm of nuclear geology, but because it is fully covered in two forthcoming volumes, *Isotope Geology* by Rankama, and *The Geochemistry of Nuclear Species* by Suess, Craig, and Urey.

The study of nuclear phenomena in geologic settings proceeds at an ever increasing pace, and one man could scarcely hope to be able to summarize the results. Of necessity, therefore, the symposium form has been chosen. Such an approach does not provide uniformity of view, coverage, and style, but it has the enormous advantage of that intangible freshness and clarity which are preserved only in first-hand accounts. There is no substitute for the eyewitness' story.

The criticism will be made, no doubt, that the present work does not have sufficient scope and that all sides of controversial questions are not fully covered. The editor is aware of these shortcomings. As an apology to the reader and in reply to the critics, a small statistic may be helpful. Of the 53 scientists invited to contribute to *Nuclear Geology,* 34 agreed to do so, but only 26 actually came through.

The authors range from Phair to Faul, and they express their own views. Their names appear on their respective Chapters and Sections, and the authorship of short contributions, where they are the work of one man, is acknowledged in footnotes. Several Sections do not bear the name of any one author. These parts, and Tables 9 and 9.1, were compiled from various sources, published and private, by a number of individuals. The editor is greatly indebted for assistance in this work. Particular thanks are due

Dr. L. Thomas Aldrich, Carnegie Institution of Washington
Dr. Ralph A. Alpher, Johns Hopkins University
Dr. Gordon L. Davis, Carnegie Institution of Washington
Prof. R. D. Evans, Massachusetts Institute of Technology
Dr. R. M. Farquhar, University of Toronto
David Gottfried, U. S. Geological Survey, Washington
Prof. F. G. Houtermans, Universität Bern
Dr. Claire C. Patterson, California Institute of Technology
Vasco C. Rhoden, U. S. Geological Survey, Denver
Dr. Leonard B. Riley, U. S. Geological Survey, Denver
Abraham Rosenzweig, University of Minnesota
Dr. R. D. Russell, University of Toronto
Arthur Y. Sakakura, U. S. Geological Survey, Denver
Thomas W. Stern, U. S. Geological Survey, Washington
Lorin R. Stieff, U. S. Geological Survey, Washington

as well as some of the authors whose names appear at the front of the book.

The editor takes full responsibility for the selection and arrangement of topics. Throughout, he has made an effort to avoid undue repetition and to maintain some semblance of a train of thought. Speculation was not hindered, but material offered as fact was scrutinized. In this task, the editor was aided immeasurably by many highly qualified anonymous reviewers.

Although this work is not intended as a textbook, it was circulated in a preliminary multigraphed edition and twice used as an outline for accelerated graduate-level courses within the Geological Survey. The classes were large—about 50 in the first course and about 100 in the second. Many errors of coverage and presentation were corrected by the students in these courses. Countless other mistakes, no doubt, remain.

The editor acknowledges the support of the U. S. Geological Survey during the preparation of the manuscript. Labor on this book was contributed, and the waiver of all royalties is reflected in the low price of the finished work.

The editor is indebted to Mrs. Carolyn Lindberg, Mrs. Virginia McGivern, and Mrs. Evelyn Nottingham for the patience and good nature with which they faced the mountain of miscellaneous work that always comes with undertakings such as this one. The invaluable assistance of the Denver Branch of the Geological Survey Library is gratefully acknowledged. Particular thanks are due Mrs. Isabel Canney, Mr. I. P. Shultz, and Miss Elizabeth Wellshear. One glance at the reference listing at the end of the book will give a measure of the magnitude of their contribution.

The sketch of the galloping prospector is by William Sanderson of Denver.

H. F.

Strasbourg
October, 1954

HISTORICAL INTRODUCTION

JOHN PUTNAM MARBLE *

The geological applications of nuclear science start in the days before natural radioactivity was known to be a nuclear property. In 1896 Henri Becquerel made his original discovery that a photographic plate is blackened by uranium salts even if they are not in direct optical contact with the emulsion. (Thirty years earlier, Niepce de Saint-Victor (1867) apparently failed to realize that he was not dealing with an ordinary photographic effect when he observed the same phenomenon.) Soon after Becquerel's first report to the Académie des Sciences, he found that uranium-bearing minerals produced the same type of effect. The exact date of this first mineral autoradiograph is difficult to confirm, but this pioneer application of radioactivity to mineralogy was presumably also made in 1896 (Curie, 1910).

In September, 1898, M. and P. Curie, through the French ambassador to Austria, made their classic request for a quantity of residues from the uranium extraction plant at Joachimsthal, and in November, 1898, the material was shipped. Insignificant as it seemed to the great scientists of the day, the Curies' request did not go unnoticed in Austria. The investigators at the Vienna Academy of Sciences began their systematic study of radioactivity in ores, minerals, rocks, and spring waters, a research which continues to this day. A very readable account of this work is given by the last survivor of that pioneer group, the late Stefan Meyer (1950).

The activity of thorium was announced independently by Mme. Curie and by C. G. Schmidt in 1898 (Rutherford and Soddy, 1902). The discovery of this curious property in a second element started

* Chairman, Committee on Measurement of Geologic Time, National Research Council, Washington 25, D. C.

investigations in many laboratories to see whether other elements also were radioactive. J. J. Thomson (1905) found that rubidium was radioactive; Campbell and Wood (1906) confirmed this, and showed that potassium also was active. The discovery of the alpha-activity of samarium came much later (Curie and Joliot, 1934; Mader, 1934), and further definite identifications of radioactive species awaited the development of modern techniques and the growth of nuclear theory. Beta-activity now has been demonstrated for isotopes of neodymium, lutecium, and rhenium and is suspected in a few other elements. All these activities are very weak (as is that of samarium) and possess, at present, little geologic interest. Needless to say, during the course of years many false findings, both as to type of activity, and parent and daughter element, have cumbered the literature, together with the retractions or corrections connected therewith. They need not be reviewed here.

When radioactivity had been discovered, the next problem was "what shall we do with it?" Apart from the therapeutic and industrial applications, two fields were thoroughly investigated in the early days. Both proved to be of considerable geologic importance. The first was the nature of the activity, its course, and its end product. The disintegration theory was first advanced in 1902 by Rutherford and Soddy, and, in 1904, Boltwood showed that the ratio of uranium to radium was constant in most old uranium minerals. Later he announced that lead was the stable end product of the radioactive decay of uranium and thorium (Boltwood, 1905; 1907). His views were based upon the meticulous chemical analyses of uraninite, performed by Hillebrand fifteen years earlier (1890, 1891). The names of Soddy, Ramsay, Rutherford, and Hahn are associated with the ultimate working out of the decay series and the identification of the daughter products of uranium and thorium. The differential equations of radioactive series decay were solved by Bateman (1910). It is interesting to note that almost all workers in the field were young people. More than 10 years went by before the most far seeing of the established scientists began to realize the significance of Becquerel's fogged plate.

The second field of study was concerned with the heat that is evolved in the process of radioactive decay, for it was soon found that radioactivity was an exothermic process. Rutherford and McClung (1900) calculated the heat equivalent of the ionization from the radioactivity of uranium, radium, and thorium. Curie and Laborde (1903) found that a sample of radium was always warmer than its surroundings. John Joly published the first important paper on the radioactive heat of the earth, using the scanty data then available. He was followed by Lord Rayleigh (then R. J. Strutt, 1906) who made the first careful quantitative measurements of the radium content of rocks and minerals and performed the first full calculations of the heat produced by the decay thereof. His results are cited in Tables 9.2.1 and 9.2.2. Today, almost fifty years later, the radium values are still reasonably good. In 1909, Joly did the first similar work on thorium.

A very large proportion of the work done in these early years on the distribution of radioactivity in natural substances and on the geologic effects of this activity we owe to Joly. In 1907 he first showed that the nucleus of the pleochroic haloes in rocks was a radioactive mineral. In 1908 he published the first paper on the radium content of sea water and followed this with the study of the radium content of deep-sea deposits. Much of his work was first published in his historically important book *Radioactivity and Geology* (1909). This book includes his pioneer work on the radioactive series represented in pleochroic haloes; on the effect of the radioactivity of rocks on temperature gradients, based on measurements made in Swiss tunnels; the first general statement as to the possibility that radioactivity may be the source of heat for mountain-building processes; and his work with H. H. Poole on the heat given off by pitchblende. In many respects, the present volume is a successor of Joly's book.

Radioactivity and its products in the air and other natural gases also received early study. Strutt (1896, 1897) showed the presence of helium in the hot springs at Bath, England, but did not at that time suspect that it was an end product of radioactive decay. Elster and Geitel (1901; 1902*a*, *b*) showed the presence of radioactivity in the air. Bumstead and Wheeler (1904) first demonstrated the presence of the gaseous products of the thorium series in air. In 1905, Strutt announced that helium also was emitted during the decay of thorium, and this result was shortly confirmed by Soddy (1908). Cady and McFarland (1907) first reported the presence of helium in natural gas.

Almost from the beginnings of geological thought students of the earth have endeavored to devise a method for the measurement of the absolute age of rocks and the earth as a whole. A large number of diverse approaches led to a large number of diverse results. Nineteenth-century geologists differed widely in their opinions. They could be classed in three groups: the uniformitarians, led by Lyell, believed that the age of the earth was essentially infinite; a more moderate group, influenced largely by Darwin, held that the age of the earth was several hundred million years; but the revolutionists, under the leadership of Lord Kelvin, had the shortest and most accurate estimate, 24 million years (King, 1893) established on the basis of erroneous heat-loss calculations. The higher estimates were roundly attacked by Lord Kelvin in his famous address, *The Age of the Earth* (1899), and it was the confident tone of this address which provoked Chamberlin's comment quoted here at the head of Chapter 9.

Rutherford (1906) made the first attempt to measure absolute geologic ages of minerals by the helium/uranium ratio. We now know that, owing to lack of knowledge of the fundamental problems of the helium method, the results were not accurate, but they indicated the incorrectness of all the earlier calculations of the age of the earth.

The first study of the radium content of meteorites was made by Strutt (1906). He also investigated native terrestrial iron, but, because of the small amount of activity in such materials and the consequent analytical difficulties, little more was done for many years until Paneth and his colleagues started their studies in the twenties.

The concept of isotopes was set forth by Soddy (1914), based on the pioneer work of Boltwood (1907), who separated thorium^{230} (ionium) and showed its chemical identity with thorium, in spite of the difference of atomic weight. This had been confirmed by Marckwald and Keetman in 1910 (Knopf et al., 1931, p. 139); and Hahn showed that thorium^{228} (radiothorium) was chemically identical with both of the two other isotopes (see Hahn, 1950).

This brief sketch outlines the high spots of the heroic age of natural radioactivity. For some years the data continued to accumulate, but the work was not done primarily from the geologic angle. In 1923, at the suggestion of the late Andrew Lawson, the National Research Council of the United States established its *Committee on the Measurement of Geologic Time by Atomic Disintegration* under the chairmanship of the late A. C. Lane. Its first report was issued April 26, 1924. This group, with changes in membership, but with A. C. Lane at the helm until shortly before his death in 1946, pursued the various available radiometric and chemical methods in their various geologic implications, striving for the cooperation of geologists, physicists, and chemists in the attack on the problems of the earth. The interested reader may consult the annual *Reports* of this Committee (National Research Council, 1924 to date).

At about the same time, the National Research Council established a joint committee on the physics of the Earth. In our field they produced two important publications: *Radioactivity* by A. F. Kovarik and L. W. McKeehan (1925, revised 1929) and *The Age of the Earth* by A. Knopf, C. Schuchert, A. F. Kovarik, A. Holmes, and E. W. Brown (1931). Virtually all work up to the date of publication is included in the bibliographies of these well-known works. Accordingly it will not be detailed here.

To conclude this opening statement, a few papers of more recent years, which the writer considers important, will be noted in chronological order:

Joly in 1923 improved the precision and widened the application of the study of pleochroic haloes.

Paneth and Peters (1928) first described the micro method for the measurement of very small amounts of helium, and in the same year Paneth, Gehlen, and Gunther published the first of many papers by many authors on the helium, radium, and thorium content and the thence-calculated age of rocks. This first paper also dealt with meteorites. In 1929, Piggot published his first paper on the precise quantitative determination of the radium content of rocks.

An important review of the earlier work on naturally occurring radioactive isotopes and their constants was published by M. Curie, A. Debierne, A. S. Eve, H. Geiger, O. Hahn, S. C. Lind, St. Meyer, E. Rutherford, and E. Schweidler (1931). This was the last concerted publication by the giants of the old days.

It should be pointed out that the use of the chemical atomic weight technique in studying problems of the isotopic composition of elements, principally lead—a topic discussed at some length in 1931—is now purely of historic interest. This work, which was started by Richards and Lembert (1914) and was continued over many years by Richards, Hönigschmid, Baxter, their students and associates, has given way to the simpler, more rapid, and more informative method of isotope ratio measurement by mass spectrometry. It must, however, be remembered that the work of Richards and Lembert first *proved* the theory of radioactive decay, by showing that radiogenic lead from uranium had an atomic weight very close to 206, as demanded by the arithmetic of alpha decay in the uranium series.

During the period 1934–1939 the late G. H. Henderson published a series of papers on his remarkably precise measurements of pleochroic haloes (Henderson et al., 1934–1939).

Nier (1935) gave the proof that the activity of potassium all lay in the isotope K^{40}. This was confirmed the same year by Hevesy (1935). Baranov and Kretschmer (1935) described the preparation and use of thick photographic emulsions for alpha-track autoradiography. From this paper stems the work in that field, with its many geologic applications. I. Curie, von Halban, and Preiswerk (1935) described artificial radioactivity. This was the start of the applied geological uses of artificial isotopes, neutron logs, and the like. Also in 1935, Hahn and Meitner first observed what later turned out to be the fission process. All in all, 1935 was quite a year!

In the early thirties the radioactivity of the oceans came under the scrutiny of Pettersson and his associates at Göteborg, and an extensive, continuing research program was started there. In 1936, Piggot of the Carnegie Institution of Washington described his apparatus for obtaining long cores of deep-sea sediments. Shortly thereafter Piggot and Urry reported on the radioactive content of the first cores (1939).

The first papers by Nier dealing with the ratios of isotopes in natural materials, and the variations in these ratios, appeared in the period 1938–1941. They are listed in the bibliography and in Tables 9 and 9.1, and need not be repeated here. With these classic measurements the present epoch of the application of nuclear processes to the problems of geology may be said to have begun. Nuclear geology was now of age.

Chapter 1

FUNDAMENTAL CONSIDERATIONS, INSTRUMENTS, AND TECHNIQUES OF DETECTION AND MEASUREMENT*

1.1 ELEMENTARY PARTICLES

Atoms have diameters of about 10^{-8} cm and are composed of electrons surrounding a central nucleus. The nucleus has a diameter of roughly 10^{-12} cm, and electrons are bound to it by the electrostatic attraction of their negative charge to the positive charge of the nucleus. The atomic binding energy of these electrons is much less than the nuclear binding energy between the particles of the nucleus, and its effect is negligible in most of the processes of nuclear physics. All nuclei consist of neutrons and protons, two types of particles of nearly equal mass. In terms of modern formalism, these two particles represent different quantum states of a single particle, the nucleon.

Neutrons have no electric charge; protons have a positive charge, equal to the charge of an ordinary electron, but of opposite sign. The simplest nucleus, that of hydrogen, consists of a single proton. All other nuclei contain a mixture of neutrons and protons, the proportion of neutrons generally increasing with the atomic weight of the nucleus. The largest naturally occurring nucleus is that of uranium^{238}, which contains 92 protons and $238 - 92 = 146$ neutrons. The diameter of this nucleus is only about seven times greater than the diameters of its individual nucleons.

The structure of the nucleus is complex and, even now, is incompletely understood. The protons, of course, are mutually repelled by the Coulomb (electrostatic) forces arising from their charge. All nucleons, however, are held together by short-range forces that have no counterpart in the macroscopic world. These very strong forces make the nucleus a tightly bound structure of extremely high density (about 1.5×10^{14} g/cm^3). The mechanics of the nucleus are more

* Most of the discussion in Sections 1.1–1.10 is taken from the writings of Robley D. Evans, released as class notes and in *The Science and Engineering of Nuclear Power,* Vol. 1, published by Addison-Wesley Press, by permission of the author and publisher.

complicated than the mechanics of the surrounding atom. Regularities exist in nuclei (Suess, in press), but they are less pronounced than the well-known regularities expressed in the periodic table of the elements. For excellent discussions of nuclear structure, see Segrè (1953). Nuclear theory is thoroughly summarized by Blatt and Weisskopf (1952).

1.2 NUCLEAR CHARGE Z AND MASS NUMBER A

The nuclear charge, or atomic number Z is the integral number of protons in the nucleus. The total number of nucleons in a nucleus is the mass number A. Nuclei of the same Z but different A are different forms of the same element and are called *isotopes*. The mass of an electron or a beta particle is only about $1/2000$ the mass of a proton. When a nucleus decays by beta emission, Z increases by 1 unit, because 1 negative charge is removed, and A remains essentially constant. The precise value of mass decreases slightly, to allow for the energy released. Alpha particles are essentially the nuclei of helium $(He^4)^{++}$, and thus have a mass of 4 atomic mass units and a double positive charge. Therefore, in a nucleus decaying by alpha emission, Z will decrease by 2 and A by 4.

1.3 ENERGY UNITS

It is customary in nuclear physics to express energy in terms of electron volts (ev), millions of electron volts (Mev), and billions (10^9) of electron volts (Bev). An electron volt is the kinetic energy acquired by an electron falling through a potential difference of 1 volt and is equal to 1.6×10^{-12} erg.

Natural alpha particles usually have energies of several Mev; beta rays range from fractions of an ev to several Mev, and most natural gamma rays have energies of the order of 1 Mev. Energies of cosmic rays go up into the Bev. In the jargon of nuclear physicists, radiation of respectively high and low energy is often referred to as *hard* and *soft* radiation.

1.4 NUCLEAR REACTIONS

Positively charged particles, such as alphas $(He^4)^{++}$, experience an electrostatic (Coulomb) repulsion as they approach a nucleus. However, if the projectile particle has sufficient kinetic energy, it penetrates inside the nuclear radius where the strong, short-range, attractive forces are acting. The projectile coalesces momentarily with the target nucleus, forming an excited compound nucleus. In a few shakes (10^{-12} second), the compound nucleus splits into a product particle and a residual nucleus. Such a reaction is usually written as follows:

Target (projectile, product) Residual.

The projectile and product particles are commonly abbreviated. For example, the production of protons and carbon^{14} from nitrogen by neutrons in the atmosphere is denoted

$$N^{14}(n, p)C^{14}$$

If the projectile and product particles are identical, the process is called *scattering*. The product (scattered) particle always has less energy than the projectile. The difference is usually transmitted to the residual nucleus in the form of kinetic *recoil* energy.

1.5 NUCLEAR CROSS SECTIONS

The probability that the projectile will interact with the target nucleus is simply expressed in terms of *cross sections*. When a reaction is likely, we say that the cross section for that reaction is large. The cross section can be thought of as the effective area presented by the target nucleus to the projectile for that particular process. Cross sections vary widely for various particles, various energies, various targets, and various processes, and are usually expressed in barns (10^{-24} cm^2).

1.6 RADIOACTIVITY

Radioactive processes are spontaneous nuclear reactions, characterized by the radiation emitted. They occur at random, and the exact moment when a given atom will decay cannot be predicted. However, in a large number of atoms a certain fraction will decay per unit of time. This fraction, called the decay constant λ, is not affected materially by any known physical or chemical process. It is reasonably certain that λ remains constant throughout geologic time.

Attempts to induce and detect changes in the rate of decay of radioactive substances were made over a period of more than thirty years after the discovery of radioactivity. The results were uniformly negative. Lambda remained constant in spite of the most drastic changes in environments, chemical state, etc. With the advance of theoretical understanding of radioactivity it was realized that the rate of one form of radioactive decay, electron capture (see Section 1.6.d, below), could be influenced slightly by the electron density around the nucleus. "If it were possible to completely strip a nucleus of all its electrons, it clearly could not decay by orbital electron capture" (Segrè and Wiegand, 1949). Experiments with decay of two artificial isotopes thought to be the most sensitive to change in atomic structure (beryllium^7 and an excited state of technetium^{99}) have shown that the decay rate can be changed, but the change is extremely small (Segrè and Wiegand, 1949; Bainbridge et al., 1953; Kraushaar et al., 1953). In the case of beryllium^7, the difference between the decay constant of beryllium metal and BF_2 is only 0.07 percent (Kraushaar et al., 1953). The greatest difference observed for different compounds of technetium is 0.27 percent (Bainbridge et al., 1953).

Differences in pressure also change the electronic environment of a nucleus, but even pressures in the interior of the earth are not sufficient to induce changes much greater than the extremes of chemical combination mentioned above. From the point of view of the geologist, the smallness of the change in λ in what are probably the most sensitive cases is more reassuring than the negative results of earlier investigations.

Given N_0 radioactive atoms at a time $t = 0$, we shall have $N = N_0e^{-\lambda t}$ atoms at any given later time t. Although λ is more convenient in calculations, the halflife T, defined as the length of time required for half of any given number of atoms to decay, is more commonly used. The relation between T and λ is

$$T = \frac{\log_e 2}{\lambda} = \frac{0.693}{\lambda}$$

Many radioactive nuclear species may decay in more than one way. Consider, for instance, the decay of radium (Figure 1.1). Radium^{226} usually emits an alpha particle of 4.9 Mev and decays to the ground state of radon^{222}. Occasionally, however, radium^{226} may emit an alpha of only 4.7 Mev, and decay to an excited state of radon^{222}, which immediately emits electromagnetic radiation (a gamma ray) of 0.2 Mev and decays to the ground state. The total energy released is always the same. Gamma rays arise in transitions from excited states to lower energy states of a nucleus. Several essentially simultaneous gamma rays may be released in a cascade decay of an excited nucleus. By definition, electromagnetic radiations originating within the atom but outside the nucleus are called X-rays. Gamma rays and X-rays are otherwise identical.

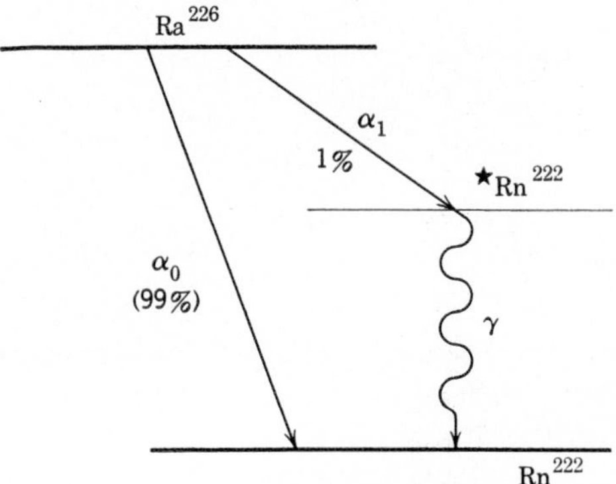

Figure 1.1 Decay scheme of radium^{226}.

Some radioactive species decay by two or more different processes into two different daughters. This process is usually called *branching*, and the ratio of the rates at which the two daughters are being produced is called the *branching ratio*. Several branching isotopes can be seen in Figure 1.2: actinium^{227}, bismuth^{214}, bismuth^{212}, and bismuth^{211}. Another important example, potassium^{40}, is discussed in Chapter 3.

1.6.a Activity units

Radioactive isotopes are measured in *curies*, originally defined as the amount of radon that is in equilibrium with 1 gram of radium. Uncertainty in the halflife of radium made it desirable to redefine the curie as 3.70×10^{10} radioactive disintegrations per second.

Thus a curie of radium^{226} is approximately 1 gram; a curie of radon^{222} is 0.66 mm^3 at standard temperature and pressure; and a curie of uranium^{238} is about 3000 kg. When a radioactive decay series (Figure 1.2) is in equilibrium, the activity of each radioactive daughter isotope, measured in curies, is the same.

1.6.b Alpha decay

Almost all natural alpha emitters are found among the heavy elements in the three decay series of uranium^{238}, uranium^{235}, and

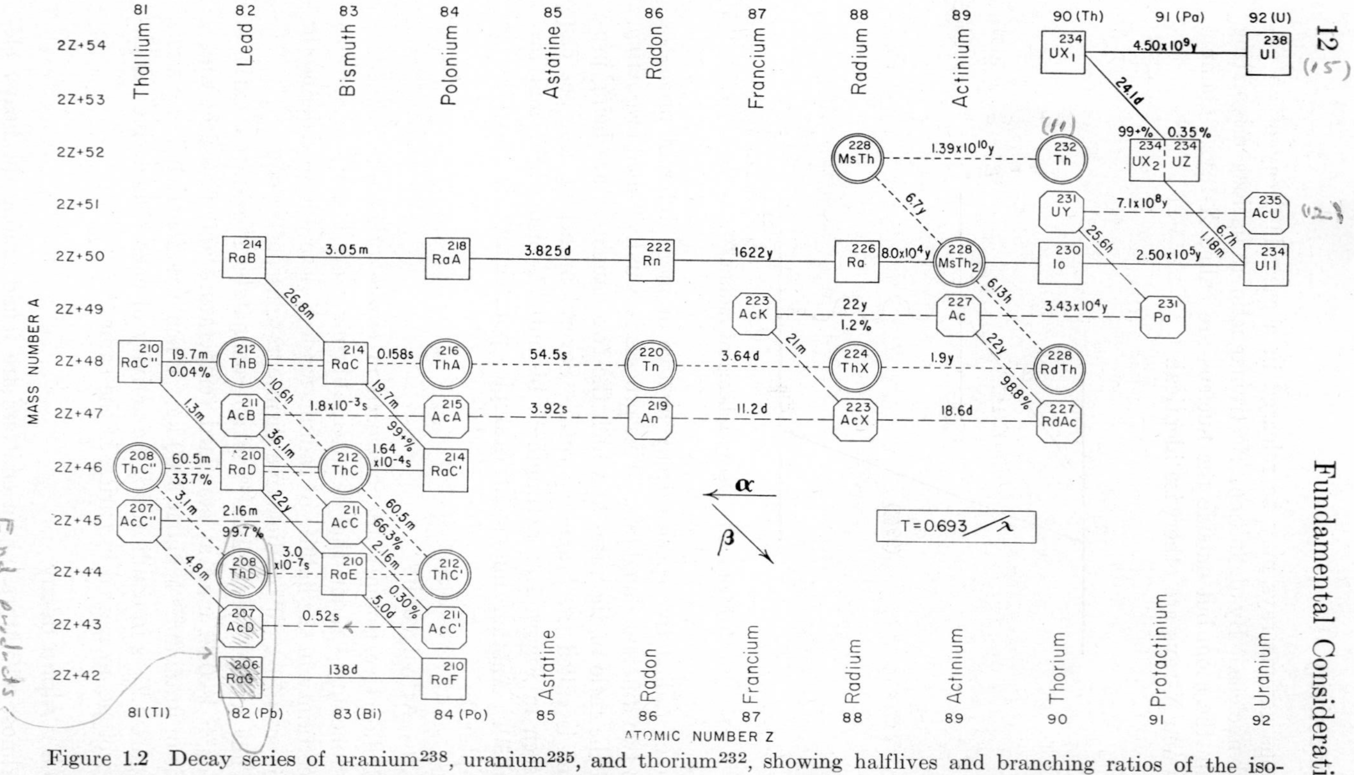

Figure 1.2 Decay series of uranium^{238}, uranium^{235}, and thorium^{232}, showing halflives and branching ratios of the isotopes. The old symbols shown in the circles, squares, and octagons in the figure are giving way to the modern terminology shown on the top and bottom, i.e., Th^{227}, not RdAc. Data from Hollander, Perlman, and Seaborg (1953).

thorium^{232}. The energy of an alpha particle is always discrete. Isotopes can be identified by the characteristic energy of their alpha particles.

Alpha particles carry considerable energy, but they are large and their penetrating power is low. A thin sheet of paper will stop most alphas, and, when a rock or mineral specimen is examined for alpha activity, only the very thin (about 30 microns) surface layer is effective.

1.6.c Beta decay

When a nucleus changes by beta decay, a beta particle is emitted, together with a *neutrino*. The neutrino was postulated by Pauli to allow conservation of energy, angular momentum, etc. It is probable that it was detected in a recent experiment (Reines and Cowan, 1953*a, b*), and there is other good evidence that it exists. Sherwin (1948) gives a popular discussion of the neutrino.

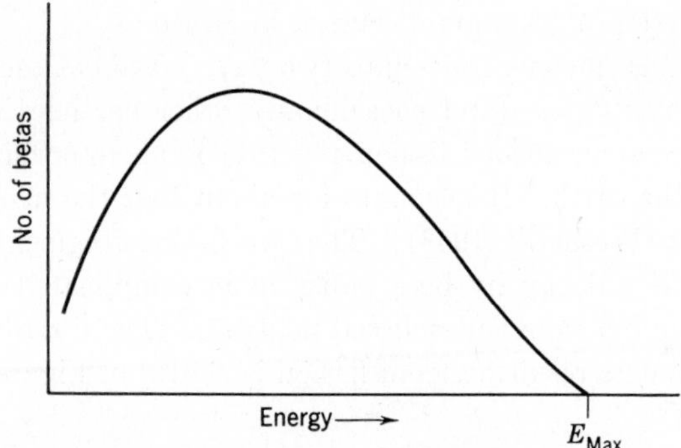

Figure 1.3 Typical continuous beta spectrum.

Because beta decay involves three bodies (the nucleus, the beta particle, and the neutrino), the energy of the beta ray may have any value from essentially zero to the definite maximum set by the total energy available in the decay. Hence the beta spectrum is continuous (Figure 1.3). Gamma rays are occasionally associated with beta decay in the manner already described for alpha decay.

The greatest penetration of energetic beta particles is of the order of a few millimeters in rocks. About 20 per cent of the beta rays from the surface of a layer of a uranium mineral will penetrate into a thin-wall counter.

1.6.d Electron capture

A nucleus may occasionally capture an orbital electron from the atom in which the nucleus is contained. The electron usually captured is in the K-orbit, and the process is often called *K-capture.* Because of the removal of an inner atomic electron, electron capture is followed by the emission of characteristic X-rays and is identified by observing these X-rays. In geology the process is significant only in potassium^{40}, of which about 10 percent decays by K-capture to argon^{40}.

1.6.e Nuclear fission

Fission, the most talked-about of nuclear reactions, may be induced by neutrons or other particles, or it may occur spontaneously. Several heavy isotopes are fissionable. Those of principal interest to us here are uranium^{235}, which undergoes neutron fission, and uranium^{238} and thorium^{232}, which are subject to spontaneous fission, apparently without external excitation (see Segrè, 1952). The geophysical implications of these processes are discussed in Section 4.2.

In fission, the nucleus splits into two parts, usually unequal in size. Two or three neutrons (and occasionally other particles as well) are emitted. The spontaneous fission reaction is an important source of neutrons in the earth. It accounts for about half the neutrons generated in rocks (Wetherill, 1953). The two fission fragments are radioactive, and they decay by beta emission in complicated chains, with associated gamma rays and delayed neutrons. The distribution of the sizes of fragments resulting from fission is shown in Figure 1.4.

1.7 RADIOACTIVE SERIES

The long-lived heavy radioactive elements decay into daughter products that are in themselves radioactive. They in turn decay and thus form series (or chains) which end when a stable daughter isotope is reached. Uranium^{238}, uranium^{235}, and thorium^{232} are each at the head of one of these series (Figure 1.2).

A series is said to be in equilibrium when for each decaying parent atom one of each intermediate daughter atoms also decays (on the average). The number of atoms of each intermediate daughter will then be in direct proportion to its halflife T, or in inverse proportion to the respective decay constant λ. The ultimate (stable) daughter will continue to increase at a decreasing rate.

Natural radioactive series are usually near equilibrium, but instances where they are not are common, and frequently very interesting. Radioactive parent and daughter are chemically different, and can be separated in nature by ordinary geological processes. Thus,

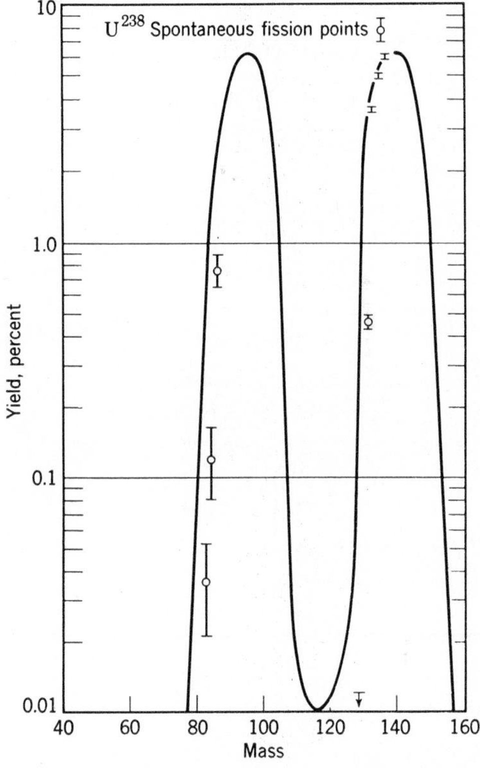

Figure 1.4 Product yield of neutron fission of uranium^{235} (smooth curve) and of spontaneous fission of uranium^{238} (experimental points). After Wetherill (1953).

the nature and degree of disequilibrium which exists in a sample frequently offers a clue to the geologic history of the sample.

The equations of radioactive series decay have been solved by Bateman (1910), but practical application of his results is laborious. Flanagan and Senftle (unpublished) have developed an approximation method of solving Bateman's equations and have compiled tables to facilitate the calculations.

Consider a radioactive series with $n + 1$ members (where the last member is stable). If the initial number of atoms of the first member of the series is N_0, then, after a given time, t, the amount of the kth member of the series will be

$$N_k = N_0(A_1e^{-0.693t/T_1} + A_2e^{-0.693t/T_2} + \cdots + A_ke^{-0.693t/T_k})$$

where

$$A_1 = \frac{T_1^{(k-2)}T_k}{(T_1 - T_2)(T_1 - T_3) \cdots (T_1 - T_k)}$$

$$A_2 = \frac{T_2^{(k-2)}T_k}{(T_2 - T_1)(T_2 - T_3) \cdots (T_2 - T_k)}$$

$$A_k = \frac{T_k^{(k-1)}}{(T_k - T_1)(T_k - T_2) \cdots (T_k - T_{k-1})}$$

1.8 INTERACTION OF RADIATION WITH MATTER

If we imagine a small radioactive sample *in vacuo,* the radiation intensity from that sample will vary inversely with the square of the distance from the sample. There will be no absorption, and all radiation will continue in straight lines to infinity. When the sample is partially or wholly surrounded by matter, however, the problem becomes more difficult. The particles or quanta collide with electrons and nuclei and are scattered or absorbed by various processes. The simplest form of scattering is called *elastic scattering* because the motion and distribution of the particles before and after the collision can be described by analogy with the motion and collision of elastic spheres. A more complex form of scattering involves exchange of energy by processes other than simple mechanical collision and is called *inelastic scattering.* Absorption takes place by various nuclear processes and is discussed separately for each type of particle.

1.8.a Absorption of alpha particles

The alpha ray is simply a stripped atom, $(He^4)^{++}$, traveling at a high velocity. A 5-Mev alpha moves with roughly $1/10$ the velocity of light. When an alpha is projected into matter, it collides with electrons, gradually slows down to a point where it can capture them, and then is rapidly stopped. The path is usually straight. In air, the range of alpha particles is several centimeters, and many authors like to express the energy of alphas in terms of air-centimeters, i.e., their range in dry air at 15° C and 760-mm pressure. Specific ionization (energy loss per unit path length) of an alpha as a function of the distance it has traveled in air is shown in Figure 1.5.

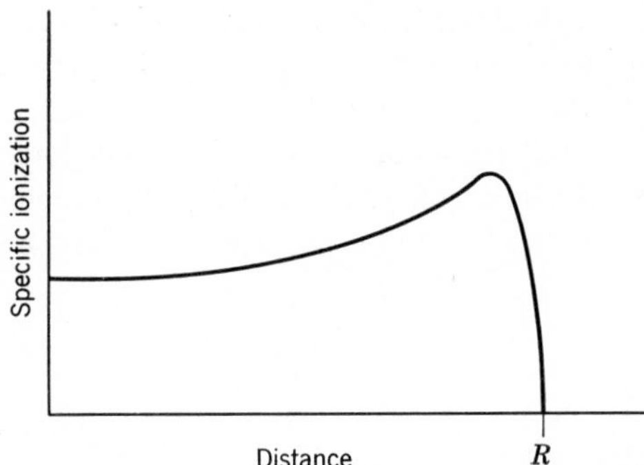

Figure 1.5 Specific ionization of an alpha particle as a function of distance traveled.

To convert alpha range from air-centimeters to a particular material with which we are dealing, a photographic emulsion for instance, we use the Bragg-Kleeman rule, which gives the relation between range in air and the length of path L in any particular medium.

$$L = R(\rho_a/\rho)\sqrt{A/A_a} = 3.2 \times 10^{-4}(R/\rho)\sqrt{A}$$

where R is the range in air, ρ_a is the density of air, ρ is the density of the particular medium, A_a is the mean mass number of air, and A is the mean mass number of the medium. It will be noted that the path length of an ordinary alpha in an average solid is a few tens of microns. For that reason, elastic scattering of alpha particles by nuclei is observed best in very thin foils. Although alpha scattering was the basis for Rutherford's postulation of the atomic nucleus, the process is unimportant in the geological sciences.

1.8.b Absorption and scattering of beta particles

(1) *Elastic scattering.* Beta particles are scattered appreciably by both atomic electrons and atomic nuclei. The elastic-scattering cross section by atomic electrons is proportional to Z, and by atomic nuclei to Z^2 of the target atom. The two effects are of nearly equal importance in hydrogen ($Z = 1$), whereas in medium or heavy nuclei the scattering is mostly nuclear. In gold ($Z = 79$) only about 1 percent of the total scattering is caused by atomic electrons. In total effect, elastic scattering is relatively unimportant in light elements.

(2) *Inelastic scattering* (Bremsstrahlung). When a beta ray enters the vicinity of an atomic nucleus it may be scattered inelastically, and lose some of its kinetic energy by X-ray emission. The cross section for such an encounter is proportional to the kinetic energy of the beta ray and to Z^2 of the target nucleus. The process is important only for energetic betas in heavy elements.

(3) *Ionization.* When a beta ray interacts electrostatically with an atomic electron, the electron may be completely removed from the atom, leaving a positive ion and a free electron. These separated electric charges are called an ion pair, regardless of whether the electron remains free or becomes attached to a neutral atom, forming a negative ion. On the average, 32.5 electron volts are required to form an ion pair in air. Ionization is the predominant process of energy loss for beta rays of low and medium energies (such as are emitted by radioactive substances) in light elements (such as constitute common rocks).

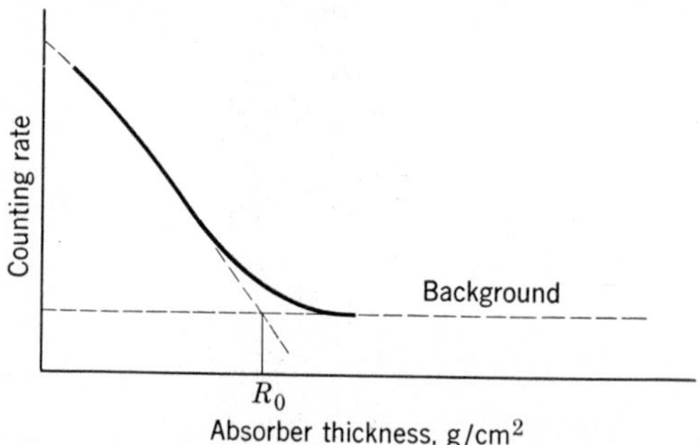

Figure 1.6 Typical absorption curve for a continuous beta spectrum.

The average straight-line range of electrons in rocks and similar absorbers is roughly independent of the atomic number Z and can be expressed in terms of grams per square centimeter. The shape of a typical absorption curve for a continuous beta spectrum is shown in Figure 1.6. The actual path of a beta ray in an absorber is tortuous, particularly toward the end (see Figure 1.7).

(4) *Self-absorption in geologic samples.* When the total beta radioactivity of powdered samples is measured it is common practice to use equal volumes of sample under a thin-window counter, empirically calibrated. The thickness of the sample is usually somewhat greater than the maximum range of the betas (a few mm), and the mean atomic number of the samples frequently varies over wide limits.

All three processes discussed above come into play, plus the variable volume concentration of the radioactive atoms, with the overall effect that total beta radiation from equal volumes of heavy samples (galena, for instance) is slightly greater than from lighter materials (such as quartz or calcite) containing equal weight percentage of radioactive matter. The effect is illustrated in Figure 1.8. It is more pronounced for uranium and thorium than for potassium.

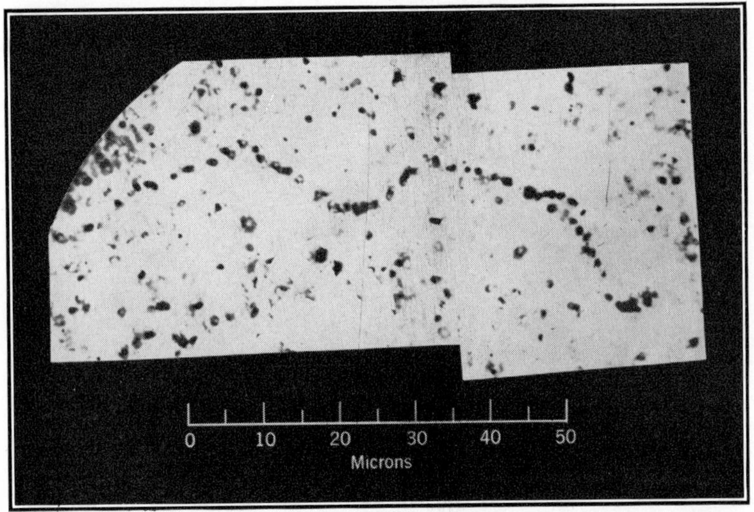

Figure 1.7 Track of a beta particle from potassium[40] in a photographic emulsion (Ilford G5). Montage of two photographs taken at different planes in the emulsion. Hée and Jarovoy (private communication).

1.8.c Absorption and scattering of gamma rays

(1) *Nature of gamma rays.* The dualistic nature of wave and corpuscular properties is particularly evident in this form of electromagnetic radiation. At any point in space the gamma-ray electromagnetic wave train is a short pulse traveling with the velocity of light ($c = 3 \times 10^{10}$ cm/sec) and with a frequency ν determined by the energy of the radiation. Hence it has a wavelength $\lambda = c/\nu$. There are three principal modes of gamma-ray interaction with matter: Compton scattering, photoelectric absorption, and pair production. The wave concept is useful in the discussion of photoelectric absorption, but Compton scattering is most easily described in terms of elastic collisions of spheres or "corpuscles." The Compton process is by

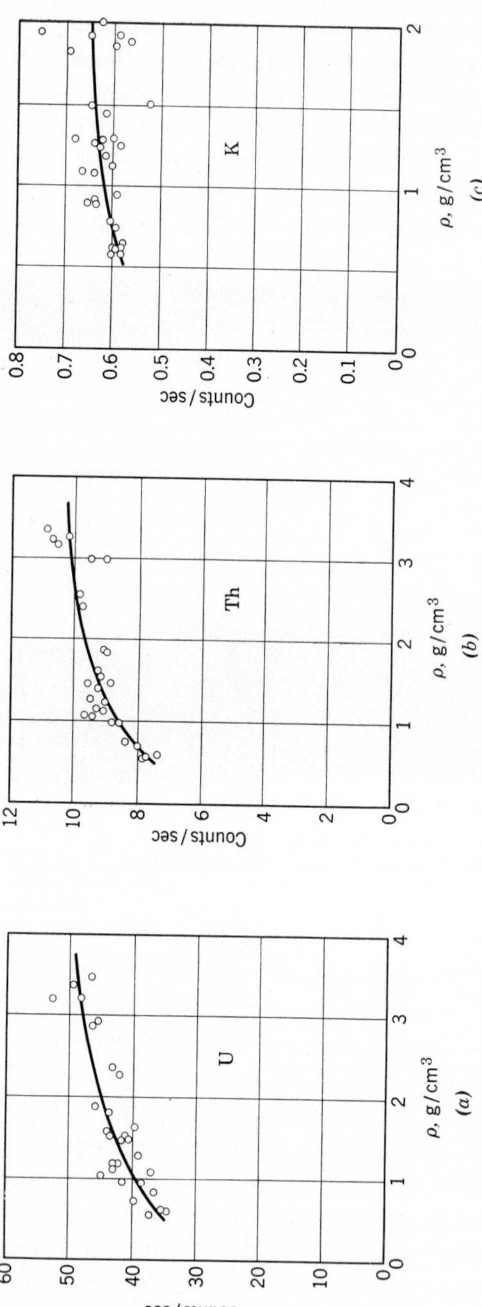

Figure 1.8 Beta radiation from equal volumes of equally radioactive samples of different bulk density.

far the most important in any consideration of gamma-ray absorption in materials predominantly composed of the lighter elements such as most rocks. A complete discussion of gamma-ray absorption is presented by Fano (1953).

(2) *Compton scattering.* We can think of the Compton effect as an elastic collision between a gamma quantum and an atomic electron. The binding energy of the electron to its atom can be ignored, so that

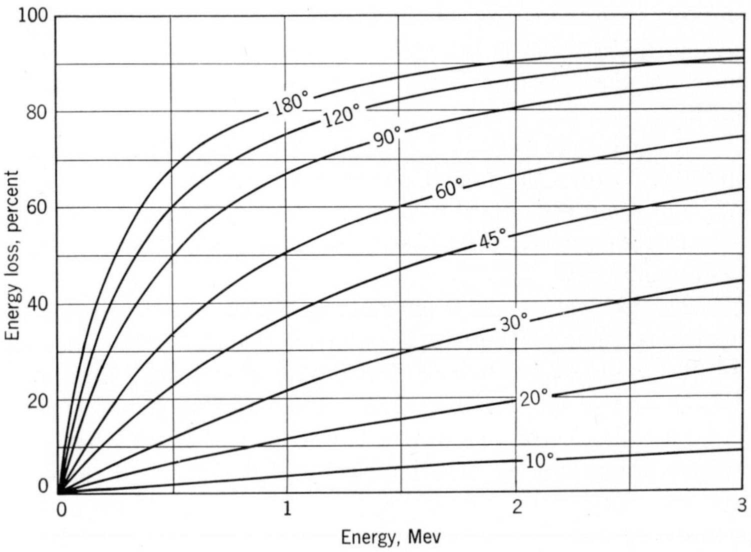

Figure 1.9 Energy loss per Compton collision for various angles of scattering, plotted as a function of energy of the incident gamma ray.

the Compton absorbing or scattering power of a material is simply proportional to the density of electrons in that material.

When the gamma quantum collides, it changes its direction and imparts part of its energy to the electron which flies off. The directions of motion are easily calculated from conservation of momentum. The change in the direction of the photon is greatest for greatest energy loss (Figure 1.9), but collisons with great energy loss are relatively improbable. Most of the scattered quanta change direction only slightly.

Although the Compton effect is thoroughly understood for individual interactions, application of the theory to geological gamma-ray absorption problems, by analytical method, is mathematically prohibitive. Various semiempirical approximations have been made for the gamma-ray logging problem and for the problem of tabular absorbers encountered in aerial gamma-ray surveys, and are discussed in the respective Sections of Chapter 8.

(3) *Photoelectric absorption.* In the photoelectric effect, the gamma ray interacts as a wave with the entire struck atom. Momentum and energy are conserved, and a single atomic electron receives all the energy of the gamma. It is ejected from the atom with a kinetic energy equal to the energy of the incident photon, minus the binding energy of the electron in the atom. After photoelectric emission, the atom emits characteristic X-rays as the electronic energy levels are refilled.

The atomic cross section for photoelectric absorption is roughly proportional to Z^4, the fourth power of the atomic number, and to $(1/h\nu)^3$, or the inverse third power of the energy. In rocks and other light materials photoelectric absorption is negligible for all but the softest gamma rays.

(4) *Pair production.* If a gamma ray has an energy greater than twice the rest mass energy of an electron (about 0.5 Mev per electron), it may produce a pair of electrons (a *positron* and a *negatron*) in the vicinity of an atomic nucleus. The positron shortly combines with an atomic electron, producing two quanta of *annihilation radiation,* and disappears; the negative electron has about half the energy of the incident gamma, minus the rest mass energy of the electron, and is absorbed in a manner already described for beta particles.

The cross section for pair production is very small for gamma rays in the energy range of radioactive materials. However, the process is very important in the interaction of cosmic rays with the atmosphere and the earth's surface.

1.9 STATISTICAL ERROR

We can think of the atomic nucleus as a barrier surrounding a group of particles that are in constant violent random turmoil. If we say that the nucleus is radioactive, we mean that the barrier is low enough or thin enough to permit a particle to escape occasionally. Each time a particle collides with the wall, it has the same fixed chance of escaping. Thus, the probability P_x that x disintegrations will occur in a given number of radioactive nuclei in a unit of time is given by Poisson's distribution

$$P_x = M^x e^{-M}/x!$$

where M is the average number of disintegrations per unit of time.

In any random procession the number of events which occur in 1 unit of time is not the same as the number of events in the following unit of time, and the fractional difference between a single measurement and an average of a large number of measurements is referred to as the *statistical error.* This quantity will be different for each individual measurement, and it cannot be given a definite numerical value. Instead, we must think of it in terms of probability. The absolute probable error of a measurement can be expressed as the *standard deviation,* given by

$$s = \sqrt{N}$$

or as the *probable error,* given by

$$p = 0.6745\sqrt{N}$$

where N is the number of events recorded. The commonly used percentage probable error is the ratio of the absolute probable error to the value of the quantity measured, expressed in percent (see Figure 1.10). We have an even chance that a measurement will differ from

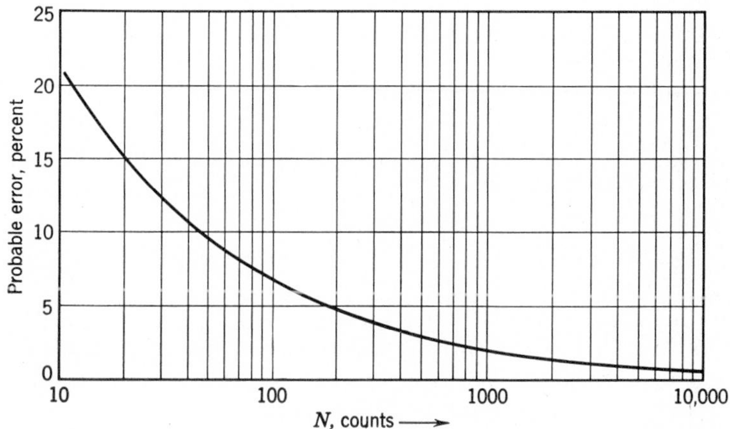

Figure 1.10 The percentage probable error of a measurement plotted as a function of the total number of counts taken.

the average of a large number of measurements by an amount smaller than p. It is important to realize that p is a function of N only, and it does not depend on the time that it took to make the measurement. The probable error, therefore, can be kept constant in a series of radioactivity measurements by measuring the time required to rack up a given number of counts rather than the number of counts per unit of time. The procedure is commonly used in routine testing of radioactive samples.

Occasionally we may be confronted with the problem of measuring an activity that is of the order of the background counting rate of our instrument. Such measurements usually take a relatively long time, at least several hours, and, if any number of them is to be made, it may be worthwhile to determine the length of time in which the measurement can be accomplished within a specified standard deviation. The problem has been treated by Loevinger and Berman (1951), who present a method for determining the total number of sample and background counts necessary to reach a result within the desired limits of error in minimum time. Their calculation is shown graphically in Figure 1.11. Corresponding to an estimate of the (total/background) count ratio r, and an adopted standard deviation, expressed in percent, the graph gives the minimum number of total and background counts that must be recorded if the result is to be within the specified standard deviation.

The use of Figure 1.11 may be somewhat clarified by a numerical example. Suppose it is desired to determine the sample counting rate to a standard deviation of 3 percent. Suppose also that $r = 1.5$. Then, from the graph, the horizontal 3 percent line crosses the $r = 1.5$ curve at the vertical line for 18,000 total counts. This point of intersection also lies about halfway between the background-counts curves for 8000 and 12,000. Hence, by interpolation, the total background count is about 10,000. For a counter with an ordinary background these measurements will run to many hours, so that the use of the optimum-time graph will be well worthwhile.

In some applications of radiation measurement, especially drill-hole logging, surveying from aircraft, radon measurement, etc., it is convenient to use integrating instruments. These devices measure the flux of radiation through an ionization chamber or the rate at which impulses are received from a counter. The statistical error of these measurements will show itself as an irregular fluctuation of the observed quantity (Figure 1.12). Again, the magnitude of the fluctuation will depend only on the total number of ionizing events recorded in the inherent interval given by the characteristics of that particular instrument. Each pulse from a counter or ionization chamber is

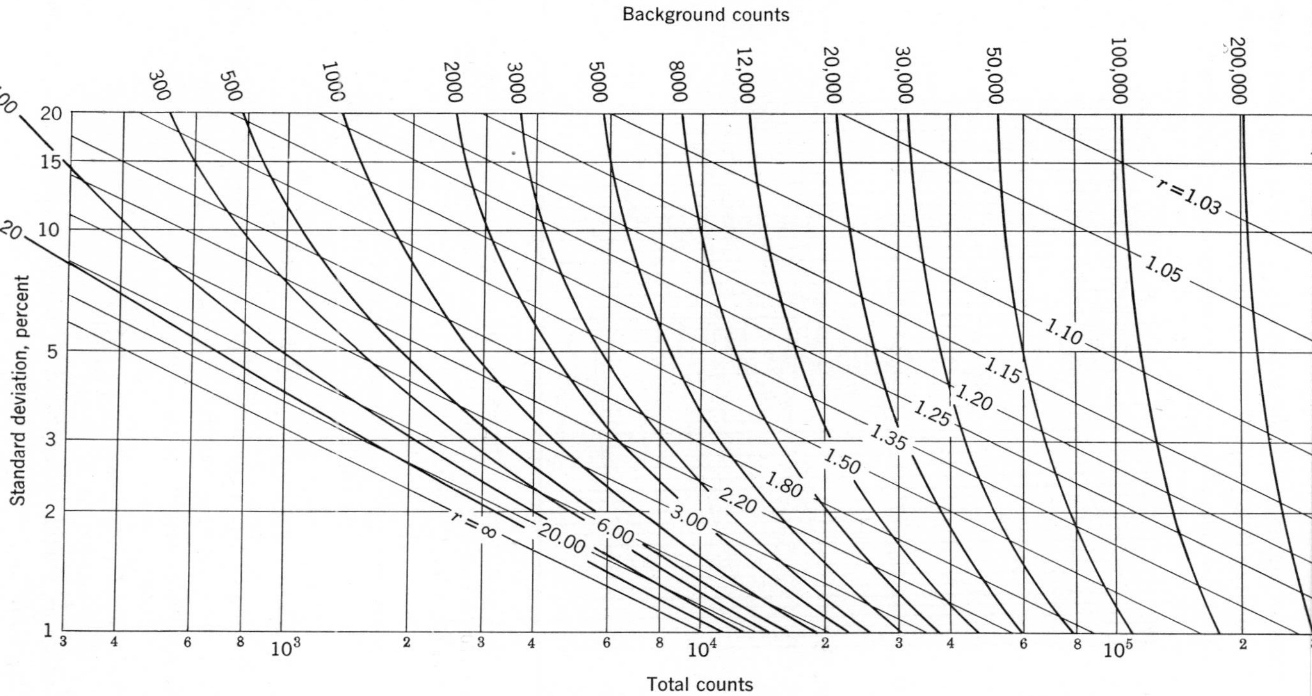

Figure 1.11 Optimum number of counts for minimizing combined counting time when the error is assigned and total-to-background ratio r is known. After Loevinger and Berman (1951).

converted electronically into a charge Δq, which is added to the charge Q, on a tank capacitance C. A resistance R shunts the tank capacitance. The charge Q is proportional to the counting rate A and may be read either by measuring the potential difference $V = Q/C = \Delta qAR$ by a device such as a vibrating-reed electrometer, or by measuring the current in the shunt,

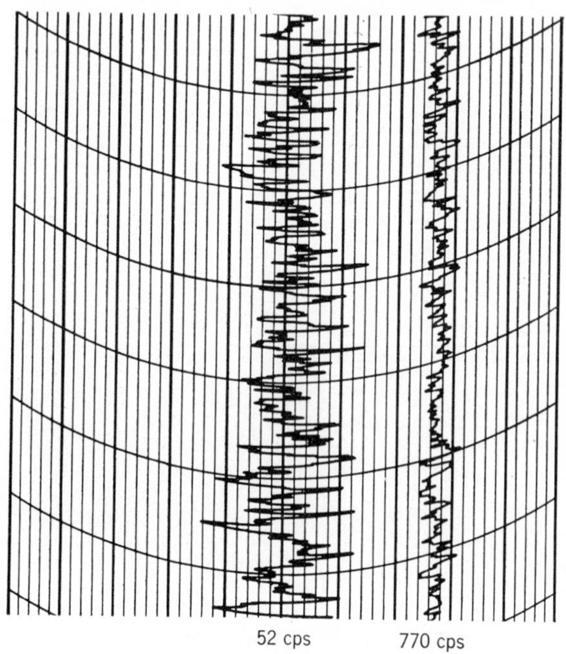

Figure 1.12 Counting-rate meter records of constant rates of 52 counts/second (left) and 770 counts/second (right). The time constant is 1 second. Note the difference in statistical fluctuation.

$$i = V/R = Q/RC = A\Delta q$$

as done in counting-rate meters. The fractional standard deviation of a single instantaneous reading of a device integrating pulses of essentially constant magnitude is

$$s = \sqrt{A/2RC}$$

or the same as would be expected in a direct counting observation over a time $2RC$.

1.10 COINCIDENCE ERROR

All pulse counting devices have finite resolving times. If two pulses occur within an interval smaller than the resolving time τ, only one pulse can be recorded. The probability that a pulse will not be missed is a function of the counting rate N and the resolving time τ:

$$p = e^{-N\tau}$$

Counting instruments used in geological research are occasionally subjected to counting rates high enough to warrant correction for this *coincidence error.*

The simplest satisfactory method for measuring the resolving time is to compare the response of the apparatus to the radiation from two approximately equal sources, taken separately and then taken simultaneously. Let N_a and N_b be the true counting rates for two sources, while n_a and n_b are the observed net counting rates after correction for background. Then, when both sources are measured simultaneously, the sum of their radiation will give a true rate of $N_s = N_a + N_b$, but the observed rate n_s will be slightly less than $n_a + n_b$. Since N is given by $N = n/(1 - n\tau)$, or approximately by $N = n(1 + n\tau)$, it follows that:

$$N_a = n_a(1 + n_a\tau)$$

$$N_b = n_b(1 + n_b\tau)$$

$$N_s = n_s(1 + n_s\tau)$$

$$N_s = N_a + N_b$$

Solving these relationships simultaneously gives:

$$\tau = \frac{n_a + n_b - n_s}{n_s^2 - n_a^2 - n_b^2}$$

or, to a satisfactory approximation:

$$\tau \cong \frac{n_a + n_b - n_s}{2n_a n_b}$$

Then, for example, if $n_a = n_b = 1000$ counts per minute, while $n_s = 1984$ cpm, we have $n_a + n_b - n_s = 16$ cpm, and $\tau = 16/2 \times 10^6 = 8 \times 10^{-6}$ minute. Then the true rates would be $N_a = N_b = 1008$ cpm, $N_s = 2016$ cpm.

1.11 IONIZATION CHAMBERS AND GEIGER-MÜLLER COUNTERS

1.11.a The ionization chamber

Radioactive particles and quanta can be detected by the ionization that they produce in gases. If we set up an electric field in a suitable vessel (Figure 1.13), we shall sweep out most of the ions and produce

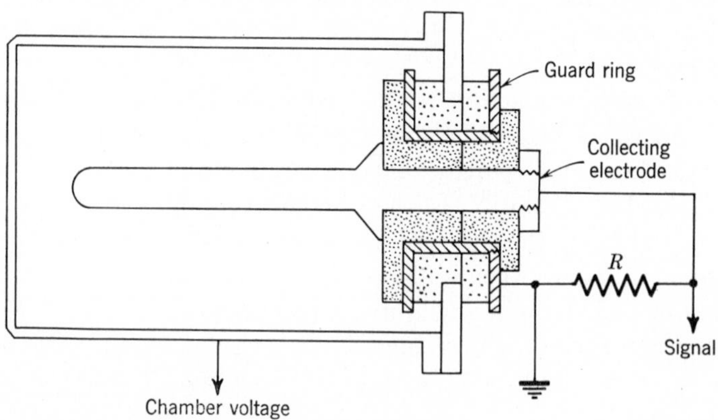

Figure 1.13 Schematic section through an ionization chamber. Insulators are shown stippled.

an electric current which will be proportional to the amount of ionization produced by the radiation in the chamber. Theory and application of ionization chambers are discussed by Korff (1946), Victoreen (1949), and Rossi and Staub (1949).

The ionization chamber will have a certain capacitance C, usually of the order of a few micromicrofarads, and the high resistance between the electrodes will be R. The product RC is called the *time constant*. If we now charge the chamber to a voltage V_0, the charge will leak off at the rate

$$\frac{dV}{dt} = \frac{V_0}{RC} \exp\left[-\frac{t}{RC}\right]$$

We may handle the ionization current in two different ways. First, the time constant can be made so small that the charge leaks off almost as fast as it accumulates. Each ionizing event will then produce a pulse proportional to the magnitude of the event. Pulse chambers are useful in the laboratory for alpha counting in a strong beta-gamma background. Suitable discriminating pulse amplifiers can easily distinguish the large alpha pulses from the ripple produced by betas and gammas.

Integrating (or direct-current) chambers have a very long time constant, on the other hand, and cannot distinguish between the different radiations. They require high-gain d-c amplifiers but can be made very sensitive when filled to a high pressure. Such chambers find their greatest geological use in the logging of oilwells (Swift, 1952).

The potential of the collecting electrode may be negative with respect to the case, to collect positive ions, or positive, to collect electrons. The ionization current will be greatest when the chamber is saturated, i.e., when an additional increase in voltage causes no further increase in ionization current, at a given flux of ionizing radiation. Direct-current chambers are best operated at saturation (about 50 volts), and positive ion (slow) pulse chambers usually work best at about the same voltage. Electron-collecting (fast) pulse chambers are usually operated at much higher voltages (500 to 1000 volts or even higher).

It is common practice to incorporate a guard ring in the insulator of ionization chambers (see Figure 1.13). The guard ring is usually connected to ground and has two functions: first, it provides an electrostatic shield; second, it collects all current that may leak across or through the high-voltage (outer) insulator. The collecting electrode is kept at a low potential with respect to the guard ring, so that the leakage across the inner insulator is kept negligible.

1.11.b The Geiger-Müller counter

In the literature and on the market we find an enormous variety of counter tubes. Their essential parts, however, have remained unchanged since Hans Geiger and Walther Müller announced their *Zählrohr* (1928, 1929). Excellent reviews of modern Geiger-Müller counter theory, technique, and application were published by S. C. Brown (1948), Friedman (1949), and Curtiss (1950).

All the tubes have a thin center wire (anode) surrounded by a usually cylindrical cathode (Figure 1.14). The volume of the counter is filled with a gas at pressures ranging from a few centimeters to atmospheric. Though a wide variety of gases can be used for the purpose, the most common mixture consists of argon with a small amount of polyatomic vapor (alcohol, amyl acetate, etc.) added to quench the discharge. Halogen gases also are used frequently as quenchers (Present, 1947; Liebson and Friedman, 1948; Franklin and Loosemore, 1951; Gimenez and Labeyrie, 1952). They have the particular advantage of not decomposing in the counter and thus giving it a long

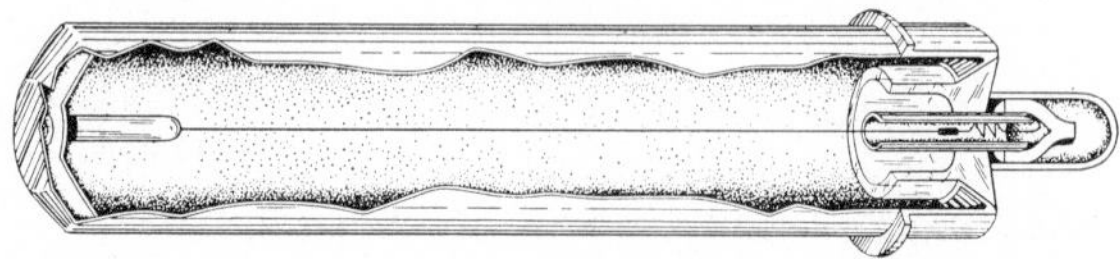

Figure 1.14 Section through a thin-wall aluminum beta-gamma Geiger-Müller tube, about ⅔ actual size. Courtesy of Victoreen Instrument Company.

useful life. Halogen counters are unusually temperature-stable, and operate reliably at relatively low voltages (300 to 400 v).

Thin-wall (beta-gamma) counters are sometimes made of glass 0.005 to 0.007 inch thick in the sensitive region, and will admit the

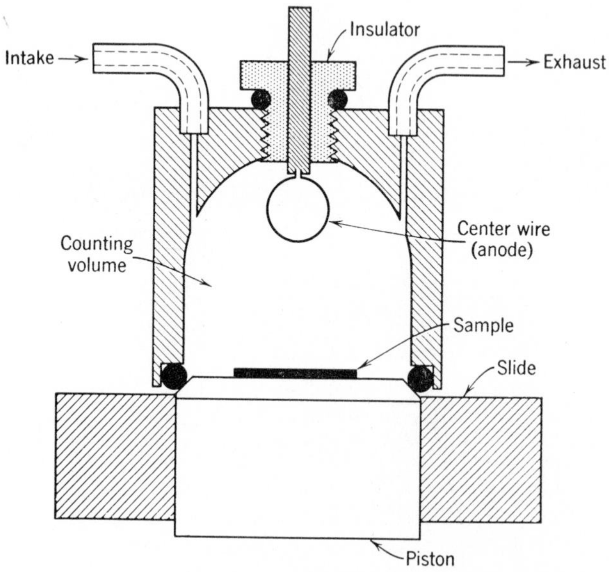

Figure 1.15 Section through a proportional (continuous-gas-flow) counter for solid samples. Courtesy of Nuclear Measurements Corporation.

more energetic betas. All-metal counters (Figure 1.14) are available with an aluminum wall only 0.005 inch thick (about 30 milligrams/ cm^2), and will count betas of medium energy very well. Counters are also frequently provided with mica windows that can be made sufficiently thin to admit even some alpha particles. The thinnest windows conveniently used in the laboratory weigh about 1.5 mg/cm^2. Almost all charged particles that penetrate into the counting volume produce pulses. Gamma rays must produce a secondary electron to be counted, and the efficiency of that process is very low (about 1 percent).

For alpha counting it is usually preferable to introduce the sample into the counting volume without any intervening wall (Figure 1.15). Such counters generally operate in the proportional region below the Geiger-Müller threshold, which makes it possible to vary the size of the pulse produced by changing the anode voltage. Thus one may first count the alpha radiation from a sample, then raise the voltage into the Geiger region, and count the alpha-plus-beta radiation from the same sample. Such measurements are useful in the study of radioactive disequilibrium in solid samples.

1.12 SCINTILLATION COUNTERS

FRANCIS J. DAVIS *

The scintillation counter is really an old instrument dressed up in new clothes. The spinthariscope used extensively early in the century was a fluorescent screen, usually of zincblende (sphalerite) on which could be observed (directly by eye or with the aid of a lens) scintillations due to alpha particles impinging on the screen. The scintillation counter is essentially the same, with an electron-multiplier phototube (Sommer and Turk, 1950; Birks, 1953, p. 21 ff.; Linden, 1953, 1954) substituted for the eye and the scintillations counted electronically. Various powdered, crystalline, and liquid phosphors have extended the use of the scintillation counter by making it sensitive not only to alpha particles but to betas, gamma rays, neutrons, and cosmic rays. (For general reference and techniques see Kallmann et al., 1952; Birks, 1953.)

Some of the advantages of the scintillation counter over the Geiger-Müller counter are: (1) Higher efficiency, especialy for gamma rays. With large, thallium-activated sodium iodide crystals the scintillation counter can approach 100 percent efficiency. (2) The pulse height is roughly proportional to the energy of the ionizing particle. In the Geiger-Müller counter the pulses are of the same size independent of the energy of the ionizing particle. (3) Lower relative cosmic ray background. This is in part the result of the first advantage men-

* Oak Ridge National Laboratory, Oak Ridge, Tennessee.

tioned. The Geiger-Müller counter and the scintillation counter both approach 100 percent efficiency of response to hard cosmic rays; therefore, for the same counting rate of gamma rays, the scintillation counter would be much smaller in size than the Geiger-Müller counter, thereby greatly reducing the sensitive volume intercepting cosmic rays. (4) The resolving time of the scintillation counter is much shorter. The decay time of the phosphorescence in the thallium-activated sodium iodide crystal is of the order of 2×10^{-7} sec, whereas the dead time in Geiger-Müller counters is of the order of 10^{-4} sec.

Some of the disadvantages of the scintillation counter are: (1) Large crystals take a long time to grow and, therefore, at the present time are high in cost. (2) The pulses from the photomultipliers are small compared to the output of a Geiger-Müller counter, thereby requiring a better amplifier circuit. (3) Photomultiplier noise pulses must be discriminated against in low-energy measurements. Commercial photomultipliers differ widely in noise level and sensitivity from tube to tube of the same make and model. (4) The scintillation crystal and photomultiplier must be kept in absolute darkness. (5) High-voltage regulation is critical. The gain of the photomultiplier tube varies roughly as the seventh power of the voltage applied to the tube.

Scintillation alpha counters can be made simply by putting a very thin coating of transparent adhesive such as stopcock grease on the photomultiplier sensitive surface (photocathode) and dipping the surface into the fluorescent powder, usually silver-activated zinc sulfide (Kulp et al., 1952*a*). The optimum amount and grain size of the powder adhering to the surface should be a compromise, maximizing the absorption of alphas in the powder and minimizing the absorption of the light emitted by fluorescence. The tube must be in a light-tight housing, which means that, if the alpha source is external to the housing, the sensitive face of the phosphor can be covered only with a very thin opaque covering, such as aluminum leaf, which will, of course, partly absorb the alpha rays. Larger areas of sensitive surface can be obtained by coating a sheet of wide cellophane tape with the phosphor. The sample is introduced through a "light lock" and placed on the phosphor side and the photomultiplier tube arranged to see the scintillations through the transparent tape (see Figure 1.16*a*). It is best to avoid lucite "lightpipes." Radon and thoron can be measured by introducing the gases into a flask with phosphor-coated walls (Damon and Hyde, 1952). A more ingenious method (Bryant and Michaelis, 1952) is to collect the radioactive daughters of radon or thoron by means of an electrostatic field on a thin aluminum foil placed over the phosphor on the phototube and to count the alpha rays penetrating the aluminum foil. This reduces the area of the phosphor and the background count from the alpha contamination of the phosphor (see page 46).

Scintillation beta counters can be made with various clear organic crystals such as anthracene. The advantages of the scintillation beta

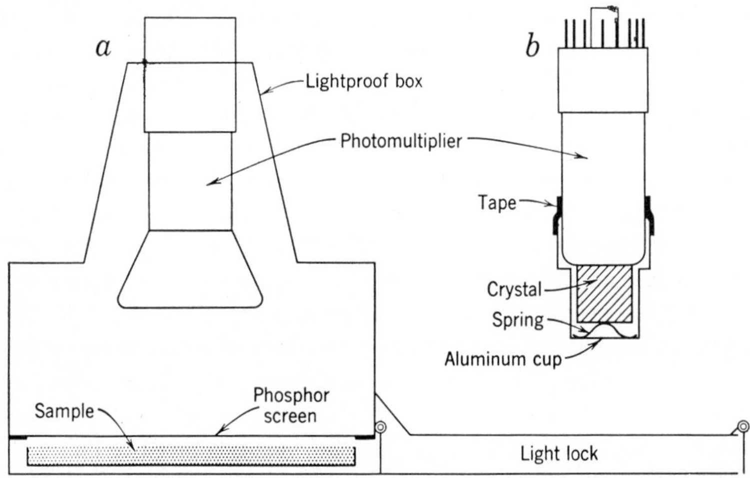

Figure 1.16 Scintillation counter for alpha counting (*a*) and gamma counting (*b*). The alpha-sensitive phosphor (silver-activated zinc sulfide) is sprinkled on the sticky side of wide cellophane tape stretched in a frame and faces the sample. The gamma-sensitive crystal (thallium-activated sodium iodide) is immersed in highly viscous silicone oil to exclude moisture and provide optical coupling, and sealed to the photomultiplier.

counter lie mostly in the fact that its pulse height is roughly proportional to the energy of the beta ray (Hopkins, 1951); thus it can be used as a beta-ray spectrometer. For integral beta counting the thin-window Geiger-Müller counter is essentially as efficient as the scintillation counter, with the Geiger-Müller counters having the advantage for they are simpler and cheaper.

The crystal commonly used in the gamma-ray scintillation counter is thallium-activated sodium iodide. Liquid scintillators such as a solution of terphenyl in toluene (Reynolds, 1952; Harrison, 1952), or plastic solutions (Buck and Swank, 1953) can be used but are less efficient. The sodium iodide crystal has a high density (3.7 grams/cm^3), which is desirable for absorption of gamma rays. It has the disadvantage of being hygroscopic and must be hermetically sealed from the atmosphere (Figure 1.16*b*). The amount of light given off when a gamma ray is absorbed by a scintillation crystal is proportional to the amount of energy dissipated in the crystal by the electrons resulting from the absorption of the gamma ray. Since the recoil electrons due to the Compton effect do not have the full energy of the gamma ray but depend on the angle of the recoil, we do not get a unique pulse height for a mono-energetic gamma ray in the Compton energy region. In the photoelectric absorption which prevails for low-energy gamma rays, we do get unique pulse height for mono-energetic gamma rays. At high energies, where pair production is the main absorption effect, we get two electrons (positive and negative). The positive electron is immediately annihilated, giving rise to two 0.51 Mev gamma rays. If both gamma rays are captured, the pulse height will be equivalent to the energy of the original gamma ray. If one or both escape, the pulse height will be less, accordingly. Thus for a mono-energetic source of gamma rays we get a continuous spectrum of pulse height with one or more peaks superimposed on it. This makes the analysis of a gamma-ray spectrum of many energies (such as radium) quite difficult with a single-crystal system; however, a spectrum consisting of only a few energies can be readily analyzed. Borkowski and Clark (1953) discuss the most advanced techniques.

The gamma-ray scintillation counter has become increasingly popular as a portable instrument for prospecting for radioactive materials (Wilson et al., in press), its high sensitivity for low weight being especially desirable. One or more scintillation detectors mounted on the roof of a car with a graphic recorder inside the car has proved to be an efficient prospecting device. Airborne scintillation counters of varying degrees of complexity have been used, from a simple battery-operated device for small planes to large crystal detectors with associated equipment for altitude correction, and with a strip film camera for determining plan positions of the plane, such as that developed by the Canadian authorities and the U. S. Geological Survey. Scintillation counters have been used in the logging of drill holes (DiGiovanni et al., 1953); however, the probes constructed with currently available photomultiplier tubes limit their diameter to sizes larger than 1⅝ inches. With the advent of the proposed small photomultiplier tube, probes with an outside diameter of ⅞ inch could be constructed, capable of exploring holes down to 1½-inch (EX) size. Carborne, airborne, and logging applications are discussed in Chapter 8.

Neutron-sensitive scintillation counters can be made with lithium iodide crystals (Schenck, 1952) and are useful in neutron logging of drill holes (see Section 8.2).

1.13 ACCESSORY ELECTRONIC EQUIPMENT *

1.13.a Scalers

The scaling circuit is commonly used for counting the random pulses from radiation detectors. The pulses frequently come at rates that are too fast for any mechanical device, and their number per unit

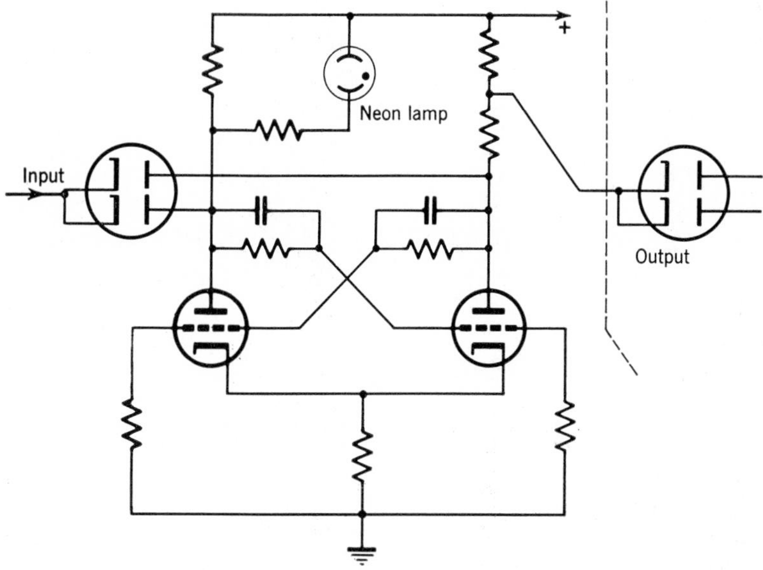

Figure 1.17 Schematic diagram of the basic scale-of-two circuit of Eccles-Jordan as modified by Higginbotham.

time must be reduced before they can be recorded. The basic scale-of-2 circuit is shown in Figure 1.17, and we shall briefly describe its action. The circuit has two stable positions: when the first triode is conducting, the second cuts off, and vice versa. Let us assume that the first tube is now off. The negative input impulse passes through one of the diodes to the grid of the tube that is conducting and cuts it off. The first triode will start to conduct, the neon lamp will glow, and a positive pulse will be transmitted to the diode of the next stage.

* Prepared by the editor.

But the diodes are biased to cut-off so that the positive output pulse has no effect. Nothing is transmitted to the next stage, but the glow of the neon lamp shows that the circuit "remembers" one pulse.

The second negative pulse arriving at the input shuts off the first triode and stops the glow of the neon bulb. A negative pulse is transmitted through the diode to the next stage. Every time the scale-of-2 receives a negative pulse, it flops over, emitting alternatively negative and positive pulses. The positive pulses have no effect, so that the scale effectively swallows every other pulse.

Scaling circuits frequently have six stages, with a preamplifier to feed the first stage and a power amplifier to actuate a mechanical pulse register after the last stage. Such an instrument registers 1 click for each 64 pulses received at the input end. Decimal scalers also have been developed, and are usually arranged as scales-of-1000. Electronically they are more complicated than instruments based on the scale-of-2, but their slightly higher cost is offset by the convenience of the decimal system in routine operation.

Some decimal scalers utilize a modification of the circuit described above, connected with suitable feedback loops. A radically different decimal scaler was designed in Great Britain (Taylor, personal communication), using the dekatron glow-transfer memory tube. This tube contains 10 electrode systems, arranged in a circle. When a suitable pulse is received, electrode 1 glows. The second pulse transfers the glow to the next electrode, and so on. The tenth pulse extinguishes the glow of electrode 9 and starts the glow on the first electrode of the next tube. Any number of tubes can be arranged in series, but each tube must have its own pulse shaping circuit. Compared to the Eccles-Jordan circuit (Figure 1.17), the dekatron circuit is relatively slow, and is useful primarily in the later stages of laboratory scalers. It will probably find its greatest geological use in portable scalers.

1.13.b Counting-rate meters

A wide variety of counting-rate meters has been used. All involve the basic principle of pulse shaping and integration. A pulse is received from the detector, amplified, and transformed into a pulse of standard size and shape. The uniform pulses are then integrated into a direct current which is measured. A counting-rate meter based on the circuit described by Cooke-Yarborough and Pulsford (1951) is commercially produced and is acclaimed for great stability and accuracy. Rate meters do not possess the inherent precision of the scaler (Bousquet, 1949), and their use is usually limited to special applications where variable intensities are to be observed and a continuous permanent record is essential. Drill-hole logging and portable instruments are the principal applications.

1.13.c Portable field instruments

Almost all portable detectors now used in the field are Geiger counters and scintillation counters. The simplest survey meter may consist of a Geiger-Müller tube, a source of high voltage, and a pair of earphones. Such a counter is very rugged and reliable, but counting the impulses by ear is tedious and limited to low counting rates. It is desirable to eliminate the necessity of counting by ear either by amplifying, scaling, and recording the Geiger impulses mechanically with an impulse register (relay-driven clock) or by integrating the current flow resulting from the passage of amplified pulses. Impulse recorders and portable scalers are most useful for relatively low rates, and rate meters are usually preferred for higher activities.

The lowest voltage conveniently used with conventional modern Geiger-Müller tubes is about 400 volts. Various types of vibrators and oscillators have supplied this voltage, but vibrator-powered high-voltage circuits are not very efficient or reliable. Oscillators or dry-cell batteries usually supply the high voltage in instruments intended for accurate surveys where good reproducibility is important.

A *univibrator* circuit * (Figure 1.18) makes a very good "amplifier" for pulses because a small trigger pulse fed into the circuit produces a much more powerful "shaped" output pulse. The effective gain per tube is considerably higher than that obtained from a conventional amplifier, resulting in small power drain which in turn permits the use of small batteries. Most of the portable Geiger and scintillation counters built in the United States use modifications of the univibrator circuit.

A different philosophy of design prevails in Great Britain, where instrument development at the A.E.R.E. (Harwell) has concentrated on cold-cathode tubes (soft valves) for portable instruments (Franklin and Loosemore, 1951; Peirson, 1951*a*, 1953). A typical circuit is shown in Figure 1.19. These rate meters have the advantages of great simplicity and ruggedness. Cold-cathode tubes have no filaments, and thus require no A batteries. Cathode emission of the soft valves

* Also known as Schmitt's trigger circuit. For extensive discussions of trigger circuits see Elmore and Sands (1949) and Puckle (1951).

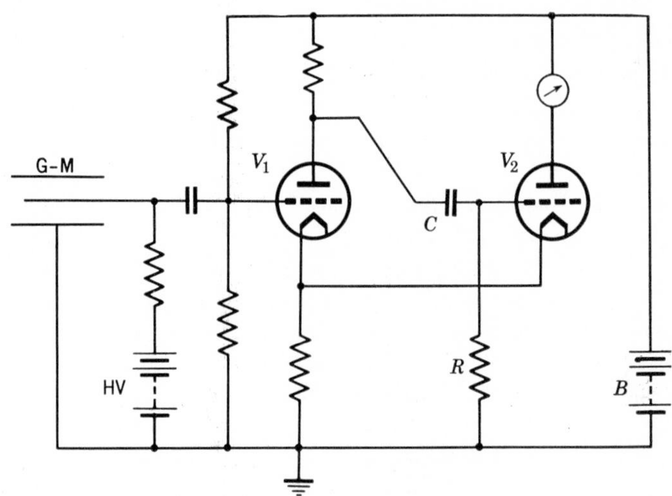

Figure 1.18 Portable counter circuit popular in the United States (modified after Schmitt, 1938). Symbols: G-M, Geiger-Müller tube; HV, high-voltage battery; V_1, first stage (normally on); V_2, second stage (normally off); RxC, coupling time constant.

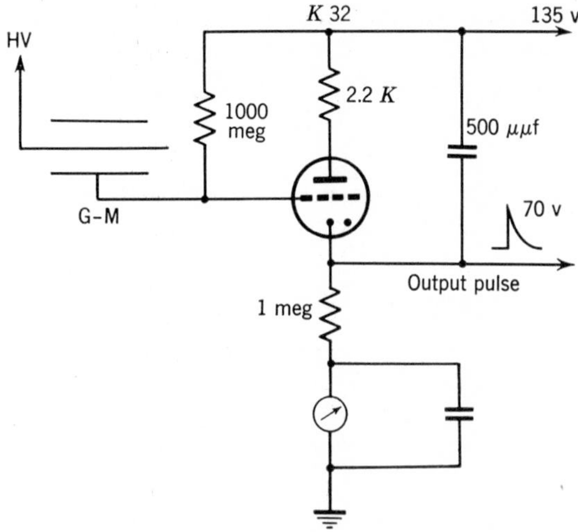

Figure 1.19. Schematic circuit diagram of a British portable rate meter using a cold-cathode valve. After Peirson (1953).

is very nearly constant with time, and, consequently, the cold-cathode rate meters have excellent stability and reproducibility. This feature is important if the instruments are to be used for accurate surveys, isorad mapping, quantitative logging, etc. On the other hand, these tubes require relatively high plate voltages and fairly large B batteries are necessary. Their deionization time is fairly long (several hundred microseconds) so that present soft-valve rate meters cannot be used at very high counting rates.

A great variety of small Geiger and scintillation counting rate meters is now commercially available, and many are specifically designed for mineral exploration. If we intend to limit ourselves to semiquantitative applications such as testing samples, almost any commercial beta-gamma instrument will do. However, before we select any particular make for accurate surveying, we should be certain that the instrument fulfills the following requirements:

a. All scales should be approximately linear, i.e., the meter reading should be directly proportional to the true counting rate.

b. The factor between the various ranges of sensitivity should be constant.

c. The reading of the instrument should not vary with temperature and humidity. All high-voltage connections should be well protected against moisture, to prevent spurious counting. Although an external probe is frequently convenient, a Geiger-Müller tube or scintillation head built into the instrument case (with short high-voltage leads) is to be preferred for work in humid surroundings, especially underground.

d. Provision should be made to check the overall instrument response easily. The reading of all counting-rate meters falls off with decreasing plate voltage, and a frequent check is essential if the measurement is to be reproducible. For the same reason, B batteries should be large enough to maintain constant voltage for at least 8 hours of continuous operation.

A small portable scintillation counter specifically designed for geological applications (Figure 1.20) was developed by the U. S. Geological Survey in cooperation with the Oak Ridge and Los Alamos National Laboratories (Wilson, et al., in press). It is commercially available from several manufacturers. The high voltage for the photomultiplier is supplied by a relaxation oscillator. Pulses are amplified and shaped by a Schmitt trigger monitored by a vacuum-tube voltmeter. When properly adjusted, the instrument is much more sensitive than the best Geiger-Müller counter, but is generally more delicate and less stable.

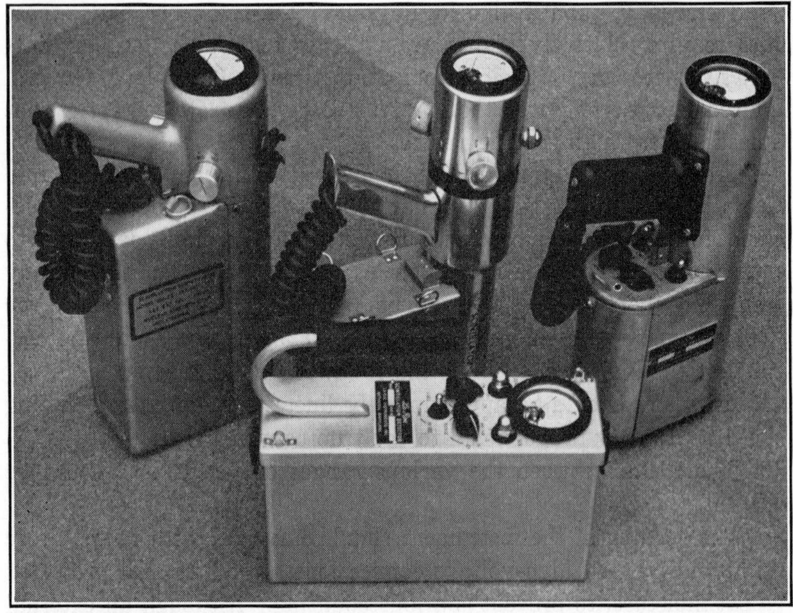

Figure 1.20 Four commercially produced versions of the portable scintillation counter designed for geological work.

1.13.d Transmission of pulses

In some operations, such as drill-hole logging, it is necessary to operate the detecting element at a distance from the counting circuit and some means must be provided to transmit the pulses without excessive attenuation. A low-impedance coaxial cable is best for this purpose, and it is necessary to provide some means for matching the high-impedance output of the Geiger-Müller tube or scintillation counter to the low impedance of the cable.

A *cathode-follower* circuit (Figure 1.21) is ideal for this purpose when there is sufficient space and power available for its operation. However, in light drill-hole logging equipment it is often inconvenient to provide for a cathode follower in the probe, and *transformer coupling* is used instead. A miniature transformer with a turns ratio of about 50:1 is used at both ends of the cable in the probe to match the high impedance of the detector to the low impedance of the cable, and at the other end to match the low impedance of the cable to the input impedance of the counting circuit (Figure 1.22). The high voltage required by the detector is supplied through the same cable, the d-c path being completed through both windings of the two trans-

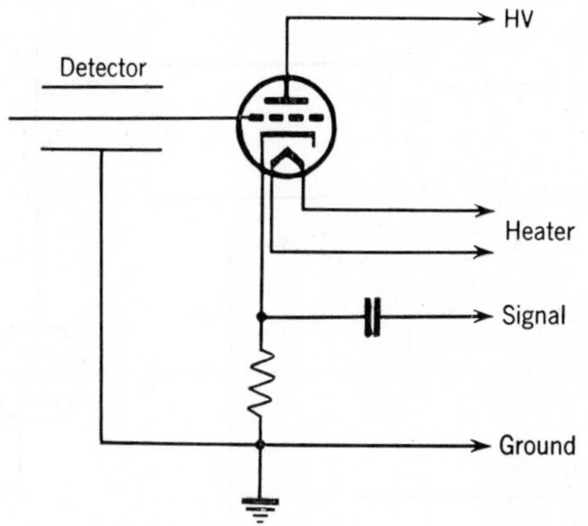

Figure 1.21 Schematic diagram of a cathode-follower circuit.

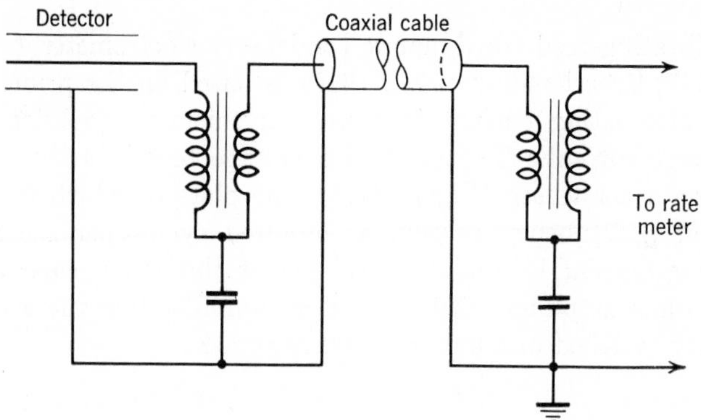

Figure 1.22 Schematic diagram of an impedance-matching circuit for pulse transmission.

formers. The capacitors are used to complete the a-c paths for the pulses. This system has been successfully used with Geiger-Müller and scintillation probes, using up to 4000 feet of cable.

1.13.e The vibrating-reed electrometer

In spite of its very high cost, the vibrating-reed electrometer is becoming widely used for the measurement of very small currents, such as are produced in ionization chambers (Horwood and McMahon,

1950; Swift, 1952), and mass spectrometers. It has excellent stability, wide range, and is readily adapted to continuous recording with any standard graphic recorder. It has largely displaced all earlier types of electrometers.

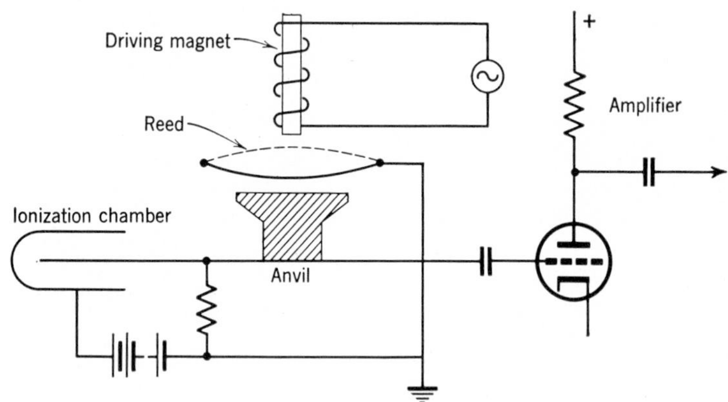

Figure 1.23 Simplified schematic diagram of the vibrating-reed electrometer.

The vibrating-reed (or dynamic condenser) electrometer (Palevsky et al., 1947; Scherbatskoy et al., 1947) is based on the principle that a small alternating current is more conveniently amplified than a small direct current. The small d-c voltage to be measured is impressed on a condenser (Figure 1.23), one plate of which is made to vibrate at a frequency of several hundred cycles per second. An alternating current is produced and passes through a capacitor into a linear audio amplifier. After sufficient amplification the a-c is synchronously rectified and measured or recorded.

1.14 THE RADON METHOD OF RADIUM ANALYSIS *

1.14.a General considerations

By a fortunate combination of physical characteristics, radon^{222} is the naturally radioactive isotope easiest to measure. First of all, it is a noble gas. It is easily separated and transferred from its parent radium by boiling or by fusion. It passes freely through various purifying agents commonly used in gas analysis (such as ascarite, drierite, catalytic platinum, hot copper, and magnesium perchlorate). It is adsorbed on organic materials such as rubber (Davis, 1947), most

* Prepared by the editor.

stopcock greases, and petroleum products, but can be handled quantitatively in minute amounts when simple precautions are taken.

Second, the combination of halflives of its parent radium, of radon itself, and of its daughters hardly could be more convenient. In all practical applications, the halflife of radium^{226} (1620 years) can be considered infinite when compared to the halflife of radon (3.82 days). Radium-radon equilibrium is established, for all practical purposes, in 30 days. The five daughters of radon^{222} down to lead^{210} have halflives of 3.05 minutes, 26.8 minutes, 19.72 minutes, 1.6×10^{-4} second, and 22.2 years, respectively (see Figure 1.2). That means that when a sample of radon is placed in an ionization chamber, it will reach equilibrium with its daughters down to lead^{210} in about 4 hours. The halflife of lead^{210} is so long (22.2 years), compared to 4 hours, that we may consider it stable in a practical calculation. Radon thus reaches effective equilibrium in a length of time that is quite small compared to its halflife.

The long halflife of lead^{210} thus makes it possible to make ionization-chamber measurements of radon without frequent decontamination of the chamber. In its decay to lead^{206} (through bismuth^{210} and polonium^{210}) lead^{210} emits only 1 alpha particle. Thus the activity of the residual deposit of lead^{210} that plates out on the walls of the chamber and is left behind after the radon has been pumped out (and after its short-lived daughters have decayed) is very small. Even comparatively large amounts of radon can reach equilibrium, be measured, and pumped out again without seriously contaminating a chamber.

The utility of the radon method was recognized by the earliest workers in radioactivity. The technique was used by many investigators for radium analysis, and the detecting apparatus was evolved from gold-leaf electroscopes through string and quadrant electrometers to electronic devices as new instruments became available. We shall describe some of the more recent apparatus.

The radon in an ionization chamber can be measured by counting the individual alpha particles as pulses or by measuring the total ionization produced in the chamber as a current. The pulse method is better for measurements of low activities, and is limited on the low end (about 10^{-14} curie) by the background count of the chamber and on the high end by the resolution of the recording apparatus (Evans and Goodman, 1941). The integrating (current-measuring) equipment produces a continuous record and has a much wider range, but it is limited on the low end by the statistical fluctuation of the recorder trace. Usually it is not convenient to make the time constant of the integrating chamber long enough to reduce the statistical fluctuation to a point where the current measuring electrometer could compete with the pulse counter on samples of low activities. On the other hand, the integrating device gives a continuous record of all operations and reduces possibility of error when large numbers of samples are handled.

1.14.b Gas handling system

Radium in solids and liquids and radon in liquids and gases can be analyzed by the radon method. Samples for radium analysis are stored for about 30 days to reach equilibrium. Samples with high emanating power may be sintered before storage. The radon is then released by fusing the sample *in vacuo* (Figure 1.24) and flushing the issuing gases into the ionization chamber with nitrogen (Goodman and Evans, 1941). (The flushing gas has been stored long enough to allow any contaminating radon to decay.) Liquids and solutions are placed in a reflux condenser (Hudgens et al., 1951) and boiled *in vacuo* while nitrogen or argon is being bubbled through. In this way 99.99 percent of the radon can be removed from an aqueous solution (Davis, 1947). The standard radium solution used to calibrate the instrument is handled in a similar manner. Most gaseous samples can be admitted directly to the system.

From the fusion furnace, the reflux condenser, or the gas sample container (Figure 1.24), the gas passes through purifying columns to remove undesirable components such as oxygen (interferes with pulse counting), water vapor, and corrosive gases. The ionization chambers are commonly made of stainless steel *bain marie* jars, commercially manufactured for the restaurant industry. The volume usually chosen is about 4 liters and should be large compared to the total volume of the rest of the system. Internal parts are usually made of brass and heavily nickel plated to absorb the alpha particles from radioelements usually present in commercial brass. Most stainless steel is sufficiently pure to make plating unnecessary.

The gas handling system is usually made of glass. For mobile use, where glass would be too fragile, systems made of tygon tubing with glass joints and stopcocks have been used at the University of Utah (Rogers, private communication). Metal systems (usually copper) are used where it is necessary to handle gases at greater than atmospheric pressure.

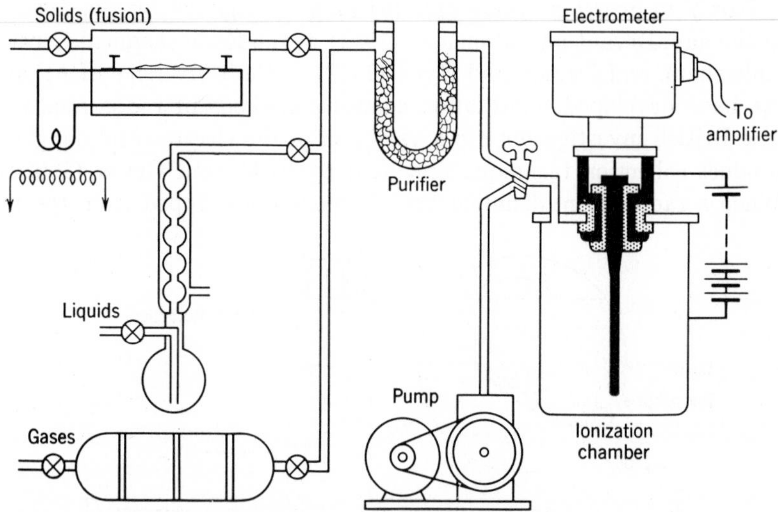

Figure 1.24 Schematic diagram of the apparatus for measurement of radon in solid, liquid, and gaseous samples.

1.14.c Pulse counting instruments

Modern versions of the pulse counting apparatus are used by Hudgens et al., (1951), Davis (Oak Ridge National Laboratory, private communication), Stockmann (National Bureau of Standards, private communication), and others. The limit of detection is about 10^{-14} curie. A high-gain pulse amplifier (Elmore and Sands, 1949; Hudgens et al., 1951) is usually mounted directly on the ionization chamber. The collecting electrode is maintained at about plus 1000 volts with respect to the walls of the ionization chamber. Oxygen must be removed carefully from the chamber atmosphere to avoid formation of negatively charged oxygen ions. The travel of electrons to the collector is very fast, so that the charge on the collector builds up rapidly and a sharp pulse results. Free oxygen captures electrons and forms ions which also travel to the collector, but more slowly, so that the resulting pulses are broad and too small to be counted. The presence of 0.2 percent of oxygen in the chamber atmosphere reduces counting efficiency by 20 percent (Davis, 1947). The oxygen is removed by passing the inlet gas over hot copper or by mixing the inlet gas with hydrogen and passing the mixture over a platinum-black catalyst.

Partly to overcome these difficulties and partly led by the fashion of the day, Bryant and Michaelis (1952) at the Radiochemical Centre, Amersham, and Damon and Hyde (1952) at the University of Arkansas have developed scintillation counting methods of radon analysis. The British investigators use a variation of the electrostatic daughter product collection technique first used by Elster and Geitel (1902*a*). When a radon atom disintegrates, electrons are stripped from the re-

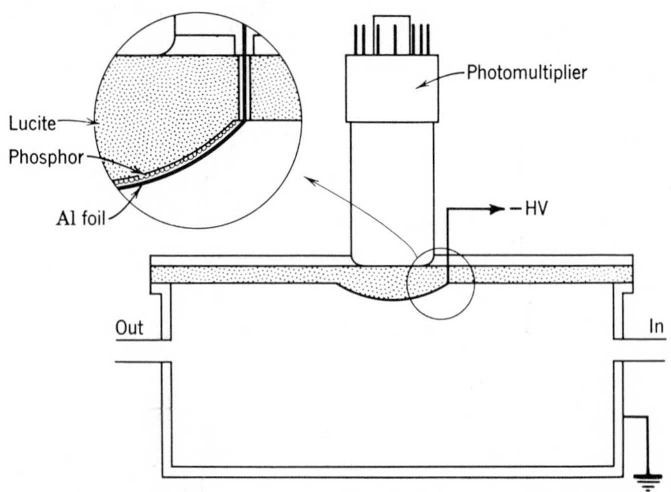

Figure 1.25 Scintillation detector for radon measurement. After Bryant and Michaelis (1952).

coiling product nucleus (polonium^{218}) and it becomes a positively charged ion. When these ions impinge on a solid surface they stick and form an active deposit. Bryant and Michaelis introduce their radon sample into a chamber with one insulating wall (Figure 1.25). A lucite window in the center of the wall is coated with a zinc sulfide phosphor and covered with a thin aluminum foil. The foil is maintained at about 1000 volts with respect to the other chamber walls so that the positive ions are attracted to the foil and the active deposit forms there. The foil is thin enough to pass the alpha particles of the active deposit, and they produce scintillations in the phosphor. The light is seen through the lucite window by a photomultiplier tube. The dimensions of the chamber are such that alpha particles emitted from possible radioactive contaminants on the chamber walls or from the natural radioactive content of the chamber materials have insufficient range to reach the zinc sulfide screen when the chamber is filled with air at atmospheric pressure. Consequently, background counting rates as low as 3 counts per hour have been achieved.

Damon and Hyde (1952) introduce the gas into a chamber internally coated with a zinc sulfide phosphor. The shape of the chamber is designed to permit the phosphor to be seen by a photomultiplier tube. Alpha particles from the radon in the chamber strike the phosphor, and the resulting pulses are amplified.

The pulses from the amplifier are scaled in a conventional scaling circuit (see Section 1.13.a) and recorded automatically. Various investigators have devised different schemes to suit their own convenience.

1.14.d Integrating instruments

The integrating apparatus described by Faul et al. (1954) uses chambers equipped with a guard ring (Figure 1.13). The chamber potential (about 67 volts) is supplied by a battery, and positive ions are collected. The leak resistance R can be varied from 10^8 to 10^{12} ohms. The ionization current passes through this resistor, and the resulting voltage is measured by a vibrating reed electrometer (see Section 1.13.e). Four ionization chambers are connected to a teflon-insulated selector switch which also contains the leak resistors, and special polystyrene-dielectric condensers in parallel with the resistors, to give sufficiently long time constants for the lower counting rates. This arrangement permits continuous operation of the apparatus at the rate of one analysis per hour.

Ionization potentials vary among different gases, and the current produced in the chamber varies slightly with the composition of the gas. Therefore, the integrating apparatus must be calibrated with a gas of roughly the same composition as the gas to be analyzed. The calibrating gas is usually stored before use to allow for the decay of any radon that might be present.

1.14.e Radon^{220} (thoron) measurement

The physical constants for radon^{220} (thoron) are much less convenient than for radon^{222}, but measurements can be made with fair accuracy. Radon^{220} has a halflife of 54.5 seconds, and its immediate daughter (polonium^{216}), 0.15 seconds. The next daughter (lead^{212}) has a halflife of 10.6 hours. Therefore, radon^{220} must be handled very much more quickly than radon^{222}. A continuous-streaming method is almost universally used (Goodman and Evans, 1941), and chambers with very short time constants are necessary. The scintillation technique offers particular advantage here because of its high speed.

1.15 NUCLEAR EMULSION TECHNIQUES *

S. H. U. BOWIE †

During the latter half of the nineteenth century Niepce de Saint-Victor (1867), Henri Becquerel (1896), and Madame Curie (1898) discovered, while experimenting with silver halide emulsions, that both uranium and thorium compounds even when separated from the emulsions by a thin sheet of paper produce a developable image in the dark. Campbell and Wood (1906) later demonstrated that potassium compounds also activate a photographic plate. The application of these discoveries to geological research has been tardy, mainly because the earlier silver halide emulsions were made primarily for ordinary photographic requirements; but more recently special nuclear emulsions have become available, possessing qualities that make them particularly useful in mineralogical studies.

Stěp and Becke (1904) were the first investigators to use autoradiographs of pitchblende to demonstrate the distribution of the radioactive mineral in specimens of ore. Mügge (1909) demonstrated that radioactive mineral grains scattered on a photographic plate produced, on development, a blackening around the grains.

Reinganum (1911) showed that this blackening, when caused by alpha particles, is due to an aggregate of tracks each represented in the developed emulsion by a row of silver grains. This discovery was one of considerable importance, for the recognition of tracks in present-day nuclear emulsions serves to discriminate between blackening caused by nuclear phenomena and that due to pseudophotographic effects. It was not, however, until 1927 that Alexandrov first employed thick nuclear-type emulsions in geological work to illustrate with detailed autoradiographs of polished sections the location of

 The writer is indebted to Dr. R. W. Berriman and Mr. C. Waller, of Kodak and Ilford Research Laboratories, respectively, for their valuable assistance in supplying new emulsion types and for technical advice. The experimental work on which this paper is based was conducted in the Atomic Energy Division of the Geological Survey of Great Britain, under the direction of the Chief Geologist, Dr. C. F. Davidson.

† Geological Survey of Great Britain, London S. W. 7.

tyuyamunite in limestone of the Tyuya Muyun district of Russian Turkestan.

The increased interest in nuclear research has hastened the production of improved emulsions of fine grain and high silver halide content. Their properties are summarized here, and it is hoped that sufficient details of the autoradiograph mechanism are given to enable the geologist to appreciate the value of autoradiographs as an aid to the location and identification of radioactive minerals. Recent advances in technique are outlined; but the more theoretical aspects are purposely omitted. Mention is made, however, of some likely sources of error in quantitative measurements, which have been ignored in previously published accounts.

1.15.a Emulsion types and their characteristics

Normal photographic emulsions are sensitive to alpha, beta, and gamma rays, and, because of the relatively high penetrating power of the beta and gamma rays, they produce a rather diffuse autoradiograph image.

Alpha-track emulsions, on the other hand, are relatively insensitive to visible light and to beta and gamma rays, but are activated by such massive particles as the proton, the meson, and the alpha particle. Since alpha particles are the least penetrating of the natural radiations they produce short-range ionization effects, and alpha-sensitive emulsions, therefore, give the best definition. Moreover, the grain size of alpha-track emulsions is some five to ten times smaller than that of ordinary photographic emulsions and permits a high degree of resolution.

Recently fine-grained dye-sensitized emulsions capable of recording the tracks of all charged particles have been produced, and these, together with normal photographic emulsions, have been grouped for convenience in Table 1.15.1 as beta-sensitive emulsions although no sharp distinctions between alpha-sensitive and beta-sensitive types is implied. The chemical composition of Ilford and Kodak emulsions is shown in Table 1.15.2.

Most emulsion types are available in thicknesses ranging from 5 to 200 microns and are usually supported on a glass plate. Some are supplied as stripping emulsions, as unhardened gels, or as hardened sheets without any support. The unhardened gel emulsions (Ilford C2, G5 and E1) are liquid under normal conditions and have a short storage life. They are particularly useful in work with thin and polished sections.

Table 1.15.1 Characteristics of some nuclear emulsions

Emulsion Type	Particular Properties	Grain Diameter * (microns)	Image Density †
	ALPHA-SENSITIVE EMULSIONS		
Ilford, E1	Emulsion of low sensitivity suitable for track length measurements	0.12	0.05
Kodak, NT-1a	More sensitive than E1; gives clearly defined alpha tracks	0.15–0.2	. . .
Ilford, C2	Similar to NT-1a	0.16	0.11
Kodak, NT-2a	Sensitive emulsion; records alpha particles and low-energy beta particles	0.2–0.3	0.26
Ilford, B2	Similar to NT-2a	0.21	0.67
	BETA-SENSITIVE EMULSIONS		
Kodak, NT-4	Sensitive to all charged particles	0.3–0.4	1.06
Ilford, G5	Similar to NT-4	. . .	. . .
Ilford Special lantern plate	Gives near linear relationship between image density and number of incident beta particles	0.6–1	0.18
Kodak Industrex-D	Double-coated film sensitive to alpha, beta, and gamma rays	3–4	1.55

* Data based on measurements by Knowles and Demers and on information supplied by Ilford and Kodak, Ltd.

† Microdensitometer measurements of image produced by standard source in unit time.

1.15.b Alpha-particle autoradiography

The precise location and determination of the radioactive mineral constituents in a plane surface of a rock are facilitated by exposing the surface in direct contact with a nuclear emulsion plate, and comparing the rock surface with the alpha emission pattern produced in the developed emulsion. When the constituent mineral grains are small there is need for the highest possible resolution. Accordingly, nuclear emulsions of the C2 and NT-1a type are normally employed when the average grain diameter of the specimen is 1 mm or less. If a density pattern only is required, the emulsion layer should be as thin as possible.

Table 1.15.2 The chemical compositions of Ilford and Kodak nuclear emulsions under normal atmospheric conditions

Ilford (g/cm³ of emulsion)		Kodak * (g/cm³ of emulsion)	
Ag	1.85	Ag	1.97
Br †	1.43	Br	1.44
I	0.052	I	0.036
C	0.27	C	0.27
H	0.052	H	0.038
O	0.27	O	0.16
N	0.067	N	0.080
S	0.010	S	n.d.
Ca, P, Cr, Si, Na,	Traces		

* Nuclear track emulsions are dried to a constant weight at 105° C.

† In the G5 emulsion the bromine and iodine contents are 1.36 and 0.024 grams, respectively.

The effective stopping power of nuclear emulsions to alpha particles varies slightly with their chemical composition; but, in general, the mean range of alpha particles of the uranium decay series is of the order of 20 to 25 microns in these emulsions. The resolving power of the autoradiographic pattern is somewhat better than 40 microns because the visible alpha-track *stellae* of two minute adjacent radioactive grains can touch and partly overlap, and yet the two sources can be recognized readily.

Polished sections and plane-ground surfaces. With any particular emulsion type the resolving power of the alpha-particle image will be at a maximum when the exposed specimen surface is in direct contact with the emulsion. For this reason, a mounted polished section of an ore affords the best surface for autoradiography (Figure 1.26). It may be necessary to impregnate friable samples with phenol formaldehyde or a similar plastic before preparing the polished surface.

Specimens with rough surfaces. Liquid emulsions and unsupported emulsions 200 microns and 300 microns thick are useful for the autoradiography of specimens with rough surfaces or uneven crystal faces which it is not practical to grind smooth or polish.

Thin sections. The thickness of a rock section suitable for microscopic examination is about 30 microns in good preparations, a thickness which is close to the mean range of most alpha particles. Thus the resolving power which can be achieved with thin sections of minerals is considerably less than that commonly attained with histological preparations, many of which can be cut to a thickness of about 2 microns.

The alpha-particle pattern of a thin section is prepared by exposing the uncovered preparation in direct contact with the emulsion. It is

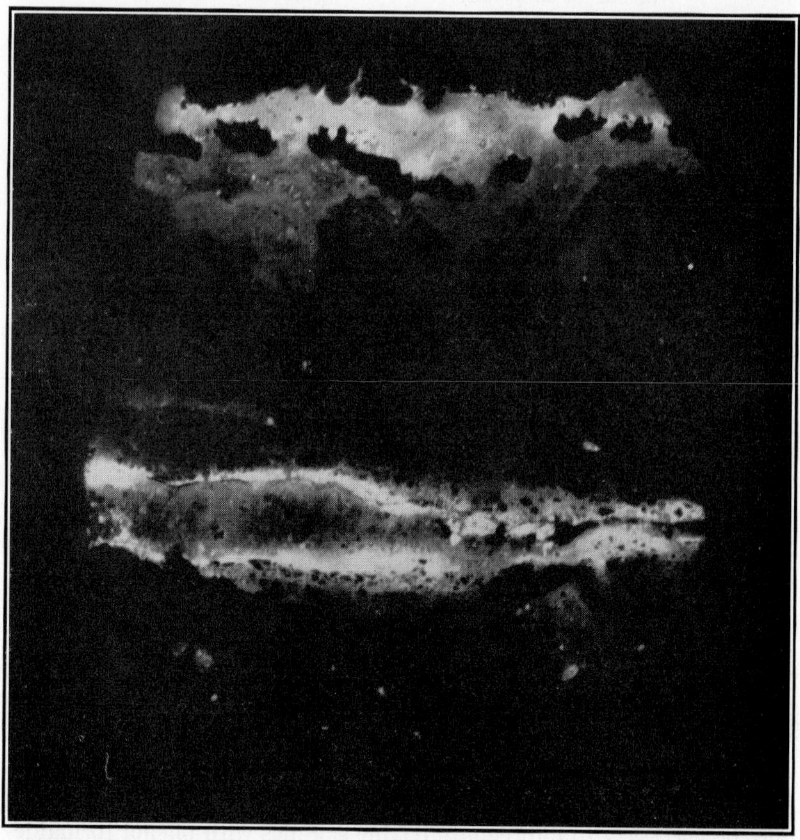

Figure 1.26 Autoradiograph of a polished section of medium-grade siliceous pitchblende ore, showing fine dissemination of microbotryoidal pitchblende in microcrystalline quartz. Areas of high radioactivity are white. Natural size, autoradiograph positive, exposure 48 hours.

important in the study of fine-grained rocks to make the section as thin as possible and to obtain the best possible contact between its upper surface and the emulsion (Figures 1.27 and 1.28).

Sands, pulps, and silts. The technique of mounting mineral grains directly on the moistened surface of a photographic plate is particularly applicable to the location of radioactive grains in sands, silts, or pulped rocks. As the emulsions can be obtained in thicknesses many times that of normal photographic preparations, the mineral grains may be embedded in the moistened emulsion layer, where they remain throughout the processing of the plate. The grains are distributed as uniformly as possible over the emulsion surface and, if necessary, pressed into it with a clean glass plate. If a little care is taken during the processing of the plate, very few mineral grains will be disturbed from their position and the radioactive particles can be recognized readily under the microscope by the stars of alpha-particle tracks radiating from the grains (Figure 1.29).

1.15.c Beta-particle autoradiography

Since Groven, Govaerts, and Guében (1938) showed that the beta particles produce a well-defined autoradiograph pattern in ordinary fast photographic emulsions, beta-sensitive emulsions have been widely used by biologists to measure the relative concentrations of artificial beta-emitting isotopes in plant and animal tissues. The records of geological applications of beta-sensitive emulsions hitherto have been confined mainly to the autoradiography of neutron-activated ore sections (Goodman, 1942) and to the location of radioactive trace elements in artificial crystals (Kolb and Comer, 1945). The reason for this paucity of geological uses for beta-sensitive preparations is to be found in the relatively long range of beta particles in such emulsions, the autoradiograph image produced thus showing a poorer resolution than that obtained by alpha techniques.

Uranium and thorium minerals. Emulsions that are sensitive to beta particles as well as to alpha particles can be used in the autoradiography of thin sections, when time is limited. In rock sections where the average grain diameter is not considerably less than 0.5 mm, the beta autoradiograph, although more diffuse than the corresponding alpha pattern, shows a sufficiently high degree of resolution to facilitate the location of uranium or thorium minerals. Most photographic and X-ray emulsions are sensitive to beta radiation, but they should be used with discretion for quantitative work as the relationship between photographic density and number of incident beta particles per unit area is by no means linear (Yagoda, 1949). Only with lantern slides does this relationship approach linearity.

Potassium minerals. The highly sensitive Kodak NT-4 emulsion which Berriman (1948) showed to be sensitive to all charged particles of any energy has been used by the writer to distinguish potassium-rich minerals from uranium or thorium minerals in ores of sub-mar-

Figure 1.27 Photomicrograph of monazite-biotite-zircon schist: biotite basal sections (black) and vertical sections (with cleavage), monazite and zircon (cracked refringent grains). Magnification 25 diameters, ordinary light.

ginal grade. Potassium is not an alpha emitter, and hence potassium-rich minerals can be readily distinguished from uranium- or thorium-bearing minerals on examination of the emission pattern. Electron tracks are thin and usually highly curved (Figure 1.7) and contrast markedly with the thicker and almost straight alpha tracks. It is difficult to follow the electron tracks to the emitting nucleus, and many short sections of tracks may go unrecognized. The problems and limitations of beta autoradiography of potassium minerals are discussed by Hée and Jarovoy (1953).

Important features of NT-4 emulsions are the stability of the latent image and the high sensitivity; but these very features impose limitations on their value as they very quickly become contaminated with tracks of charged particles of external origin.

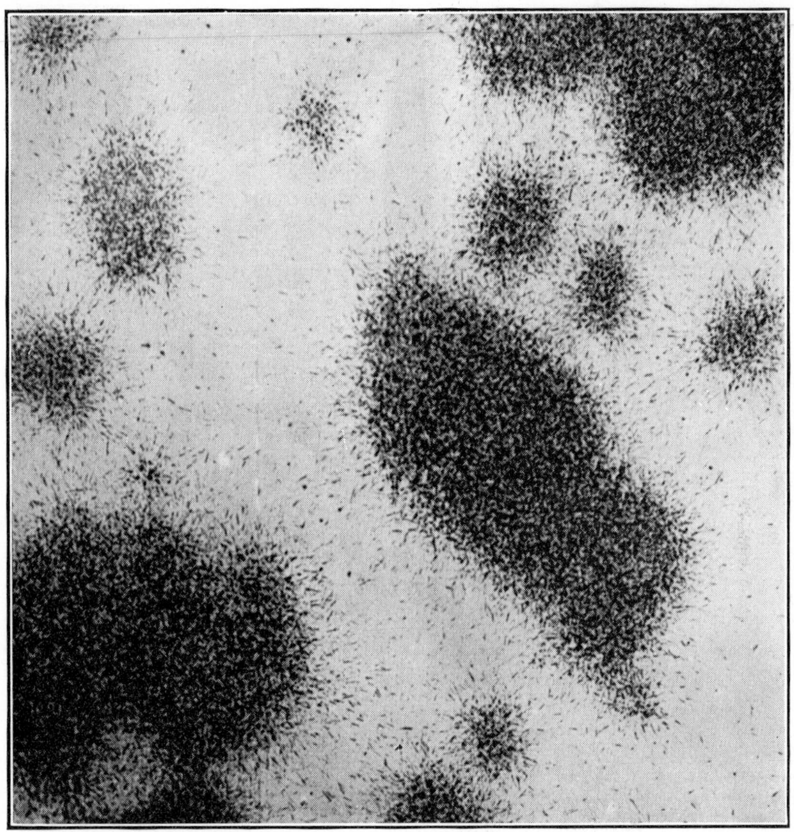

Figure 1.28 Autoradiograph of same field as Figure 1.27, showing alpha-particle emission pattern of monazite grains (dark gray). Magnification 25 diameters, autoradiograph negative.

1.15.d Autoradiograph exposure

Cameras and containers. Various types of clamps, containers, and so-called cameras have been used and described by research workers for holding the specimen in position on the emulsion; but when a large number of samples has to be examined such gadgetry is neither necessary nor advantageous. The writer concludes from experience that the exposure procedure should be kept as simple as possible. The specimen is placed directly on the emulsion surface, unless pseudo-photographic interferences are anticipated, and put in a lightproof box for exposure. Most nuclear emulsions are sensitive to mechanical shock and abrasion, and care must be taken in establishing contact between the specimen surface and the emulsion. Once the two sur-

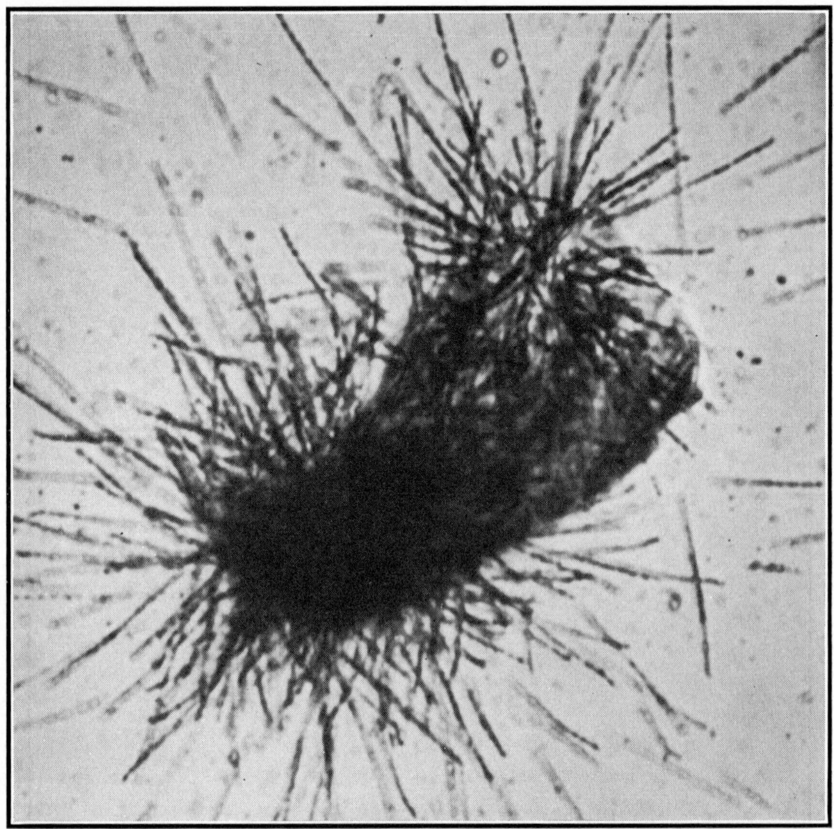

Figure 1.29 Autoradiograph of a barite grain from the Bitter Creek Mine, Montrose County, Colorado, magnified about 1200 diameters. Activity from radium and its daughter products is concentrated at the tips of the barite crystal. T. W. Stern (private communication).

faces are in contact, the specimen should not be moved horizontally; otherwise abrasion marks will result on development.

The box used for storing plates during exposure should be capable of holding a dozen or more small labeled containers arranged so that individual plates may be removed for processing without disturbing the remaining plates. Beta-sensitive emulsions in particular should not be stored in wooden boxes, for the potash in certain woods fogs sensitive emulsions. The containers used for high-grade samples should be thoroughly washed to remove contamination by the solid decay products of radon.

High humidity accelerates the decay of the latent image, and where such conditions prevail the plate and the specimen should be stored in a desiccator. This precaution will also preclude any possibility of the emulsion being desensitized by the mercury vapor which may be present under laboratory conditions.

Duration of exposure. For any particular alpha-sensitive emulsion the density of the image produced is almost directly proportional to the number of alpha particles emitted by a source of unit area in unit time. The exposure time required will depend largely on the emulsion sensitivity, on the grade of the radioactive material, and on the image density desired. Sufficient alpha particles are emitted by high-grade minerals, such as uraninite or pitchblende (90 percent U_3O_8), for an estimate of the activity to be made by counting the track population after exposing the plate to a polished section for one or two minutes. When Ilford type B2 or Kodak type NT-2a emulsions are used a megascopic image is produced by uraninite in 10 minutes and an image dense enough to be reproduced on ordinary bromide paper in 2 hours. These emulsions, since they record low-energy electrons as well as alpha particles, produce an image of the same density as the desensitized alpha-track emulsions types C2, E1, and NT-1a (Figure 1.26) in about half the exposure time.

1.15.e Processing

The development of thick nuclear emulsions has not been standardized because the best results are obtained by varying the techniques with the type and thickness of the emulsions and with the particular purpose in view, e.g., whether the investigator is concerned with the examination of individual alpha tracks, with the density of the aggregate alpha-track image, with uniform depth development, or with maximum differentiation between beta and alpha tracks. For general purposes the metol-hydroquinone developers, D19 and ID19, recommended by Kodak and Ilford, respectively, are satisfactory.

Yagoda (1946*a*) recommended heating the developing solution to 32° C to produce a sharply defined reproducible image, but this procedure is likely to cause reticulation of the emulsion if the temperatures of the processing baths are not carefully controlled. The writer, since 1947, has used a caustic-hydroquinone developer which produces alpha tracks of great density.

The developer is prepared by dissolving the following chemicals, in the given order, in 1000 cc of distilled water:

Sodium sulfite crystals	180 grams
Caustic soda	35 grams
Hydroquinone	45 grams
Potassium bromide	30 grams

For use, 2 parts of stock solution are mixed with 1 part of water. The development of 50-micron emulsions is complete in 2 minutes at 65° F, but somewhat longer time will be required for the thicker emulsions to be developed in depth. Where it is inconvenient to lower the temperature of the developer below 75° F it is recommended that half the quantity of caustic soda be employed and an emulsion hardener introduced between developing and fixing or as a combined fixing-hardener. Approximate times for complete fixation are 30 minutes for 50-micron emulsions and 60 minutes for 100-micron emulsions at 65° F. As a precaution against staining, the plate should be rinsed in water or a stop-bath of 2 per cent acetic acid solution immediately after development.

The exposure time necessary to produce a macro-image of material of low radioactivity can be reduced considerably if the image produced after a comparatively short exposure is intensified. The mercuric intensifier recommended by Jones (1896) as giving the most reproducible results is still satisfactory.

1.15.f Examination and interpretation of emission patterns

Technique. The images in the nuclear emulsion can be correlated directly with the mineral surfaces exposed in the section by inverting the plate, emulsion side down, and matching the autoradiograph pattern with the mineral grains.

When magnifications in excess of 100 diameters are employed exact correlation becomes difficult, and to facilitate this operation in work on ores the writer suggests the incorporation of radioactive grains in the polished section mounts in the plane of the polished surface. For examination, the polished ore section and the corresponding autoradiograph are mounted in the mechanical stages of separate identical microscopes and oriented correctly by reference to the marker grains and their image in the emulsions.

With thin sections this problem is less difficult; the autoradiograph can be superimposed on the microslide, and the exact location of the radioactive material noted by differential focusing. When this technique is employed a low-density autoradiograph image is most suitable. In 1947 the writer devised a frame to hold the microslide and nuclear plate in fixed positions relative to one another. After exposure in the frame the plate is removed for processing and later returned to its original position in the frame for examination under the microscope. If such an apparatus is constructed with precision the location of grains of the order of 20 to 25 microns presents little difficulty. Poole and Bremner (1949) have independently employed a similar method.

Hée (1948) and Picciotto (1949) suggest that the thin section and nuclear plate be exposed to light so that the image of the thin section as well as the alpha tracks are recorded in the emulsion; but it is difficult, and in feebly radioactive transparent minerals virtually impossible, to regulate the exposure to light so that the autoradiograph pattern is not masked by the photo-image.

The stripping emulsion technique outlined by Pelc (1947) has been used for geological studies by Stieff and Stern (1952) and by the writer. More recently, improved gelatin-supported emulsions and liquid emulsions have been prepared in Britain and are now widely available. The main advantage of these emulsions is that they can be placed in direct contact with the specimen to be autoradiographed and after a suitable exposure time the latent image can be developed while the emulsion remains permanently in position on the section. The manual application of liquid emulsion described by Ford (1951) is useful in studies where intimate contact between emulsion and specimen is otherwise impossible, but with this technique it is difficult to obtain a thin uniform coating, and there is added work in hardening the emulsion before development.

Pseudophotographic effects. When rocks or ores are exposed in direct contact with silver halide emulsions a latent image may be produced by pseudophotographic effects, and caution is therefore necessary in interpreting the effects produced on development.

(1) CHEMICAL EFFECTS. Hydrogen sulfide is frequently produced in polished sections of ores rich in metallic sulfides after acid etch tests, and unless such polished surfaces are washed and dried thoroughly before exposure brown stains of silver sulfide are likely to form on the emulsion. Hydrogen peroxide has a fogging action on beta-sensitive emulsions, but, as mentioned below, is employed for the eradication of background alpha tracks in alpha-sensitive emul-

sions. Mercury vapor also has a dual action on silver halide emulsions; it increases the photosensitivity of panchromatic emulsions, but has a marked desensitizing effect on alpha-track plates.

(2) PRESSURE EFFECT. Taylor (1935) has demonstrated that the early nuclear emulsions were very sensitive to localized pressure: if a soft hair brush is drawn across the emulsion surface before development, a large number of subparallel marks resembling long nuclear tracks appear after processing. Experiments with the latest types of emulsions show that they are also sensitive to abrasion, but that, if care is exercised in placing the specimen on the plate, abrasion marks can be eliminated.

(3) PHOSPHORESCENT EFFECTS. Secondary photographic effects can be produced by phosphorescent minerals when they are exposed on ordinary photographic or beta-sensitive emulsions. Alpha-sensitive emulsions, however, are not activated by natural phosphorescence. Phosphorescent effects can be overcome by storing the material in a lightproof box before it is exposed in contact with the emulsion surface.

Fading of the latent image. Several investigators, particularly Blau and Wambacher (1933), Lauda (1936), Yagoda (1946*a*), and Occhialini and Powell (1947), have shown that fading during exposure causes a marked decrease in the image density recorded in alpha-track emulsions. This decay of the latent image varies with different emulsion types, and Yagoda has demonstrated that with emulsions of low silver halide content complete obliteration of the image occurs when development is delayed for 5 days, whereas with emulsions of high silver halide content the tracks are still apparent after a delay of 20 days. Lauda (1936) noted that the fading is somewhat less at lower temperatures and is only slight when the emulsion is stored in an evacuated desiccator. Preliminary tests with boron-loaded emulsions indicate that the presence of boron increases the stability of the latent image and also increases the stopping power of the emulsion to alpha particles, with a resulting improvement in resolving power.

It has been established with reasonable certainty that the latent-image decay under normal atmospheric conditions is due to the decomposition of water in the emulsion gelatine by alpha-particle bombardment (Yagoda and Kaplan, 1947; Bonét-Maury and Lefort, 1948). Delay in development will cause the hydrogen peroxide to diffuse into the silver halide grains and dissolve the metallic silver which is formed during the exposure, thus causing a fading of the latent image. The chemical action of dilute hydrogen peroxide, as already mentioned, is utilized to eliminate random alpha tracks, before exposure of the plate.

1.15.g Quantitative measurements of radioactive intensity

Nuclear emulsions can be employed for quantitative estimations of the uranium, thorium, samarium, rubidium, or potassium contents of minerals or ores.

Estimations based on image density. Homogeneous radioactive minerals produce an alpha-particle image of uniform density, and the image density varies directly as the alpha activity of the material. Hence an estimate of the active element in the mineral can be made with a microdensitometer, using a suitable chemically analyzed standard as control. It is preferable to expose the standard and unknown on the same plate, or on plates belonging to the same batch, for the same period. Preparations from low-grade material, exposed for several days or weeks, should not be compared with those from a high-grade standard exposed for only a few hours.

Estimations based on track population counts. The presentation of the radioactive source to the emulsion is of extreme importance when it is proposed to make assays by counting the track population. Three methods of presentation are normally employed and each has its limitations.

(1) A thin source of known weight is placed in contact with the emulsion or at a measured small distance from the emulsion surface.

(2) The source is incorporated in the emulsion, the emulsion being "loaded" by allowing a measured volume of solution of known concentration to evaporate to dryness on the emulsion.

(3) A thick source, such as a polished section, is placed in direct contact with the emulsion.

The mathematical aspects of such measurements have been treated by Evans (1934), Keevil and Grasham (1943), I. Curie (1946), Coppens and Vernois (1953), and Senftle et al. (in press). It is possible, theoretically at least, to calculate the uranium, thorium, or samarium content of an ore or mineral and to evaluate the proportion of each should they occur together; but in practice this involves the counting of a very large number of tracks, and, in ores containing more than one radioactive element, the accurate measurement of the track lengths.

The sampling error involved in all assay techniques which are dependent on counting alpha tracks is likely to be considerable. Other important sources of error are the difficulties in recognizing alpha tracks which dip into the emulsion at a high angle, equilibrium disturbances, differences in surface diffusion, variations in the effective stopping power of mineral species, fading of the latent image, and the uncertainty of whether one is measuring the activity of a thick or thin source when dealing with opaque minerals in polished section.

Estimations of uranium-thorium ratio. Uranium and thorium minerals can readily be distinguished from potassium-rich minerals by autoradiography since potassium is not an alpha emitter. The distinction between uranium and thorium minerals and the assessment of their ratio are more difficult. Fortunately, the mean ranges of the alpha particles emitted by polonium^{214} (mean range in dry air at standard temperature and pressure is 6.91 cm) and polonium^{212} (mean range in dry air 8.57 cm), the most energetic of the uranium and thorium series, respectively, are sufficiently different to be used as a means of establishing the percentage of uranium and thorium in an unknown source in radioactive equilibrium.

A practical method which obviates the tedious task of counting and measuring a large number of alpha tracks is to make a dual exposure of the section, firstly, in direct contact with the emulsion and then with a thin layer of a plastic introduced between the specimen and the emulsion. The correct screen thickness can be determined by experiment; the writer has found that five layers of 0.0005-inch Distrene have a stopping power approximately equivalent to 7.5 cm of air, and give satisfactory discrimination. The number of alpha particles emitted per unit area of a thick uranium source in unit time is approximately 3.3 times that emitted by thorium under the same conditions.

If the grade of the ore is too low to produce an image of suitable density for measurement by densitometer, the alpha tracks per unit area can be counted with the aid of a microscope fitted with some form of graticule. The attendant statistical error is likely to be great (see Section 1.9).

1.15.h Track length measurement

The photographic technique offers the opportunity to identify an alpha-emitting nucleus by measuring the length of the track and thus determining its energy. The method is relatively laborious, but is used frequently because it can be applied to minute grains and thin sections where the radiating mineral can be identified petrographically.

In order to translate track length into energy, it is necessary to know the range-energy relationship for alphas in that particular emulsion (see Section 1.8.a). This relationship has been determined by Lattes et al. (1947) for Ilford emulsions, but it may be desirable for individual workers to calibrate their own emulsions for most accurate results. Such empirical calibrations can be made by using known finely ground uranium or thorium minerals or chemical separates such as thorium^{230} which gives the characteristic *ionium stars* when exposed in a nuclear emulsion (Isaac and Picciotto, 1953).

The best available optical conditions are necessary for quantitative track measurements. An oil-immersion 100 × 1.32 N.A. apochromatic objective with 25 × oculars of the periplan type is normally used in a microscope with a fine motion calibrated in units of 1 micron. The actual length of the track is determined by measuring its horizontally projected length with a filar micrometer and its depth with the fine motion of the microscope. Great care must be taken to check that the measured track has terminated within the emulsion. Theoretical aspects of the technique are discussed by Demers (1947).

1.15.i Conclusions

Nuclear emulsions afford a method of localizing the radioactive constituents of mineral aggregates. Alpha-sensitive emulsions are useful for assessing the uranium and thorium contents of mineral grains in polished sections, thin sections, and pulps. Assays may also be made of minerals, rocks, or ores in solution.

Alpha-particle autoradiographs provide a record of the distribution of radioactive minerals in a rock section, and can assist the geologist in obtaining information on the paragenesis of the radioactive and associated constituents. The technique facilitates the recognition of changes in the chemical composition of minerals due to leaching, weathering, and deposition of radiocolloids (Yagoda, 1946*b*). The importance of autoradiography in the selection of material for age determination measurements has been discussed by Marble (1937). The homogeneity of radioactive minerals for chemical analysis can be verified by autoradiographs.

The application of silver halide emulsions to the assay of rocks by counting and measuring the individual alpha tracks is at present valuable to the specialist in this field, but the routine application of this method to the evaluation of uranium or thorium in ores would present an extremely tedious task.

1.16 MASS SPECTROMETRY

IRVING FRIEDMAN *

1.16.a Determination of isotopic abundance

The mass spectrometer is becoming increasing important in geochemistry and nuclear geology. It is being used not only in geochronological research but also in the more general field of isotope abundances as related to geologic and cosmologic processes. The number of papers containing data obtained by the mass spectrometer is rapidly increasing, and it is necessary for the modern geologist to add an understanding of this instrument and its limitations to his curriculum.

Of the different types of problems that have been attacked with the mass spectrometer one may select a few examples:

1. Geochronology.
   a. lead-lead and lead-uranium age method.
   b. K^{40}/A^{40} age method.
   c. K^{40}/Ca^{40} age method.
   d. Sr^{87}/Rb^{87} age method.
2. Geothermometry.
   a. O^{18}/O^{16} in carbonate fossils.
3. Cosmochemistry.
   a. Isotopic abundances in meteorites.
   b. He^4/He^3 in meteorites.
   c. S^{34}/S^{32} in meteorites and terrestrial material.
   d. C^{13}/C^{12} in meteorites.
4. Miscellaneous.
   a. S^{34}/S^{32} and the origin of life.
   b. Composition of the upper atmosphere.

The above examples are some of the researches that have made use of the mass spectrometer. More can be found in the reviews of isotopes in geology (Ingerson, 1953; Jensen, 1953; and Rankama, in press).

Although the mass spectrometer is a relatively old instrument, its popularization as a tool for geologic problems is primarily due to Nier and his coworkers. Excellent treatments of the principles of the mass spectrograph and spectrometer are given by Inghram (1948), by

* U. S. Geological Survey, Washington 25, D. C.

Barnard (1953), and by Ewald and Hintenberger (1953). In general, the mass spectrometer consists of a source of ions, the ions containing the element whose isotopic composition is to be determined, an analyzer that separates the ion beam, and a collector and electronic circuit to measure the ion currents produced (Figure 1.30). Most of the

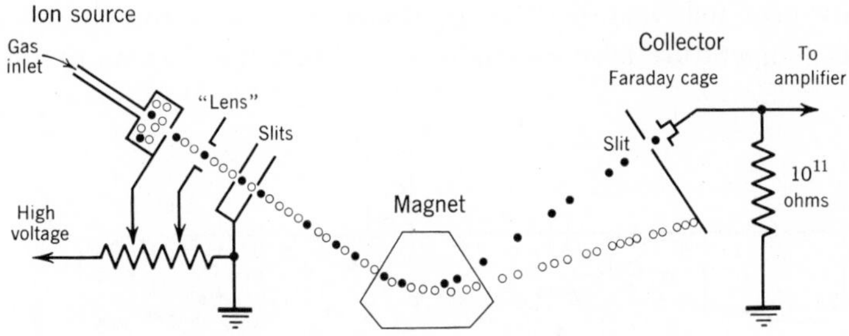

Figure 1.30 Essentials of a mass spectrometer.

geochemical work to date has made use of the magnetic analyzer to separate the components of the ion beam, but it is expected that the newer "time of flight" and velocity selector spectrometers that bunch ions into discrete bundles according to their charge to mass ratio (see *Nat. Bur. Standards,* 1953, pp. 111–122) will find increasing application in this field.

1.16.b Ion sources

Mass-spectrometer ion sources are of two types. In one, the material is introduced as a gas, and, in the other, the sample is introduced as a solid. For most purposes the gas source described by Nier (1940, 1947) is useful. The gas is introduced by means of a "leak" into a region that is being traversed by an electron beam. Electron impact ionizes the gas. The ions pass through a succession of slits, being accelerated, focused, and collimated. The final collimating slits are an important factor in defining the ultimate resolution of the instrument, and in determining beam intensity and relative accuracy of the measurements. Figure 1.31 will help make the operation of this source clear.

The electron beam that ionizes the gas is usually adjustable from 0 to 100 volts. Close control of this variable is necessary for optimum performance. In general, for any gas there is a threshold electron energy below which ionization will not take place. Too high an electron energy often leads to multiple ionization and also yields an ion beam containing ions of widely different initial energies. In the popular single-focusing machines, the focusing properties of the magnetic field are realized only for ions of the same charge/mass ratio and of the same velocity. Velocity spread of the initial ion beam gives a broad focus and results in poor resolution.

Some control method is necessary to give an ion beam whose intensity does not vary with time. Usually the electron source (filament) temperature is so controlled that either the electron flux or the

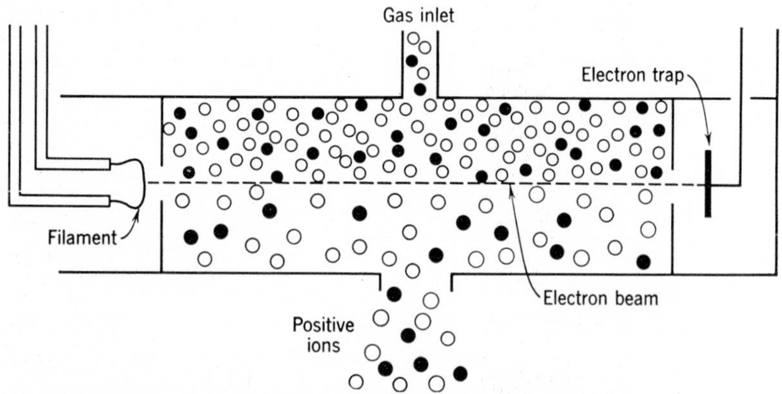

Figure 1.31 Details of the ion source of a mass spectrometer.

resultant ion beam is kept constant. Winn and Nier (1949) have described an emission regulator where space charge controls the electron flux.

The two types of leaks used for gas-sample introduction are the molecular-flow and capillary leaks. The molecular-flow leak consists of two units: a large volume containing the sample gas under reduced pressure, and a pinhole leak connecting the gas container to the mass spectrometer. Fractionation will occur as the gas traverses the leak, for the ratio of the diffusion velocities of the two isotopic species M_1 and M_2 is given by Graham's law:

$$v_1/v_2 = \sqrt{M_2/M_1}$$

The composition of the gas mixture will change with time. This effect is minimized by using large gas volumes.

In the capillary leak the sample gas container is joined to the spectrometer source by means of a long fine capillary tube containing a constriction close to the source end of the capillary. The viscous flow of the gas through the capillary overcomes the tendency for back diffusion of gas at the constriction and prevents fractionation of the gas entering the source. The composition of the gas in the source differs in any event from the original gas mixture, for molecular fractionation will occur during diffusion of the gas out of the tube via the high-vacuum pumping system. More detailed and exact discussions of leaks are given by Inghram (1948), Halsted and Nier (1950), and Barnard (1953).

In order to avoid extensive calibration of the leak systems, a comparison method is often used in which two identical leak systems are connected to the source by a valve system arranged so that either one can be switched into the source, while the other one is connected to an independent waste vacuum system. One leak system contains the sample gas to be measured; the other leak system contains an arbitrary standard gas. The standard gas is chosen so that its isotopic composition will be close to that of the sample gas. By rapidly switching alternately one gas and then the other into the source, one can compare the composition of the sample gas with that of the standard. Relative differences can be determined with far greater accuracy than the absolute isotopic composition. The rapid switching of sample and standard gas was used by McKinney et al. (1950) for the extremely precise measurement of O^{18}/O^{16} ratios in carbonate shells as a method of paleotemperature measurement. Such switching also helps to average out changes in the instrument that shift the zero reference level.

Volatile liquids, such as lead tetramethyl, can be introduced into the leak system, and, in general, the instrumentation problems are similar to those encountered with gas samples. The gas source has been used for the analysis of sulfur dioxide for S^{34}/S^{32}, hydrogen for D/H, carbon dioxide for O^{18}/O^{16} and C^{13}/C^{12}, oxygen for $O^{18}/^{16}$, nitrogen for N^{15}/N^{14}, lead tetramethyl for Pb^{206}/Pb^{204}, Pb^{207}/Pb^{206}, and Pb^{208}/Pb^{207}, argon for A^{40}/A^{36}, and silicon tetrafluoride for Si^{30}/Si^{28}, to mention a few examples of geologic interest.

For the analysis of solid materials of relatively low vapor pressures, such as lead iodide (for lead) and strontium carbonate or strontium sulfate (for Sr^{87}/Sr^{85}), other techniques for the production of a molecular beam are necessary:

(1) A small amount of sample may be placed on a tungsten or platinum filament which is then introduced into the source. If the hot filament material has a higher work function than the sample material, it will pull electrons from the neutral molecules of the sample, thereby ionizing them. The ions are then accelerated and collimated in the

same manner as gas samples. This method has the advantage of requiring only a small sample. Samples of lead iodide as small as one microgram have been successfully analyzed isotopically for lead. The method suffers from the disadvantage that the small amount of material evaporates rapidly, making the method difficult and less precise than an analysis in which one has time to run the sample sufficiently long to average out possible slight fluctuations in the instrument itself.

(2) If the material to be tested has a reasonable vapor pressure (10^{-5} to 10^{-2} mm of mercury) at temperatures under 1200° C, the sample material can be heated in a small furnace placed within the source.

(3) Various other techniques, such as sparking and arcing, have been used. Inghram (1948) discusses this aspect fully.

The introduction of the solid sample into the source usually requires that the spectrometer tube be opened to air, the source removed, the sample applied, and the instrument reassembled, evacuated, and degassed before the sample can be run. The last two steps may require 6 to 24 hours. To overcome this basic objection to the use of solid samples, elaborate vacuum locks have been designed which eliminate the breaking of the vacuum within the spectrometer tube. Owing to their complexity, these locks have not come into general use. Multiple sample sources in which several samples to be analyzed can be run in succession without removing the source also have been used.

1.16.c Ion collectors

The ion collector may be of the Faraday cage type, in which the ion current is collected in a small metal bucket (Nier, 1947). For exceedingly weak ion beams, an electron multiplier is commonly used. The multiplier consists of a series of metal plates arranged so that secondary electrons emitted from the first plate by the collision of the ions focused upon it will be accelerated and strike the second plate. These secondary electrons will cause additional electrons to be emitted from this plate, which are in turn accelerated and focused onto the third plate, etc. During each collision 2 to 5 electrons per collision are emitted. If one uses a multiplier containing 10 dynodes (emitting plates), a current gain of 10^3 to 10^6 will result.

The final current from a collection of either the Faraday cage type or the electron multiplier is passed through a high resistance to ground. The flow of current through this resistor (usually 10^9 to 10^{12} ohms) develops a difference in potential which is amplified by a d-c amplifier or vibrating-reed electrometer (see Section 1.13.e).

1.16.d Limitations of the technique

The natural differences in isotope ratios are relatively minor, and great precision is necessary to secure significant results. For example, the maximum difference in the D/H ratio in nature is about 15 per cent. In order to measure this quantity with an accuracy of about ½ percent, we must measure the difference between 1.000/6700 and 1.005/6700. In order to do this, the electronic components must be stable to 1 part in 1000 or better for periods of several hours and to 1 part in 10,000 for shorter periods. Because we are measuring an ion current composed of individual particles generated by random events, the statistics of random processes operate (see Section 1.9), and, in order to secure favorable statistics, rather sizable ion beams are favored. However, the securing of large ion currents means a loss of resolution, and some compromise is usually adopted.

With the usual magnetic analyzer instrument of fixed radius of curvature, the resolution is fixed by the source and collector slit size, by the gas pressure in the source and analyzer tube, as well as by the ionization method. The resolution is usually expressed by the number of mass units that can be separated; i.e., 1 in 100 indicates that mass 99 and 100 can just be separated. As the resolution tends to be linear, this means that ½ mass unit can be resolved at mass 50 and that 2 mass units will enter the collector at mass 200 and cannot be resolved.

The usual Nier type 6-inch–60° gas source instrument has a resolution of about 1 in 100, using 0.010-inch slits in the source and a 0.025-inch collector slit. Obviously this resolution is a function of the previously mentioned variables and can be changed. At this resolution a reproducibility of better than ± 0.01 percent has been achieved for O^{18}/O^{16} analysis, using carbon dioxide as the gas to be analyzed. This precision is obtainable only by the use of intense ion beams, very stable electronic circuits, close temperature and humidity control of the entire instrument ($\pm 1°$ F, relative humidity less than 50 percent at 72° F), and by a system of simultaneous collection of the two ion beams whose ratio is to be compared to the ratio in a standard gas.

In this double collection method both ion beams are simultaneously collected on two separate collectors. In O^{18}/O^{16} analysis using carbon dioxide, mass 44 ($C^{12}O^{16}O^{16}$) would be collected on one collector while mass 46 ($C^{12}O^{16}O^{18}$) would be collected on the second collector. The more intense ion beam is amplified as before, and a portion of the amplified current is used to buck out (counteract) the weaker ion beam. The small residual voltage not completely bucked out, is amplified and recorded. The double collection method is described by Nier, Ney, and Inghram (1947), and the method of comparison of two gases is discussed by McKinney et al. (1950).

By using smaller slits with the forementioned instrument, weaker ion beams, and single collection (collecting and measuring one mass peak at a time) it has been possible to measure the lead isotopes 204, 206, 207, and 208 to about ± 0.1 percent. This accuracy has been achieved on samples where the ratio of the mass 208/207 peaks is not less than 1/20. For lower ratios, the limited resolution has resulted in overlap of peaks and correspondingly poor accuracy.

If one desires to make absolute ratio determinations, great care must be taken to avoid isotopic fractionation while the sample is being prepared. In addition, one must correct for fractionations in the leak and source units. The calibration of the high-resistance resistors through which the ion currents flow is of great importance, as these resistors are seldom ohmic (i.e., the voltage developed across them is not a linear function of the current flow through them). They usually suffer from hysteresis effects (a memory probably due to polarization), and their temperature coefficient of resistance is usually large (0.15 percent per degree C for one popular make). These are but a few of the reasons why absolute ratios measured by one investigator do not always agree with those of another.

The trend in recent years has been to instruments of inherently greater resolution (larger radius of curvature) for mass measurements above mass 100. By the use of 12-inch-radius instruments rather than the popular 6-inch-radius, larger slit widths can be used, yielding more intense ion beams.

1.17 ISOTOPE DILUTION TECHNIQUES *

The availability of separated stable isotopes from the Atomic Energy Commission has made the method of isotope dilution practicable for a large number of elements. The requirements for the determination of any element possessing more than one stable isotope by isotope dilution are:

* By George Tilton, Carnegie Institution of Washington, Washington 8, D. C.

1. A standardized solution (sometimes called the *spike*) of an isotopically altered carrier of the element to be determined.
2. A procedure for equlibrating a known weight of the carrier (spike) with the sample to be analyzed and for extracting enough of the element to be determined to permit isotope analysis.
3. A mass spectrometer to perform the isotpe analyses required. These analyses include those of the carrier, of the carrier plus sample, and, for elements of variable isotopic composition, of the sample alone. In addition a blank is usually necessary.

Figure 1.32 illustrates the various measurements required for the determination of the thorium content of a zircon mineral. The tho-

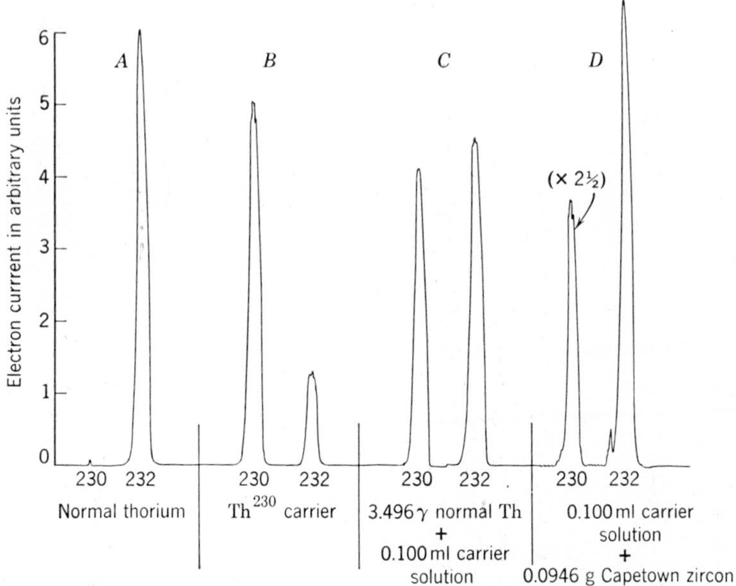

Figure 1.32 Mass spectrograms for a thorium analysis of zircon from the Capetown granite, South Africa, by the isotope dilution method. Carnegie Institution (1954).

rium^{230} carrier in this case has been separated from a thorium-deficient uranium ore from the Colorado Plateau (Tilton et al., 1952). The carrier solution has been standardized by equilibrating an aliquot of a solution of the carrier with an aliquot of a solution of normal thorium of known strength.

Chemical processing need be quantitative only during the dissolution of the sample and its equilibration with the isotopicallly altered carrier. Beyond this point the result will depend only upon the new ratio(s) produced in the carrier by the sample rather than upon the degree of recovery of the element under analysis. This is strictly true only if contamination introduced in processing is less than a few percent of the amount of the analyzed element contributed by the sample. When contamination is high the result depends on the chemical yield of the sample and that of the blank, which may not be the same if the procedure is not quantitative, and on the assumption that the contamination introduced into the sample and the blank are the same. The last assumption will be true if contamination is coming from reagents, but may not be true when it is coming from dust or glassware. It is usually possible to select a sample that is large enough to eliminate the influence of contamination on the result. In an analysis for microgram amounts of an element it is a tremendous advantage to the chemist to be freed from the necessity for quantitative recoveries throughout the procedure.

A further advantage of isotope dilution is the fact that the chemical separation of the element to be determined need not be complete since the mass spectrometer will discriminate between any impurities of a different mass. Even when an impurity peak falls on the same mass unit as the element under investigation, differences in volatility may permit the impurity to be distilled off before the determination is made. A specific example of this occurs in strontium determinations. Varying amounts of rubidium are almost always present which will contribute an impurity to the strontium^{87} peak. In actual practice it is possible to distill off the rubidium in the early stages of the run and finally to obtain pure strontium peaks for analysis. In the thorium determination cited here it is not necessary to achieve complete separation from zirconium, cerium, or uranium as is usually required in analytical procedures for the element. The exact amount of impurities that can be tolerated in an analysis varies with the emitting characteristics of the impurities. The total amount of impurities usually must be reduced to an amount of the same order of magnitude as the element that is being analyzed; otherwise it is usually found that peak intensities vary somewhat erratically over the course of the run and reduce the accuracy of the ratio measurement.

In general it has been possible to determine a few micrograms of a given element to an accuracy of a few percent with the mass spectrometer. The actual sensitivity for any particular element varies with the purity of the enriched isotope used as the carrier and the amount of the isotope that must be used to obtain a satisfactory run with the mass spectrometer. Ordinary surface ionization technique requires some tens of micrograms for a satisfactory run; however, this amount can be reduced to a microgram or less by electron multiplier techniques. Rubidium analyses have been reported on as little as 0.01 microgram (Tomlinson and DasGupta, 1953).

For many elements, isotope dilution has the highest sensitivity of any method known. To take thorium as an example, recent work indicates that it is possible to measure 1 microgram of thorium with an accuracy of ± 15 percent with the best radiometric technique (Dalton et al., 1953). With the mass spectrometer equipped with an electron multiplier and with 5 micrograms of the thorium^{230} carrier shown in Figure 1.32, it is possible to measure 1 microgram of thorium with an accuracy of $\pm 1\frac{1}{2}$ percent (Tilton et al., 1952). For uranium, the sensitivity of the mass spectrometric method can be made to surpass that of the fluorimetric method.

Geologic problems in which isotopic dilution has been utilized include age determination by the lead-uranium method and by the rubidium-strontium method (Davis and Aldrich, 1953), and the measurement of the branching ratio of potassium^{40} (Inghram et al., 1950). The method obviously will be of great use in the determination of the abundance and distribution of trace constituents, particularly, in meteorites.

SUGGESTED READING

Introductory

Semat, Henry, 1946, *Introduction to Atomic Physics,* Rinehart and Company, New York.

Goodman, C. (editor), 1947, *The Science and Engineering of Nuclear Power, Volume 1,* Addison-Wesley, Cambridge, Massachusetts.

Friedlander, G., and J. W. Kennedy, 1949, *Introduction to Radiochemistry,* John Wiley & Sons, New York. (Contains excellent introduction to the elements of nuclear physics.)

Siri, W. E., 1949, *Isotopic Tracers and Nuclear Radiations,* McGraw-Hill, New York.

Bitter, Francis, 1950, *Nuclear Physics,* Addison-Wesley, Cambridge, Massachusetts.

Lapp, R. E., and H. L. Andrews, 1954, *Nuclear Radiation Physics,* Prentice-Hall, New York.

Advanced

Fermi, Enrico, 1950, *Nuclear Physics,* University of Chicago Press.

Blatt, J. M., and V. F. Weisskopf, 1952, *Theoretical Nuclear Physics,* John Wiley & Sons, New York.

Segrè, S. (editor), 1953, *Experimental Nuclear Physics* (3 volumes), John Wiley & Sons, New York.

Reviews

Beckerley, J. G. (editor), 1951 and annually thereafter, *Annual Review of Nuclear Science,* Ann. Reviews, Inc., Stanford, California.

Frisch, O. R. (editor), 1950, continuing series, *Progress in Nuclear Physics,* Academic Press, New York.

Chapter 2

URANIUM AND THORIUM

2.1 THE DISTRIBUTION OF URANIUM AND THORIUM IN IGNEOUS ROCKS *

E. S. LARSEN, JR.,† AND GEORGE PHAIR †

The distribution of uranium and thorium in igneous rocks is not yet well documented. Many problems of sampling, analysis, and interpretation remain. This account describes the present state of progress. The work of the last few years has served to point up the variability of the different igneous rock groups. Although most of the fresh igneous rocks have uranium contents lower than 7 ppm, some radioactive samples contain as much as 200 ppm uranium and 500 ppm thorium. High contents of uranium and thorium usually can be correlated with other compositional peculiarities. In this summary we have followed Evans and Goodman's implicit recommendation (1941) in attaching greater significance to work done since 1936.

2.1.a Sampling and analytical errors involved in radioactivity, uranium, and thorium determinations on igneous rocks

In part the higher values reported in the older literature seem to be due to radioactive contamination in the chemicals used and in part to less reliable radium and thorium standards (Evans and Goodman, 1941). Some of the differences remain unexplained. Prior to 1941 the most complete summary of the radioactivities of igneous rocks was that of Jeffreys (1936). Evans and Goodman's (1941) average radium contents run about 40 percent less than Jeffreys' (1936) figures for average igneous rocks and about 60 percent less for basic rocks.

Uranium and thorium give complex spectra lacking in persistent strong lines and as a result cannot be determined by standard spec-

* The research reported here was supported in part by the Division of Raw Materials and the Division of Research of the Atomic Energy Commission.

† U. S. Geological Survey, Washington 25, D. C.

trographic procedures in most igneous rocks. A highly sensitive analytical method, the fluorimetric technique, has been developed (Grimaldi et al., 1952). It gives reproducible results for uranium contents as low as a fraction of a part per million. The precision of the method is believed to be about ±15 percent for uranium contents lower than 10 ppm. Previous workers determined radium by the radon method (see Section 1.14) and calculated the uranium content from the known radium content, assuming equilibrium. However, part of the uranium in most granitic rocks is readily leachable. Such uranium may not be in equilibrium with its daughter products.

The determination of small amounts of thorium poses a difficult problem. New chemical methods (Grimaldi et al., 1954) and radiochemical methods (Rosholt, in press) give useful results when the thorium content is greater than about 0.01 percent, but these methods are inadequate when applied to lower concentrations. In the low range represented by the great bulk of igneous rocks, thorium at present must be determined either directly by the thoron streaming method (see Section 1.14) or indirectly by alpha counting combined with fluorimetric analysis for uranium. Neither of these methods is very satisfactory.

In resolving the fine details of the distribution of uranium and thorium in igneous rocks, alpha-sensitive photographic emulsions applied to uncovered thin sections are the most useful (see Section 1.15). Under ideal conditions many of the radioactive elements can be identified by their characteristic track lengths and track patterns. Because of the short halflives of its four daughters, thorium gives characteristic stars consisting of five tracks.

The accessory minerals in granitic rocks are generally more erratically distributed throughout the rock than are the essential minerals. In banded rocks many of the radioactive minerals, zircon, sphene, allanite, and even uraninite, tend to segregate with the dark minerals. Such dark bands are particularly common along the contaminated border of igneous bodies and may account for some of the increased radioactivity commonly localized within the border zones of stocks and batholiths. Samples must be large and properly distributed to be representative.

Much of the radioactivity in igneous rocks is concentrated in the mildly radioactive common accessories, zircon, sphene, and apatite. The highly radioactive minerals, monazite, allanite, pyrochlore, xenotime, uraninite, and thorite, though much scarcer than the common accessories, may be of widespread but spotty distribution in igneous rocks showing normal radioactivity. A single grain of uraninite in a million of the normal rock minerals contributes nearly half of the total uranium of a sample averaging 4 ppm uranium by weight. To design the sampling procedure so as to insure that such stray grains be adequately represented poses a knotty problem. Part of the answer lies in preparing a sufficiently large sample, adequately mixed, ground and split.

Evidence also has been accumulated which suggests that the leachable uranium content of an igneous rock is not uniformly distributed. Preliminary data suggest that the non-leachable uranium content of some species of accessory minerals varies rather widely from crystal to crystal within a single hand specimen. Metamict and non-metamict zircon from the same rock may differ in radioactivity by as much as tenfold, and a similar difference in radioactivity may be found from zone to zone in a single zircon crystal (Larsen et al., 1953). More data on these phenomena will be given in later sections.

2.1.b Generalized averages and their limitations

Averages for the alpha activity and for the uranium and thorium contents of broad igneous rock types have been compiled by several investigators as a basis for specific geophysical calculations (Chapter 5). The averages for the different rock types are known only within wide limits, and the boundaries of the rock types themselves are often poorly defined. Much analytical care has been lavished on material which, for geologic purposes, is inadequately described. Table 2.1.1 summarizes that data which in our opinion is the most reliable for North America.

Table 2.1.1 Average radioactivity, uranium, and thorium contents of broad igneous rock types with particular reference to North America

	Alpha Activity (alpha/mg-hour)	Radium ($\times 10^{-12}$ g/g)	Uranium (ppm)	Thorium (ppm)
Stony meteorites				
Paneth (1948)			0.35	1.0
Davis (1950)		0.0034 ± 0.0013	1.0	
Ultramafic rocks				
Davis (1947)		0.01	0.03	
Gabbroic rocks				
Evans & Goodman (1941)	0.61 ± 0.07	0.38 ± 0.03	0.96 ± 0.11	3.9 ± 0.6
Keevil (1938*a*)			0.94	2.83
Intermediate rocks				
Evans & Goodman (1941)	0.90 ± 0.16	0.51 ± 0.05	1.4 ± 0.2	4.4 ± 1.2
Senftle & Keevil (1947)			2.27 to 3.03	9.28 to 10.5
Granitic rocks				
Evans & Goodman (1941)	2.2 ± 0.2	1.37 ± 0.17	3.0 ± 0.3	13 ± 2.0
Keevil (1938*a*)			2.77	7.94
Senftle & Keevil (1947)			3.84 to 4.02	13.1 to 13.5

Jeffreys (1952) notes that in a small set of samples of a single rock type from a single region the difference in radioactivity contents between the two extremes may be six to eight times the smaller of the two measurements. He concludes that in such a set of measurements the individual radioactivities are distributed according to a Pearson type III curve "showing a concentration at values less than the mean and a long tail extending far above the mean." Ahrens (1954) observes that the distribution of trace elements in granites and gabbros from Canada and the United States appears to be normal only when the dispersion is small. All elements, irrespective of whether they have a small or large dispersion, show a distribution that is lognormal or at least roughly so. An assumption of normal distribution leads to erroneous predictions about the prevalence of various concentrations of an element if its dispersion is large. The radioelements in igneous rocks are so dilute as to approach zero concentration in all but the most radioactive types. As a result the range of permissible downward deviation is limited from the outset; the permissible upward range knows no such restrictions.

Several writers have studied the variation in radioelement content of the broad rock types as a function of world-wide geography. Davidson (1951) notes that regional radiometric surveys have outlined broad areas of unusually high radioactivity of igneous rocks in northern Michigan, Africa, and Canada. He implies that the present averages may have to be drastically revised. Jeffreys (1952) noted systematic differences among the radium and thorium averages for given rock types determined for different regions. Jeffreys' subdivisions are shown in Table 2.1.2. A more detailed breakdown on a geographic basis is given by Birch (Table 5.4).

Regional averages differentiated solely on the basis of geography are open to much the same objections as are the world-wide averages —they ignore the petrologic facts. The lumping of variable rocks under generalized categories obscures mineralogical and chemical distinctions which might go far toward explaining the dispersion of the data. For example, both the common calc-alkaline granites and the less common alkalic varieties are included under a common heading, yet the difference in radioactivity contents between the two subtypes is commonly many times greater than that between calc-alkaline granite and gabbro.

Table 2.1.2 Mean radium and thorium contents of various rock types in different geographic regions

After Jeffreys, 1952

	Ra (10^{-12} g/g)	Th (10^{-6} g/g)
Granites		
North America, Greenland, Iceland, Ireland, and Japan	1.59 ± 0.12	8.1
Finland	4.66 ± 0.40	28.0 ± 2.4
Alps	4.43 ± 0.68	33.0 ± 5.0
South Africa	2.36 ± 0.16	
Basalts		
North America,* Greenland, Scotland, and Ireland	0.96 ± 0.06	9.8 ± 0.8
England, Germany, France, and Hungary	1.30 ± 0.13	8.8 ± 1.0
Plateau Basalts	0.73 ± 0.03	5.2 ± 0.2
Oceanic Island Basalts	0.90 ± 0.03	4.6 ± 0.3
Dunites (world)	0.42 ± 0.06	3.3 ± 0.3

* Jeffreys notes that in view of the variability found by Evans and Goodman (1941), North American basalts are probably too complex to be included under one heading.

2.1.c Studies of special interest to geologists

From the geologist's point of view, a smaller number of samples, taken from a single structural province, magma series, or large intrusion gives more information than the generalized averages presented in Table 2.1.1. Many such studies have been concerned primarily with the distribution of radioactivity *per se* within single intrusive bodies. The source of the radioactivity, whether uranium or thorium, usually is not known. Most of the systematic work along these lines has been done by Keevil and coworkers at Toronto, particularly by Slack and Whitham (1951). "The distribution of radioactivity in related rock types is such that it has correlative value. The results of several hundred determinations of radioactivity have shown a tendency for the elements to concentrate in the periphery of batholiths or stocks. In intrusives greater than two miles across, a core of lower than average radioactivity may be present if erosion has removed the roof" (Ingham and Keevil, 1951).

This inhomogeneity poses another sampling problem in the field. Normally it would be expected that the enriched border of any large batholith is small in comparison with the area of the whole complex.

One must not weight the averages by taking too much data from the border zone.

A study of several hundred unusually radioactive porphyry dikes and small stocks in the Front Range, Colorado, indicates that the distribution of radioactive constituents in these small fine-grained intrusions is more nearly uniform than in the large bodies except where hydrothermal alteration has been particularly intense. No systematic contact effect is noted.

Poole and Joly (1924), Piggot (1938), and Barth (1938) have studied the variation of radium content in Finnish granites. Sahama (1946) has made a detailed study of the regional variation in trace element content of the Rapakivi granite of Finland. Rankama (1946) has assembled data on the trace element content (including radium and thorium) of granites of widely different ages throughout the world. He has advanced the interesting hypothesis that the content of lithophile trace elements decreases with geologic age of the granite.

Adams and coworkers at the University of Wisconsin measured the alpha activity and uranium contents of glassy rocks, including obsidians, pitchstones, and tektites, few of which have as much as 0.5 percent CaO. The results are summarized in Section 2.2. Preliminary evidence from several sources suggests that volcanic rocks and hypabyssal rocks (Black Hills porphyries—Friedman, unpublished; Front Range porphyries—Phair, unpublished) may average somewhat higher in radioactivity and in uranium content than do plutonic rocks of similar composition.

Commonly, as much as 40 percent of the uranium in most fresh-appearing igneous rocks is readily leachable. The exact distribution of this radioactivity is largely unknown. The leachable radioactivity may occur: (1) in metamict phases of primary silicates, (2) as interstitial material derived from late-magmatic, deuteric, or hydrothermal solutions, (3) in certain non-metamict partly soluble radioactive accessories, such as apatite, and (4) as adsorbed ions in disseminated weathering products such as iron oxide. At present none of these possibilities can be ruled out entirely; the question is one of degree.

Davis and Hess (1949) in their study of the distribution of radioactivity in ultramafic rocks suggested that virtually all the radium content of these rocks is contained in a small volume of late-stage minerals: kaemmerite, talc, tremolite, and serpentine. These late-stage minerals are believed to have been formed from the residual solutions in the normal course of crystallization of the rock.

Hurley (1950) noted that granulated samples of several granites gave much higher alpha-particle emission rates than one would expect from the known uranium and thorium contents of the bulk rocks. He found that the excess radioactivity, amounting to as much as 90 percent of the total radioactivity, could be removed by leaching in 1:5 HCl. Prior to leaching, a very high proportion of the alpha particles gave abnormally high pulses. Together these facts implied that the excess radioactivity was present as coatings along fractures and on grain surfaces. Because the surface samples of granites tested contained a larger quantity of leachable radioelements than did the samples of granite at depth, Hurley suggested that the excess radioelements may have been due to actual supergene enrichment.

Working with highly radioactive quartz bostonite, Phair (unpublished) found that about 50 percent of the actual uranium content was removed on the average under leaching conditions similar to those described by Hurley. Larsen (unpublished), working with heavy mineral separates from granites, found that a substantial part of the uranium and also part of the lead content could be leached from some samples by concentrated acid.

Brown and coworkers at the California Institute of Technology have spent much time in an effort to determine the chemical constituents of the leachable materials. They found (Brown et al., 1953*a*, *b*) that, although the total content of leachable material in the granitic rocks is variable, ranging from about 0.009 percent to 0.55 percent of the total rock, the actual composition of the leachable material is remarkably similar for all. SiO_2 is low in all cases, ranging from 2 percent to 6 percent. Major constituents are CaO (15 to 45 percent), Fe_2O_3 (11 to 46 percent), and Al_2O_3 (20 to 32 percent). The concentrations of minor constituents in the leachable fraction vary widely, and are related to the amounts of trace elements in the original rock and to the chemical nature of the elements. As much as 40 percent of the rare earths in granite is in the leachable fraction.

One interpretation now popular is that the leachable material may represent a sample of the last material to solidify in the igneous rock. As noted by Brown et al. (1953*b*), "the greatest trace element enrichment (in the leachable material) occurs where ionic radius and charge hinder admission of the element to the major mineral phases."

2.1.d Distribution of uranium and thorium in calc-alkaline magma series

Table 2.1.1 shows that, in general, rocks rich in magnesium, iron, and calcium and poor in silica and alkalies tend to be poor in radioactive elements. These results are shown more clearly by comparing the rocks of a single petrographic province or magma series.

Such a series is made up of igneous rocks that are related genetically and are of nearly the same age, usually within a few million years. They are confined to some geologic or structural province such as a mountain range or group of ranges, occupying an area of any size from a few miles long to one several thousand miles in length. These related igneous rocks may vary widely in chemical and mineral composition, and in structure and texture, but they have certain broad family characteristics.

An example of a petrographic province is the batholith of Southern California. The rocks are Middle Cretaceous in age and form the backbone of a mountain range over 1000 miles long and over 75 miles wide in its northern part. Structural relations and lead-alpha age determinations strongly suggest that the Idaho, Southern California, and Sierra Nevada batholiths are parts of a single body (see Table 9). The Coast Range batholiths of British Columbia and Alaska probably represent its northward extensions. The entire body thus represents an appreciable segment of the earth's crust.

The rocks of the Southern California batholith range from gabbro with less than 40 percent silica to granite with over 75 percent, but the major oxides when plotted on a variation diagram vary systematically and fall near smooth curves that are characteristic of the province. Compared to these, the radioactive elements when similarly plotted scatter widely.

This scattering is to be expected. Unlike the major rock-forming oxides, the amounts of thorium and uranium contained in the solid phases of the mineral assemblage forming at any particular stage depend not only upon concentration of those elements in the magma but also upon the rate of precipitation of suitable host minerals, such as zircon. In view of the complications arising from this cause, as well as the sampling error, one can hardly expect the uranium and thorium contents or radioactivity to fit the curves of variation diagrams as smoothly as do the major components. Broad belts rather than sharp curves are the rule. Nevertheless, when the number of samples analyzed is sufficiently large, the trend is clear (Figure 2.1).

Our present data on the Idaho batholith rocks and Evans and Williams' (1935) and Adams' (Section 2.2) data on the Mt. Lassen volcanics are quite similar to those for the Southern California batholith. All indicate low radioactivity in the dark gabbros, moderate in the diorites, and rising sharply to high values in the silica-rich rocks.

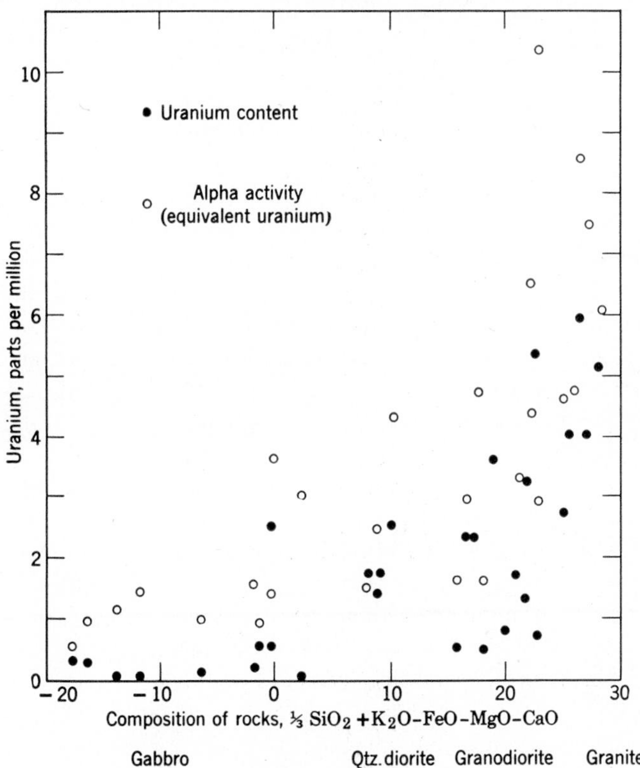

Figure 2.1 Distribution of uranium and radioactivity in rocks of the Southern California batholith plotted as a function of the composition of the rocks.

In contrast to their systematic variation in these magma series, uranium and radioactivity in the lavas of the San Juan region of Colorado are erratically distributed. In general the Potosi rocks, near the middle of the sequence are about 50 percent more radioactive than the Southern California rocks, and the alkali rocks of the Hinsdale Formation and in the pre-Potosi sequence of the eastern area are even higher.

We believe that the Southern California batholith contains about the average amount of uranium for batholithic rocks in general. By way of contrast, the Carboniferous White Mountain rocks in New England contain on the average about twice as much uranium as do the comparable rocks from the Southern California batholith. The White Mountain rocks are, however, more sodic than their western counterparts, and underlie a very much smaller area. It seems to be generally true that highly radioactive igneous rocks have unusual composition and are restricted to small areas.

2.1.e Radioactive minerals

Although most of the radioactivity of igneous rocks appears to be present in minerals with only moderate amounts of uranium and thorium, 7 out of 100 samples studied by us contained from 1 to 20 parts per million of thorite and one contained uraninite. The minerals of moderate to high radioactivity listed in what we believe is a decreasing order of abundance in igneous rocks are: zircon, allanite, monazite, xenotime, thorite, pyrochlore, and uraninite. Zircon is present in most granular igneous rocks, but is rare in gabbros and in ultramafic rocks. In most rocks it averages less than 100 ppm, but in some it is much more abundant. In leucogranites it is commonly present in only very small amounts. In gabbro not only is the zircon sparse but its alpha activity is very low. In one norite the alpha activity of the zircon was only 18 alphas/mg-hour.

In our studies of the California batholith, zircons from nine quartz diorites were found to have an average of about 320 alphas/mg-hour; those from six granodiorites, about 900; and those from four granites, 1960; the ratio for the three rock types was about 1:3:6. The granites from the White Mountain series of New England contain as much as 0.1 percent zircon and the zircon is high in radioactivity, averaging about 1500 alphas/mg-hour. Generally speaking, zircons from pegmatites even when collected from the same area are variable in radioactivity. Zircon is sparse in the lavas of the San Juan Mountains of Colorado, and it is low in radioactivity, commonly not above 100 alphas/mg-hour. The abundance and radioactivity of the zircon in the granular intrusive rocks associated with the lavas are normal.

The radioactivity of zircons from a single rock is generally variable, and individual crystals commonly show alternating fresh and metamict zones. It is not unusual for the metamict part to yield ten times as high an alpha count as the fresh part. Zircon with less than 100 ppm of lead is not metamict and has remarkably uniform optical properties. When more than 100 ppm of lead are present, the zircon shows at least some metamictization, and an approximate estimate of the lead can be made from the optical and other physical properties of the zircon. The average zircon contains about equal amounts by weight of uranium and thorium, but some zircons carry five times as much thorium as uranium and a few contain almost no thorium.

The data available for the uranium content of the common minerals of igneous rocks are poor and inconsistent. In most minerals the uranium content is low and variable. Our estimates for the uranium content of minerals in typical granodiorite, calc-alkaline granite, and sodic granite are given in Table 2.1.3.

Table 2.1.3 Measured uranium content of common rock-forming minerals and radioactive accessory minerals in a typical granodiorite, a calc-alkaline granite, and a sodic granite, in parts per million

Mineral	Woodson Granodiorite, California Batholith	Rattlesnake Granite, California Batholith	Conway Granite, White Mountains, N. H.
Quartz	2.2	2.4	2.3
Orthoclase		1.2	2.6
Perthite	8.2		2.1
Plagioclase	6.0	1.9	5.1
Biotite	2.6	5.2	38
Hornblende	2.8		43
Magnetite	3.5		30,* 14 *
Garnet	7.5	5	
Zircon	1750	4600	1450
Monazite	820		1750
Apatite	62	47	
Xenotime	12,700	360	
Muscovite		8.1	
Allanite			540
Ilmenite			48

* Analyses of two separate fractions of magnetite.

The minerals which contribute most largely to the thorium content of the bulk rock are sphene, allanite, apatite, monazite, zircon, and thorite. Some of the rare-earth minerals are appreciably radioactive and contain up to several percent of equivalent uranium. The minerals rich in cerium and related elements (for instance, allanite and monazite) commonly contain chiefly thorium, and those rich in yttrium (such as xenotime) contain chiefly uranium. Certain niobates and tantalates (pyrochlore, for instance) are known to contribute significantly to the radioactivity of some sodic granites.

2.1.f Uranium and thorium in late-stage differentiates exclusive of pegmatites

"Acid" rocks, in general, have higher contents of radioactive constituents than do the intermediate and "basic" rocks. In some alkalic series, however, as in the Front Range intrusive sequence of Colorado, silica followed an erratic path throughout differentiation (Lovering and Goddard, 1950) whereas uranium and thorium showed a more or less steady increase (Phair, unpublished). Again in the Cripple Creek series in Colorado we have found the older, more silica-rich latite phonolites to be definitely poorer in uranium and thorium than the younger phonolites which are richer in nepheline. Among dike rocks, many lamprophyres contain uranium in amounts quite out of keeping with their low silica contents.

Perhaps the safest generalization that can be made at this time is that the maximum concentration of uranium and thorium is found in the youngest member of a series, regardless of the particular liquid line of descent that the magma may have followed. Most of the igneous rocks greatly enriched in uranium turn out to be late-stage differentiates of granite or of syenite. These include leucogranite, late rhyolite, aplite, alkali syenite, and phonolite. These rocks approach pegmatites in their poorness in CaO and MgO and in the scarcity of mafic minerals. More rarely do they approach pegmatites in texture. Pegmatites themselves must be excluded from consideration here because of the formidable sampling problem presented by these inhomogeneous coarse-grained rocks. At this stage we cannot say whether pegmatites as a group are unusually radioactive, in spite of the occasional find of uranium and thorium minerals of spectacular size in some pegmatites.

The only instance known to us of high radioactivity genetically associated with an early differentiate is found in Mozambique (*Mining World*, 1953). There, deposits of davidite, uranium, and titanite occur in a large body of gabbro-anorthosite. These deposits bear many resemblances to the much more widespread deposits of ilmenite associated with gabbro-anorthosite and generally interpreted to be the result of magmatic segregation.

Nearly all samples of alkali granite and syenite tested to date exceed the average uranium and thorium content of calc-alkaline granite not uncommonly by a several-fold factor. All three most radioactive rocks so far reported are alkalic granites, and are shown in Table 2.1.4.

Table 2.1.4 Uranium and equivalent uranium contents of three unusually radioactive igneous rocks

	Samples	Av. U (ppm)	Av. eU (ppm)
Albite granite, Nigeria	117	130(?)	260
Quartz bostonite, Colorado	67	33	120
Conway biotite granite, New Hampshire	10	9	13(?)
"Average" granite (for comparison)		4	8

All three are the silicic end members of predominantly sodic series, the intermediate members of which are monzonites and syenites. Their compositions are close to the valley of low-melting liquids in the system Albite-Anorthite-Silica, called by Bowen (1937) "petrogeny's residua." Such liquids would be among the last of any magmatic succession to crystallize and, if regenerated, would be the first to form. It may be significant that all three rocks were intruded, if not under conditions of actual tension, at least after the major folding. The Nigerian and New Hampshire granites were emplaced as stock and ring structures, the Colorado quartz bostonite as long narrow dikes. They were intruded at no great depth; fine-grained to porphyritic contacts are common, and the intrusions are generally unfoliated from wall to wall.

All three contain abundant albite, but, in addition to phenocrysts of high-temperature alkali feldspar, potash-rich cryptoperthite is common in the quartz bostonite. Sodic pyrabole is present in all three, but in the quartz bostonite mafic minerals are scarce and nearly completely replaced by late-stage magnetite. Perhaps the most interesting common accessory in all three is fluorite which forms discrete grains interstitial to quartz and feldspar and has the textural relationships of a late magmatic mineral. It does not form cross-cutting veinlets. As noted by Phair and Shimamoto (1952), association of fluorite with uranium and thorium minerals is marked throughout the world. The general affinity of the one for the other can be explained on geochemical and mineralogical grounds (*ibid.*).

The major host minerals for the uranium and thorium differ in all three rocks. Billings and Keevil (1946) found that much of the alpha activity in the Conway biotite granite was localized in zircon and in allanite. In addition we have found monazite and/or pyrochlore sparsely disseminated in some phases of this granite. In the Nigerian granite most of the uranium is said to be present in pyrochlore. Much of the uranium and thorium in the Front Range quartz bostonite is present in zircon, allanite, and xenotime. However, one grain of thorite, clear but completely metamict, has been identified in a thin section covered by a nuclear emulsion; others are thought to be present.

A covariation of uranium and potassium has been noted in the Mt. Lassen volcanic series (Evans and Williams, 1935; Adams, Section 2.2) and in the Southern California batholith rocks (Larsen and Keevil, 1947). The highly radioactive quartz bostonites from the Colorado Front Range belong to a predominantly sodic series but contain as much K_2O as Na_2O. In each of the above illustrations, the rocks richest in K_2O are the youngest members of their respective series.

In the sodic rocks already described most of the albite has the appearance of a primary mineral. We have omitted all mention of "albitized" rocks from the discussion of alkaline suites, in part because of a lack of data, and in part because these are more properly classified as products of hydrothermal alteration than as primary igneous rocks. In general, our studies of the radioactive alkalic porphyries of the Colorado Front Range have shown that hydrothermal alteration, sufficient to bleach the porphyry by removing most of the iron from the groundmass, removes on the average about half the uranium.

2.1.g Geochemical controls of uranium and thorium fractionation

During most of the magmatic cycle uranium, like thorium, is in the tetravalent state, and the crystallization paths of both elements are parallel owing to close similarities in ionic radius. During this interval, when the water content of the melt is very low, magmas saturated with either constituent probably do not exist and no precipitation of discrete uranium or thorium minerals takes place. Instead, their ionic radius and charge dictate that part of U^{4+} and Th^{4+} present enter appropriate host minerals; the U^{4+} and Th^{4+} proxy particularly for zirconium in zircon and for calcium^{2+} in apatite and sphene. Coordination requirements prevent uranium and thorium from entering the plagioclase in place of Ca^{2+}.

Nearly all compounds of U^{4+} and of Th^{4+} are known to be highly insoluble in aqueous solutions in the laboratory. It seems possible that at some time during the "granite" stage the buildup of water may so reduce the solubility of both uranium and thorium that sporadic precipitation of actual uranium and thorium minerals may occur.

Meanwhile, a part of the uranium and thorium present continues to enter the solid solution minerals. As differentiation proceeds to the highly hydrous pegmatite stage, more and more uranium forms discrete minerals and less and less enters the common accessory minerals. Although highly radioactive zircon (var. cyrtolite) does occur sporadically in some pegmatites, the bulk of the zircon from pegmatites studied by us contains less uranium and thorium than that in related granodiorites and granites.

Commonly, at a very late magmatic stage, a change takes place which brings the uranium and thorium to a parting of the ways, the uranium going with the hydrothermal solutions and leaving the thorium to crystallize with the final silicate-rich fraction. It is this change which, in our opinion, makes possible the formation of thorium-free pitchblende ores.

This change, we believe, is brought on by a shift towards more oxidizing conditions. It may result from a relief of pressure caused by intrusion of the magma into higher hearths. Evidence for this shift in oxidation-reduction equilibria is found in the replacement of early-formed ferrous magnesium silicates by magnetite.

Less energy is required to oxidize U^{4+} to U^{6+} than to oxidize Fe^{2+} to Fe^{3+} in standard solutions. In the hexavalent state uranium forms compounds which by contrast to those of U^{4+} are highly soluble in aqueous solutions. Thorium has only the one stable valence, and, as a result, it is not directly affected by the shift to more oxidizing conditions.

Once in solution, uranium will precipitate when for reasons of declining temperature, changing pH, etc., conditions become once again reducing. The fact that the phase so formed is pitchblende, the one richest in low-valent uranium, and the fact that the pitchblende is generally an integral part of a sulfide sequence, give support to such an interpretation.

2.2 URANIUM AND THORIUM CONTENTS OF VOLCANIC ROCKS *

J. A. S. ADAMS †

The average uranium and thorium content of volcanic rocks has been of special interest in several studies: (1) the relation of radio-

* The author is indebted to the Atomic Energy Commission, Research Division, for its support of a research program of which this work is part.

† Department of Chemistry, University of Wisconsin, Madison, Wisconsin.

activity to volcanism, (2) the hypothetical volatilization of uranium from volcanoes, and (3) the possible leaching of uranium from tuffs. For these and other studies, the average and range of thorium and uranium concentrations in these rocks are of fundamental importance.

2.2.a Sampling of volcanic rocks

The sampling of all common rocks is complicated by their very large weight-to-sample ratio, already discussed in Section 2.1.a. Furthermore the possible existence of volcanic uraniferous provinces must be taken into account in any sampling procedure. It is difficult to estimate the relative abundances of the various volcanic rock types. The great volume of the basic lavas and tuffs makes them the most important single factor in calculating an average uranium content for volcanic rocks. Published analyses give values from 0.6 to 1.1 ppm for the average uranium content of basic rocks (Evans and Goodman, 1941; Davis and Hess, 1949; Paneth, 1953). Thus ordinary basic lavas can be expected to have an uranium content somewhat less than 1 ppm. The less abundant acidic volcanics have long been known to have higher uranium concentrations than the basic ones. In order to see how much higher the uranium content of acidic volcanics can range, it is useful to discuss a suite from Lassen Volcanic National Park, California, and a collection of unweathered obsidians and other volcanic glasses from widely separated localities.

2.2.b Analytical errors

The alkali analyses in Tables 2.2.1 and 2.2.2 were done with a flame photometer. One National Bureau of Standards standard sample is included for evaluation of the technique. The average error in the alkali analyses is believed to be less than ± 4 percent of the amount present in these samples. The uranium analyses were done fluorimetrically, using procedures essentially the same as those described by Grimaldi et al. (1952). Cross-checks with other laboratories using the fluorimetric technique gave agreement to within 5 to 10 percent of the amount present in granites, phosphate rocks, and low-grade carnotites. Cross-checks between the fluorimetric and other methods of uranium analysis in the range of a few parts per million are rare. The obsidian from Obsidian Cliff in Yellowstone National Park (see Table 2.2.1) was analyzed by Evans and Goodman (1941), using the radon technique (see Section 1.14). Their value for uranium in this obsidian was 3.9 ± 0.8 ppm as compared with 6.2 ± 0.4 ppm (9 determinations) by the fluorimetric method in this laboratory. The two

Table 2.2.1 Analyses of volcanic glasses from various localities

Locality	% Na_2O	% K_2O	Relative Alpha Counts/ Hour	Average U (ppm)	Number of U Analyses
Lipari, Italy	4.40	5.04	138	15.4	6
Vulcano Island, Italy	4.35	4.82	122	14.1	6
Rocky Mt. Park, Colorado	3.08	5.10	125	10.9	3
Corbitz, Germany	3.32	3.17	81	7.9	5
Grants, New Mexico	5.27	4.28	76	7.9	6
Silverton, Colorado	4.15	5.00	79	7.7	5
Lake County, California	3.94	4.75	77	7.6	5
Frijoles Canyon, New Mexico	4.35	4.42	74	6.9	8
Mt. Taylor, New Mexico	4.78	4.52	60	6.3	9
Yellowstone Pk., Wyoming	4.03	4.90	78	6.3	4
Yellowstone Pk., Wyoming	3.67	5.31	81	6.3	5
McKinley Park, Alaska	3.15	4.36	46	6.0	4
Mono Craters, California	4.16	4.66	52	5.9	4
Götterfelsen, Meissen, Germany	4.40	3.15	61	5.3	7
Tokaj, Hungary	4.19	4.70	59	5.0	5
Ascension Island	4.18	4.50	40	4.9	3
Boulder City, Nevada	3.49	5.27	66	4.9	3
Magdaleno, Mexico	4.72	4.91	44	4.6	3
Newberry Crater, Oregon	5.59	4.05	38	4.5	4
Valle Grande, New Mexico	3.81	4.30	47	4.1	5
New Zealand	5.90	3.45	35	3.9	4
La Piedad, Mexico	4.61	4.15	30	3.2	3
Stromboli, Italy	2.40	2.00	56	3.1	3
Glass Buttes, Oregon	4.17	4.38	27	2.9	6
San Benedicto Is., Mexico	3.51	5.30	36	2.4	3
Amchitka Is., Alaska	4.32	3.50	26	2.3	4
Kanaga Island, Alaska	4.03	3.09	19	2.0	3
Paricutin, Mexico	3.11	3.74	16	1.7	3
Little Sitkin Is., Alaska	4.52	2.09	12	1.0	3
Shizuoka Pref., Japan	4.55	1.86	8	0.80	4
Bur. of Standards standard 91 opal glass					
flame photometer	8.72	3.23			
accepted value	8.48	3.25			

methods were used on different samplings, and at least part of the discrepancy may be due to a real difference in various parts of Obsidian Cliff. However, two samples from different parts of the cliff gave the same value fluorimetrically for U, but different alkali analyses (see Table 2.2.1). Dalton et al. (1953) placed more reliance on

Table 2.2.2 Analyses of volcanic rocks from Lassen Volcanic National Park, California

Rock Description	% Na_2O	% K_2O	Relative Alpha Counts/ Hour	Average U (ppm)	Number of U Analyses
Raker Peak pyroxene andesite	3.26	1.26	11	1.0	2
Andesite	3.83	1.76	16	1.3	3
Twin Lakes andesite	4.13	1.44	16	1.4	3
Basalt	4.36	1.89	23	1.6	4
Flat iron andesite	3.88	1.93	20	1.7	3
Pilot Mt. rhyolite	3.70	1.95	18	1.8	3
Table Mt. basalt	3.81	2.05	23	1.9	3
Raker Peak dacite	3.80	2.15	26	2.0	4
1915 Lava dacite	4.29	2.39	28	2.1	4
1915 Mud flow	4.27	2.52	34	2.1	4
Raker Peak dacite	4.29	2.16	31	2.2	4
Chaos Jumbles dacite	4.32	2.53	32	2.2	3
Dacite tuff	4.53	2.80	39	2.5	4
Raker Peak dacite	4.80	2.65	40	2.6	2
Chaos Crags dacite	4.54	2.99	42	3.0	4
Manzanita dacite	4.73	2.91	49	3.1	2
Dacite pumice	4.43	3.11	46	3.2	3
Pre-Lassen dacite	4.58	2.95	47	3.2	3
Raker Peak dacite	4.30	3.34	51	3.6	4

their fluorimetric determinations of uranium than on their radon determinations. Preliminary results on the one granite sample available show agreement to within 10 per cent between the fluorimetric and isotope dilution methods of uranium analysis for the 3 ppm present. The average error is believed to be within ± 15 per cent of the uranium present for the values from this laboratory given in Tables 2.2.1 and 2.2.2. The alpha activities given are relative to one of the samples selected as arbitrary standard. Thick-source alpha scintillation counters were used (see Section 1.12) with a sample area 20.3 cm^2. Counting on each sample was continued long enough to give a statistical precision of at least ± 20 percent at the 90 percent confidence level.

2.2.c Uranium content

The uranium analyses in Table 2.2.1 give an average of 5.6 ppm for volcanic glasses, including obsidians, giving each locality equal weight. Omission of the low-uranium, low-alkali glasses from the list would not change the average figure much, since nearly two-thirds of the samples are within the range 4.1 to 7.9 ppm, and most obsidians could be expected to fall within that range. The localities have a wide geographical distribution, and the figure is fairly representative. The relative abundance of obsidians is quite small, and, even if the rhyolites were grouped with them, it would be difficult to estimate what weight should be attached to the uranium content of obsidians in the calculation of the average abundance of uranium in volcanics. The average of 5.6 ppm probably does represent a fair upper limit for the average uranium contents of acidic volcanics.

On the assumption that differentiation of the Bowen reaction series type is the dominant process in enriching obsidians in uranium, it is interesting to see how much the differentiation can vary the uranium content of a series of lavas. The uranium and alkali analyses of the Lassen suite are useful in this connection (see Table 2.2.2, Figures 2.2 and 2.3). Williams (1932) has published a variation diagram for

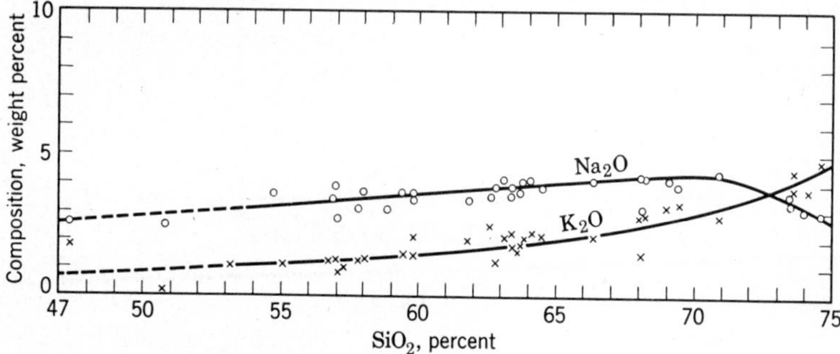

Figure 2.2 Variation of soda and potash content with silica content of the rocks in the Lassen Peak region, California. After Williams (1932).

Lassen, and Figure 2.2 is based upon his diagram. Nockolds and Allen (1953) have studied the trace-element distribution in the Lassen suite. Potassium increases systematically during differentiation, whereas sodium passes through a low maximum. A plot of uranium in parts per million versus potassium oxide in weight percent is surprisingly linear (Figure 2.3) and indicates that both uranium and potassium were systematically concentrated in the liquid phase as differentiation (crystal fractionation) proceeded. Evans and Williams (1935) found a correlation between potassium and radium in the Lassen suite. Their data is independent substantiation for linearity in Figure 2.3. The linearity in Figure 2.3 can be explained on the basis of the exclusion of these two elements from the common minerals formed during the crystallization of the Lassen magmas. The different space requirements of potassium and uranium, as represented by their ionic radii and coordination numbers with respect to oxygen, do not permit them to substitute readily for other common ions. The slope of a trend line in Figure 2.3 is about 0.75, indicating that ura-

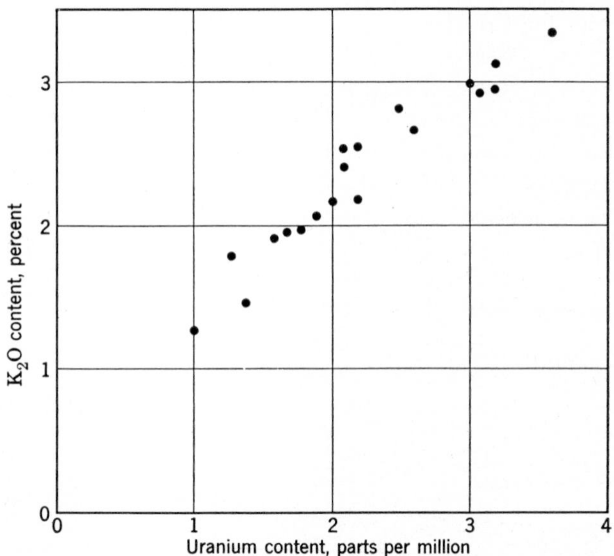

Figure 2.3 Relation between potash and uranium content of rocks in the Lassen Peak region, California (see Table 2.2.2).

nium was concentrated faster than potassium, probably because the latter entered the crystalline phases to some extent.

The data from Lassen show that the differentiation produced a fourfold enrichment of uranium in the most acidic Lassen lavas. Differentiation at Lassen is not very extreme; the most acidic lava is dacitic. Where more acidic lavas are formed, a larger enrichment factor may be attained.

Assuming that crystal fractionation is primarily responsible for concentrating uranium in acidic volcanics and taking 1 ppm for the average uranium content of basaltic parent magma, we find that the average volcanic glass is enriched about 6 times in uranium. The Lipari samples would then be enriched 15 times. However, the possibility should not be excluded that at Lipari other enrichment mechanisms are operative or that Lipari and Vulcano, but not Stromboli, are in a volcanic uraniferous province. It should be noted that the Lipari uranium value is based on 3 different samples from two independent collections, whereas the other values are based on replicate determinations on a single hand specimen.

The differentiation mechanisms just described for potassium and uranium would require that other ions with uncommon space requirements be concentrated along with the uranium. One such ion is tetravalent thorium, which has the same space requirements as tetravalent uranium. Analytical difficulties greatly restrict the number of trace thorium analyses available. A plot of total relative alpha activity versus uranium (Figures 2.4 and 2.5) can give some indirect evi-

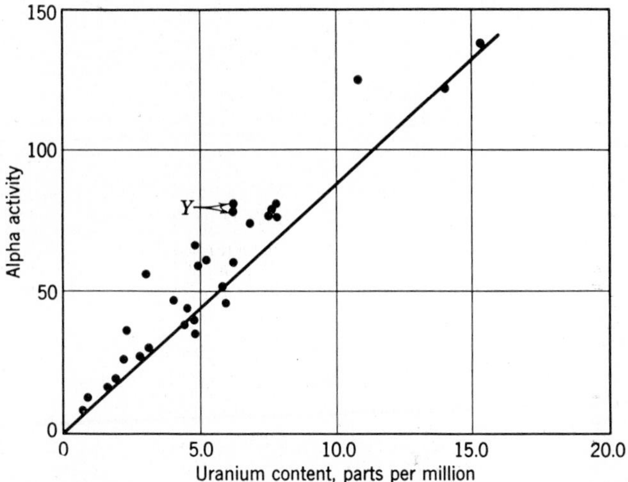

Figure 2.4 Relative alpha activity (in counts per hour) plotted as a function of the uranium content of volcanic glasses from various localities (see Table 2.2.1). *Y* denotes samples from Obsidian Cliff, Yellowstone National Park, Wyoming.

dence of what is happening to thorium during differentiation. Neglecting uranium[235], the total alpha activity can be divided into 4 terms:

$$\text{Alpha activity} = \text{U} + \text{Daughters}_{\text{U}} + \text{Th} + \text{Daughters}_{\text{Th}} \qquad (1)$$

At radioactive equilibrium there is a fixed relationship between parents and their daughters that permits equation 1 to become:

$$\text{Alpha activity} = \text{U} + 7\text{U} + \frac{\text{Th}}{K} + \frac{5\text{Th}}{K} \qquad (2)$$

where K is a constant correcting for the difference between the decay constants and concentrations of thorium and uranium. The decay constant of uranium is about three times that of thorium, and the total relative activity of thorium and thorium daughters will be three times less on this account. Therefore, assuming equal amounts of uranium^{238} and thorium^{232}, equation 2 becomes:

$$\text{Alpha activity} = \text{U} + 7\text{U} + \frac{\text{Th}}{3} + \frac{5\text{Th}}{3} \tag{3}$$

The energies of the alpha particles from the two series under discussion are about equal, and thus their likelihood of being counted in a scintillation instrument is almost equal, as a first approximation. The average thorium:uranium ratio in the accessible part of the earth and in meteorites is about 3 according to Keevil (1944) and Paneth (1953), and, using that figure in equation 3, it is reduced back to equation 2 with K equal to 1. These approximate relations show that if radioactive equilibrium exists and all of the three-times-more-abundant thorium is removed with its daughters, the total alpha activity would be decreased by only about 43 percent. A counting uncertainty of 15 percent would prevent the determination of a one-third reduction in the relative amount of thorium and its daughters.

2.2.d Thorium : uranium ratio

Figure 2.4 is a plot of relative alpha activity versus uranium in parts per million for the obsidians and other volcanic glasses listed in Table 2.2.1. The curve is almost linear, indicating that the thorium: uranium ratio does not vary greatly. Some of the deviations may be due to a lack of radioactive equilibrium. Assuming that Keevil's average thorium:uranium ratio of 3 holds for most of these samples, it is interesting to note that the obsidian from Yellowstone either has a higher-than-average thorium:uranium ratio or is not in radioactive equilibrium. Evans and Goodman (1941) give a value of 5.4 for the thorium:uranium ratio in this obsidian. The precision of the alpha counts and the uranium analyses (about ± 15 percent) does not justify more exact calculations. Figure 2.5 is a plot of relative alpha activity versus uranium for the Lassen volcanics listed in Table 2.2.2. The main deviations are in partially weathered samples, which are almost certainly not in radioactive equilibrium. These data indicate no large shift in the thorium:uranium ratio during differentiation at Lassen. They do provide independent analytical substantiation for earlier conclusions in the literature, based on many fewer samples, that the thorium:uranium ratio in volcanics is fairly constant. Exact and rapid analytical techniques to determine thorium in parts per million concentrations are needed. Several possible methods based upon nuclear track techniques are under study at the U. S. Geological Survey (Senftle et al., in press), the University of Wisconsin, and in France (Coppens and Vernois, 1953).

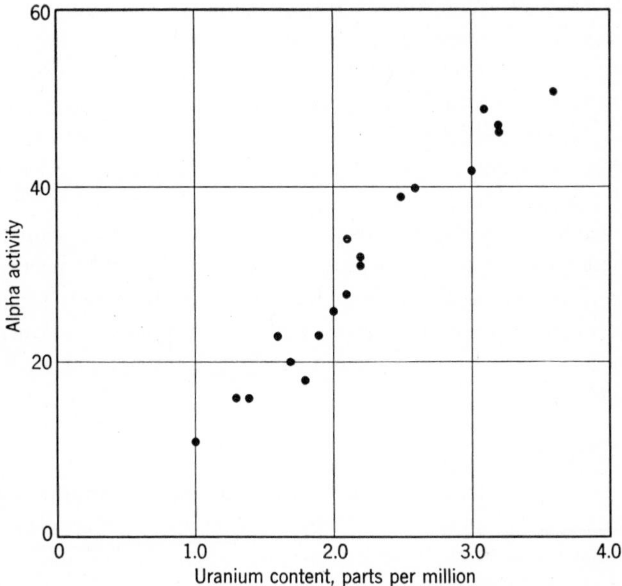

Figure 2.5 Relative alpha activity (in counts per hour) plotted as a function of the uranium content of volcanic rocks from Lassen National Park, California (see Table 2.2.2). The plot suggests that the thorium:uranium ratio is roughly constant in these rocks.

By detailed studies of the thorium:uranium ratio, one may obtain insight into the volcanic and general geochemistry of these two elements. First of all, the fair constancy of thorium:uranium ratios in the volcanics so far studied points to an average thorium abundance that is about 3 times the average uranium abundance. Second, this constancy during differentiation locally as at Lassen (Figure 2.5) and after differentiation in 30 localities (Figure 2.4) shows that uranium and thorium are separated little, if at all, during differentiation. This lack of separation indicates that uranium is probably tetravalent during magmatic volcanic processes. The similarity of the oxidizing potentials of bivalent iron and tetravalent uranium and the high bivalent:trivalent iron ratio in fresh volcanics also make the tetravalent the most likely state for the uranium in fresh volcanics.

Mason (unpublished thesis, Univ. of Wis., 1954) made a thermodynamic and experimental study of the formation of uranium hexafluoride and other volatile uranium compounds under molten volcanic conditions. The results were negative. The formation and removal of this gaseous fluoride or its chloride analogs would have greatly changed the thorium:uranium ratio. Finally, the thorium:uranium ratios may be very useful in discriminating between those volcanic and plutonic rocks derived in part from sediments and those volcanics containing iron and uranium that have never been oxidized. The oxidation of tetravalent uranium to the hexavalent uranyl ion gives it an entirely different chemistry from that of thorium, since thorium does not form an analog to the uranyl ion. Uranium in the uranyl state is leached out of rocks during weathering (see Section 2.3) but tetravalent thorium is left behind. Thus, one might expect the thorium:uranium ratios in oxidized sediments to be much higher than the same ratios in rocks that have never been oxidized. However the present state of the art of thorium analysis does not permit a test of this hypothesis.

2.2.e Conclusions

On the basis of available analyses, the average uranium content of basic lavas is between 0.6 and 1.1 ppm. At Lassen differentiation produced dacitic lavas with 4 times as much uranium as the most basic lava analyzed, and differentiation can be expected to produce acidic volcanic rocks with at least 6 times as much uranium as the average basic lavas. Obsidians with 15 ppm are known, and extreme differentiates may have even higher concentrations of uranium. Present data indicate that thorium is about 3 times more abundant than uranium in unweathered volcanic rocks and that this ratio probably holds constant during differentiation.

2.3 URANIUM AND THORIUM IN SEDIMENTARY ROCKS

KENNETH G. BELL *

Uranium is an oxyphile element which, during the course of magmatic differentiation, becomes concentrated in residual magmas. Oxy-

* U. S. Geological Survey, Washington 25, D. C.

gen is present in all its minerals. Almost all the uranium contained in the earth is believed to be present in the upper lithosphere, preferentially concentrated in acidic or felsic rocks. Uranium occurs in igneous rocks, in part as discrete uranium minerals, and to a greater extent in minerals in isomorphous substitution for elements such as calcium and the rare earths. Some uranium exists in extremely thin intergranular films formed by solidification of the last residual traces of magmatic fluid, or by supergene enrichment (Hurley, 1950; see Section 2.1.c).

Weathering of igneous rocks, and also metamorphic and sedimentary rocks, releases uranium which is later deposited syngenetically in many kinds of sediments and sometimes epigenetically in all kinds of sediments and rocks. Uraninite and pitchblende, which occur as primary constituents of some pegmatites and mesothermal fissure veins and as epigenetic minerals in other kinds of rocks, are readily susceptible to alteration. During weathering processes they are altered to hydrated oxides, phosphates, and silicates, and some uranium is leached from them, probably as soluble uranyl complexes. Some uranium- and thorium-bearing minerals, such as monazite, euxenite, and samarskite, which are primary constituents of igneous rocks, are not readily altered in place but are rather easily reduced by attrition during transportation with clastic sediments. Some other minerals which carry uranium and thorium and which are minor primary constituents of igneous rocks are highly resistant to chemical decomposition and mechanical disintegration. These minerals, of which zircon is the most abundant, accumulate in placers and the heavy mineral fraction of clastic sediments. Most secondary uranium minerals are susceptible to alteration and leaching and are quickly reduced by attrition during transportation with clastic sediments.

Uranium, which is dissolved in surface and ground waters during alteration and weathering of rocks, may be redeposited nearby or may be carried into the drainage system and ultimately into the oceans (Section 2.4). It is removed from aqueous solutions by precipitation as insoluble compounds, by adsorption on several kinds of sediments, and by isomorphous substitution for calcium and possibly other elements deposited in chemical sediments. Some may be extracted by organisms. Uraniferous compounds are precipitated in strongly reducing environments, as for example in the presence of sapropelic compounds or sulfides. Uranium can be adsorbed by hydroxylate gel precipitates of iron, aluminum, and manganese, by gel precipitates of silica, by some clay minerals, and by some organic compounds. The adsorption appears to be rather slight when deposition occurs in waters containing either free oxygen or carbonate ion and increases markedly with decreasing oxygen and carbonate contents. Some phosphatic sediments are uraniferous, and it is probable that the phosphatic material and uranium were deposited simultaneously with some of the uranium being in isomorphous substitution for calcium. Inasmuch as uranium is readily dissolved by weathering processes and subsequently much of it is adsorbed by gel precipitates, clay minerals, and organic sediments, no highly concentrated deposits are formed by deposition of weathering products, and it becomes dispersed in sedimentary formations.

The geologic distribution and geochemistry of thorium have not been investigated as thoroughly as those of uranium. Quantitative analysis for thorium is difficult and inaccurate, and there has been no need to conduct intensive searches for thorium raw materials. Thorium is an oxyphile element. Most of the thorium contained in the earth is believed to be present in the upper lithosphere and preferentially concentrated in acidic rocks. It occurs in igneous rocks in part as discrete thorium minerals and in part in isomorphous substitution for calcium, the rare earths, and possibly other elements. Thorium-bearing minerals generally are resistant to chemical weathering and tend to become concentrated in placers and in the heavy-mineral resistate fraction of clastic sediments. Some thorium is dissolved during the weathering of rocks, but it is easily hydrolyzed in an oxidizing environment; therefore much of it is deposited with hydrolyzate sediments. The remainder is carried into the oceans.

An attempt is made here to summarize the vast literature on uranium and thorium in sedimentary rocks. A complete tabulation of all data pertaining to the uranium and thorium contents of all kinds of sediments and sedimentary rocks, and detailed descriptions of the processes by which these elements are deposited in sediments and rocks, is beyond the scope of this book.

2.3.a Types of uranium concentrations in sedimentary rocks

Uranium existing in sediments and sedimentary rocks falls into three categories, (1) that which is indigenous to clastic sediments, (2) that which is deposited syngenetically with the sediments, and (3) that which is deposited epigenetically after sedimentation ceases. It is probable that all clastic sediments contain some indigenous uranium. Syngenetic deposition of uranium occurs when many clays, gel precipitates, evaporites, phosphatic sediments, and carbonaceous sediments are laid down. Epigenetic deposition of uranium occurs in all kinds of sediments and sedimentary rocks. Some sediments and sedimentary rocks contain uranium belonging to two, or possibly all, of these categories.

Uranium which is indigenous to clastic sediments is contained partly in grains and fragments of discrete uranium minerals, partly in isomorphous substitution in other minerals, and possibly in part in intergranular films between the crystalline constituents of particles and pebbles of igneous rocks. Most of the indigenous uranium content of clastic sediments exists in heavy-mineral resistates, but some samples of sediments and rocks containing infinitesimal amounts of resistates contain measurable quantities of uranium which is probably dispersed in isomorphous substitution in the major constituents. Some residual soils contain uraniferous resistates.

Syngenetic deposition of uranium occurs predominantly in chemical sediments. Uranium may be removed from solutions by direct precipitation as insoluble compounds or by adsorption in several varieties of sediments. Uranium compounds may be precipitated from solutions saturated by evaporation, and they may be precipitated from solutions which have become strongly reducing. Uranium is adsorbed on some gel precipitates, in clays (Beers and Goodman, 1944; Hoogteijling and Sizoo, 1948; Frederickson, 1948), and in some carbonaceous materials (Beers, 1945; Tolmachev, 1943).

Uranium is deposited epigenetically in all kinds of rocks and in many kinds of sediments by a variety of processes. It is introduced by hydrothermal solutions or ground waters and deposited where evaporation or the chemical environment causes precipitation. Uranium compounds are capable of replacing some organic substances (Hess, 1933; Waters and Granger, 1953). Uranium compounds being transported by ground waters, and possibly also by hydrothermal solutions, are deposited as evaporites or as caliche-type deposits above the ground-water table in both consolidated and unconsolidated sediments of semiarid regions (Hillebrand and Ransome, 1905; Hess, 1933). It is probable that some uranium is removed from aqueous solutions by adsorption in clays and other sediments and by base exchange reactions.

2.3.b Indigenous uranium in sediments

Weathering of rocks of all kinds releases uranium and uranium-bearing minerals contained in them. Some uraniferous heavy minerals are not readily susceptible to decomposition or alteration, and these accumulate in residual soils or are carried away to be deposited elsewhere as part of the heavy-mineral fraction of clastic sediments. Most of the uranium contained in minerals which are decomposed during weathering is dissolved in surface and ground waters and is removed in the run-off.

Residual soils. The uranium content of residual lateritic soils formed in warm humid climates is believed to be somewhat higher than that of soils in general. Decomposition and profound leaching are the predominant weathering processes under such climatic conditions. Those heavy minerals which are highly resistant to decomposition remain as resistates, and, if uraniferous, tend to build up a slight concentration of uranium in the residual soil. Such concentrations can be expected to be greater where the bedrock is granitic or syenitic than where it is composed of more basic igneous rocks, metamorphic rocks, or sedimentary rocks.

Clastics. The largest part of the uranium content of clastic sediments and sedimentary rocks is contained in uraniferous resistates. The volume of these resistates varies widely and depends upon the kind of bedrock forming the terrain from which the sediments were derived, the distance the sediments were transported, and the amount of working over that they were subjected to after arriving at the site of deposition.

Most of the discrete primary uranium and thorium minerals found in igneous rocks are readily altered and are quickly reduced by attrition during transportation with clastic sediments. This category includes uraninite, pitchblende, samarskite, euxenite, brannerite, thorite, thorianite, and other less common species. These minerals are not commonly found in clastic sediments, although under favorable conditions the most resistant species are sometimes deposited with sands and gravels which have been transported short distances. Brannerite has been found in the placers of the Boise Basin, Idaho (Hess and Wells, 1920), samarskite is reported to have been found in placers of Japan, Korea, and Manchuria (Iimori, 1938; Kimura, 1936), euxenite occurs in cassiterite placers of southeastern Asia (Scrivenor, 1928), and thorianite is reported in gravels of Balangoda, Ceylon (Palache et al., 1944).

Some common minor primary constituents of igneous rocks carry uranium and thorium in isomorphous substitution for calcium, some of the rare earths, and possibly other elements. Monazite, apatite, zircon, xenotime, and sphene are some of the most abundant minerals belonging to this category. Most of these minerals are resistant to alteration, but they differ greatly in their resistance to attrition during transportation with clastics. Monazite, apatite, and xenotime are most readily reduced by attrition, but under favorable conditions these minerals become enriched in sands and gravels which have been transported short distances. They are found frequently in the heavy-mineral resistate fraction of terrestially deposited clastics. Stream and beach monazite-bearing placers are found in many parts of the world. Xenotime has been reported in the cassiterite-bearing placers of southeastern Asia (Scrivenor, 1928). Prolonged attrition at the sites of deposition, as for example, by wave action along a shoreline, tends to eliminate these minerals. Zircon, which carries a large portion of the uranium and thorium contents of felsic rocks, is a common constituent of the resistate fraction of all kinds of clastic sediments.

Uranium minerals found in vein-type deposits are readily altered and reduced by attrition and therefore are not found in clastic sediments. The most common of these minerals are uraninite and pitchblende, which occur in primary deposits, and torbernite and autunite, which occur in secondary deposits. Fluorite may carry small amounts of uranium, but it is easily reduced by attrition and therefore is not found in clastic sediments except in the vicinity of outcropping veins.

Unconsolidated deposits of clastic sediments in which concentrations of uranium- and thorium-bearing resistates are great enough to be of economic importance are uncommon. No clastic sedimentary rocks are being mined exclusively for their content of these minerals. Granites, syenites, and pegmatites are the principal source rocks for the uranium- and thorium-bearing resistates. These resistates may be removed from erosional terrains of the igneous rocks and become concentrated in placer deposits in environments where rock destruction by decomposition is predominant over that by disintegration. This action takes place readily in tropical climates and uncommonly in temperate zones. The thorium content of the minerals contained in these placers is considerably greater than the uranium content; therefore the deposits are classified primarily as thorium-bearing placers. Monazite beach placers occur along the Travancore Coast, India (Tripper, 1914; Fermor, 1935; Brown, 1936), along the coast of Brazil between Cape Frio and Recife (Bain, 1950), and on the Florida Coast (De Mille, 1947). Sands on the Florida Coast are reported to contain 0.09 percent monazite (Hess, 1937). Beach sands of India average 2 to 5 percent monazite, and recoveries up to 46 percent have been made in small areas (De Mille, 1947). The cassiterite-producing stream placers of southeastern Asia and the East Indies have a monazite content almost equal to that of cassiterite (Bain, 1950). In the United States stream placers in the San Luis Valley, Colorado, have been found to carry about 0.15 percent monazite and those of the Boise Basin, Idaho, about 0.08 percent (U. S. Bur. Mines, 1906). Monazite has been recovered from the stream gravels of Mitchell, Madison, Burke, and McDowell Counties, North Carolina. Monazite commonly contains from 6 to 12 percent of ThO_2 (Palache et al., 1951) and a few tenths percent U_3O_8 (Hess, 1937). The monazite content of placers is rarely more than 3 percent, and recoveries exceeding this figure are usually made from only small areas. It appears that the maximum concentrations of uranium and thorium in placer-type deposits are about 70 and 3000 ppm of sediment, respectively, and the average concentrations are probably about 2 and 60 ppm, respectively.

The uranium content of clastic sediments and sedimentary rocks varies from a small fraction of a part per million to some 10's of parts per million. An average content of about 1.2 ppm has been given for all sedimentary rocks exclusive of limestones (Evans and Goodman, 1941). The distribution pattern is irregular.

It is probable that all terrestrially deposited clastic sediments include uraniferous resistates. First-cycle sediments derived from igneous terranes can be expected to contain more uranium than reworked material derived from terranes of sedimentary rocks. Weathering and attrition during repeated cycles of sedimentation tend to remove all but the most resistant uranium-bearing minerals, and, unless there is a significant enrichment of persistent resistates like zircon, an impoverishment of uranium results. A poorly sorted rubble of disintegrated rock or coarse-grained clastics deposited in alluvial fans and along streams close to the sources of the sediments can be expected to contain about the same amount of uranium as the parent rocks. There is some removal of the readily altered uranium-bearing minerals, and, locally, uraniferous resistates become enriched. Silts, sands, and gravels which have been transported long distances can be expected to have lower uranium contents than the parent rocks of the sediments except where there are significant enrichments of uranium-bearing resistates. The uranium contents of aeolian deposits tend to be lower than those of the parent rocks of the sediments. The soft and readily altered uranium-bearing minerals are removed by decomposition and leaching before windblown action starts or are reduced to dust by attrition and are blown from the area of deposition of the larger-sized particles.

Quantitative values for the uranium contents of terrestrially deposited clastics are rather meaningless except when presented with detailed geologic data. The character of these sediments often changes within very short distances, both laterally and vertically, and the uranium contents are equally variable.

Marine-deposited clastics often are transported long distances and are subjected to the chemical action of water and materials dissolved in it for long periods. Attrition begins as transportation is initiated and may continue because of wave action for a long time after sediments arrive at sites of deposition. Uraniferous resistates are largely eliminated. Well-graded marine sands and sandstones composed predominantly of quartz commonly have uranium contents of less than 1 ppm. Marine-deposited clastics which are contaminated with gelatinous, colloidal, phosphatic, or carbonaceous sediments may have slightly higher uranium contents. It is probable that most of the increased uranium content is deposited syngenetically with the contaminating materials. There is a continuous gradation from the low contents of sands and sandstones to contents of several parts per million in some mixed sediments. Clastic limestones composed of detrital remains of shellfish, corals, and other organisms contain only minute traces of uranium.

Muds, clays, and shales often contain more uranium than do coarser clastics and sedimentary rocks. There are continuous gradations between pure fine-grained clastics and several varieties of chemical and carbonaceous sediments. The pure fine-grained clastics contain very small amounts of uranium, generally less than 2 ppm. The chemical and carbonaceous sediments may have uranium contents ranging up to 100 ppm. The uranium content of the fine-grained clastics is predominantly indigenous; that of the chemical and carbonaceous sediments is deposited syngenetically with the sediments. Complete gradational series exist between fine-grained clastics and the various chemical and carbonaceous sediments, and therefore the uranium contents may range up to 100 ppm. The uranium of pure or nearly pure fine-grained clastic sediments is found in part in uraniferous resistates and in part adsorbed on clays, chemical precipitates, and carbonaceous sediments. The lowest uranium contents are found in muds and clays deposited in oxidizing chemical environments and are accounted for predominantly by resistates. Only the most persistent uraniferous resistates, such as zircon, survive to be deposited with these sediments which include many muds and clays deposited in fluviatile, delta, and many off-shore marine environments where turbulence maintains oxygen in the water, and in lacustrine environments where turbulence and seasonal inversions do likewise. Fine-grained glacial deposits also fall into this group. Fine-grained clastics deposited in stagnant waters and where chemically reducing environments exist generally are mixed with chemical and carbonaceous sediments. The uranium contents tend to increase because of syngenetic deposition with the sediments.

Volcanic sediments. Volcanic ejectamenta which are blown into the atmosphere and then fall to the ground without cohering are properly classified as clastic sediments. Such material varies from coarse fragments to fine dust. The dust probably is blown about the world and contributes to the bulk of all sedimentary deposits. Generally it does not significantly alter the uranium content of the sediments with which it is mixed. Deposits formed in the vicinity of volcanic vents, if unaltered, have chemical compositions essentially identical to those of the igneous rocks. Basaltic volcanic sediments have low uranium contents, which probably do not exceed 2 ppm. Rhyolitic sediments have higher contents and probably average about 9 ppm. Some volcanic beds, as for example, those included in the White River formation of Wyoming and South Dakota, are thought to be the source of the uranium contained in secondary deposits in adjacent formations (see Love, 1952). Mudstone beds carrying substantial amounts of altered volcanic ash and bentonite occur in the Chinle and Morrison formations of the Colorado Plateaus (Waters and Granger, 1953). Some of these mudstones have uranium contents ranging up to about 50 ppm, but it has not been definitely determined that the uranium is either a part of the volcanic constituents or has been derived from them. Analyses of some volcanic rocks are given in Section 2.2.

2.3.c Syngenetic deposition of uranium

Uranium is deposited syngenetically by chemical processes in a large variety of aqueous sediments. The chemical reactions which take place during the extraction of uranium from aqueous solutions and its inclusion in sediments are not fully known. Uranium can be removed from aqueous solutions by direct precipitation as insoluble compounds. It is adsorbed by several materials, notably by clays having layered sheetlike structures (Beers and Goodman, 1944; Frederickson, 1948), by carbonaceous materials (Tolmachev, 1943; McKelvey and Nelson, 1950), and apparently in lesser amounts by gel precipitates of iron, aluminum, manganese, and silica. It may be a constituent of some organic compounds present in carbonaceous sediments. Uranium may enter some minerals in isomorphous substitution for calcium, as for example, in the calcium phosphate minerals of phosphatic sediments. The distribution of uranium in chemical sediments and sedimentary rocks shows that its separation from aqueous solutions can take place in reducing environments in the presence of organic material and sulfides and in the absence of dissolved oxygen. It also accumulates with marine-deposited phosphatic sediments, but the chemical reactions involved are not fully known. Both laboratory and geologic observations indicate that the precipitation or adsorption of uranium is inhibited by the presence of the carbonate ion (Piggot and Urry, 1941; McKelvey and Nelson, 1950). It is possible that several processes may be involved in the accumulation of uranium in chemical sediments. There is still much to be learned about them.

Carbonaceous sediments. The two principal groups of carbonaceous sediments are the humic group which has low hydrogen and high carbon and oxygen contents and the sapropelic group which has high hydrogen and carbon contents and little, if any, oxygen content. Peats, lignites, and coals are humic sediments. They consist of plant remains which may be partially altered. Cannels are nearly pure sapropelic sediments. They may consist of waxy and fatty plant remains or of bituminous materials produced from plant remains by microbian action. Complete gradational series exist between pure humic, pure sapropelic, and pure inorganic sediments. Sapropelic sediments are deposited in open waters where very little inorganic sediment is introduced and where organic materials are available. The waters are deep enough to allow microbian action to convert plant material to bitumens before deposition on the bottom. The deeper parts of the waters are toxic, and there is no circulation between the surface and deeper layers. Sapropelic sediments may be deposited in ponds, lakes, sloughs, inland seas, and bays and gulfs where tides and currents are weak. Humic sediments are deposited in swamps, marshes, and open bodies of water where there is an abundance of woody plant material. Deposition of plant remains on the bottom takes place before decomposition is complete. There may be considerable circulation of the water, and it seldom becomes completely toxic. The uranium content of carbonaceous sediments ranges from very minute amounts to several hundreds of parts per million and appear to have been controlled mainly by the chemical environments which existed during deposition.

The highest concentrations of uranium contained in sedimentary rocks, with the exceptions of epigenetic deposits introduced by ground waters and hydrothermal solutions, exist in some black marine sapropelic shales. All of the uraniferous black shales contain large amounts of organic matter and sulfides and hardly any carbonates. Oil can be distilled from them, and they are considered to be probable source beds of petroleum. All of the uraniferous black shale formations are thin, generally less than 100 feet thick, and were deposited very slowly during long periods of geologic time. The highest uranium contents are found in nodules and layers of nearly pure bitumen. In general, the uranium content increases with increasing carbon content, as in the Sunbury and Antrim shales of Kentucky, Ohio, and Michigan (Beers and Goodman, 1944). The mineralogy of uranium in black shales is unknown except for the fact that the uranium is in an acid-soluble form.

The distribution of radioactive atoms in black slates from the Carboniferous of northern France has been studied by Coppens (1953) with the aid of nuclear emulsions. He finds uranium contents from about 5 to 20 ppm, assuming a thorium:uranium ratio of 3, uniformly distributed through the rock. Alpha tracks indicate that the actual ratio may be much lower in the slate. The processes involved in the deposition of uranium in carbonaceous shales have not been definitely determined, but they may include precipitation as insoluble compounds and adsorption on clays or other finely divided inorganic sediments and on carbonaceous materials. This subject has been discussed by McKelvey and Nelson (1950).

Many marine black shales are not uraniferous. All of those known to be uraniferous are of pre-Mesozoic age. It is not known whether this is a significant feature of these deposits or whether incomplete investigations merely have not disclosed uraniferous shales of younger ages. It is not possible to state conclusively why some of these shales contain appreciable quantities of uranium and others do not.

Non-marine black shales, oil shales, asphaltites, and coals have very low uranium contents, and according to Russell (1944) they are the least radioactive of all sedimentary rocks.

Uraniferous black shales are found in all parts of the world. Some examples are the Antrim and Chattanooga shales of the United States which carry about 0.01 percent U_3O_8 (Russell, 1944), the alum shale of Sweden, which in places carries up to 0.023 percent U_3O_8 (Westergård, 1944), the Cambro-Ordovician shales of the Leningrad district, Russia, which are reported to carry from 0.008 to 0.03 percent U_3O_8 (Orlov and Kurbatov, 1936), and the metamorphosed black siliceous Cambro-Silurian schist of the Ferghana region, Russia, which is reported to carry from 0.03 to 0.08 percent U_3O_8 (Fersman, 1930). The outcrops of that formation are probably surface-enriched, according to Bain (1950).

Some lignites of Tertiary and Cretaceous age are uraniferous. It is significant that they are found in regions of widespread beds of uraniferous volcanic ash or hydrothermal uranium deposits. Not all lignites in these regions are uraniferous, and even different parts of the same bed may vary in content of uranium. The manner in which the uranium was introduced into the organic sediments is a controversial subject. Some geologists believe that the uranium has been leached from adjacent formations and deposited epigenetically in the lignites; others consider the uranium to have been deposited syngenetically with the carbonaceous sediments. It is possible that both hypotheses apply to individual deposits. The source of both syngenetic and epigenetic uranium would be the surrounding terrane from which it is removed by leaching. It is not completely known whether uranium has been deposited in lignites as inorganic compounds or combined in organic compounds or has been absorbed in inorganic and carbonaceous sediments.

The presence of uranium in lignites, and in coals, appears to be in no way related to the age of these deposits. It is probable that most of the coals and lignites of the world contain only minute quantities of uranium. This circumstance is attributed mainly to the fact that the carbonaceous sediments comprising most coals and lignites trend toward the humic varieties and were deposited in waters unsuitable for the precipitation of uranium.

Carbonate sediments. Carbonate sediments are notably low in uranium. Marine limestones and dolomites generally contain less than 4 ppm of uranium. There are few data in the literature pertaining to the uranium contents of non-marine carbonate sediments, probably because such deposits are small and rather uncommon. Marine carbonate sediments consist predominantly of either skeletal parts and shells of organisms or chemically precipitated carbonates. Organisms that use calcium carbonate for skeletons and shells live mostly in shallow water and require oxygen. The oxygen-rich environment is unfavorable for precipitation of uranium. Some carbonate sediments are chemically precipitated from both marine and fresh waters as a result of changing conditions which reduce the dissolved carbon dioxide content. Turbulence and temperature changes are the chief factors. The environment is seldom, if ever, reducing and, therefore, uranium is not precipitated with these sediments, which include marine limestones, muds, oolites, magnesites and siderites, and hot-spring and mineral-spring deposited travertines and tufas. The presence of carbonate ion inhibits precipitation and adsorption of uranium (Piggot and Urry, 1941), as already noted.

Radioactivity logging of oil wells has indicated that some dolomitic limestone strata given anomalously high radioactivity values. The radioisotopes present in these formations have not been positively identified. Studies of carbonate rocks in the Rocky Mountain region indicate that most, if not all, of the radioactivity in these rocks is epigenetic, contained in asphaltic residues and "dead oil" stains in the porosity openings (Erickson et al., in press; Faul et al., 1954).

Phosphatic sediments. Some phosphatic sediments carry appreciable quantities of uranium. Phosphatic sediments are deposited under a variety of circumstances in various environments. Some are deposited in the sea under reducing conditions and in the presence of a considerable amount of organic matter; calcium phosphate may also be precipitated in the presence of calcium carbonate (Twenhofel, 1939). Phosphatic nodules form on the ocean floor along coasts subject to rapid and considerable changes of temperature and at depths ranging from 200 to 500 fathoms (Twenhofel, 1939). Such nodules are found in many limestones and black shales.

According to McKelvey and Nelson (1950) all marine phosphate formations that had been tested up to the time of their report had been found to contain significant quantities of uranium. The phosphates are similar to the black shales in that they are thin and were deposited slowly during long periods of time. The sites of deposition were probably along the edges of continental shelves where ascending cold, phosphate-rich waters were warmed and the partial pressure of carbon dioxide decreased (McKelvey and Nelson, 1950). It appears probable that the uranium is combined with phosphate minerals inasmuch as they cannot be separated by physical methods. It is probable that this uranium enters the phosphate minerals in isomorphous substitution for calcium. The presence of organic material in a reducing environment enhances adsorption of uranium in carbonaceous and inorganic sediments and thus may be a factor in its concentration in phosphatic sediments. Here again the presence of the carbonate ion inhibits deposition of uranium in phosphatic sediments (McKelvey and Nelson, 1950).

Phosphatic nodules enclosed in some black shales, as for example those at the top of the Checkerboard limestone and of the Fort Scott limestone of Oklahoma, are uraniferous (McKelvey and Nelson, 1950). Phosphatic black shales in Kansas and Oklahoma contain uranium in non-phosphatic shale layers. Nodules, when present, generally contain more uranium than the enclosing shale (*ibid.*).

Non-marine phosphatic rocks are guano and some residual deposits. Generally they do not contain appreciable quantities of uranium.

Phosphatic formations occur in many parts of the world. The Phosphoria formation of the northwestern United States is a typical marine deposit in which thinly bedded uraniferous phosphate strata are separated by slightly phosphatic shales. The so-called land-pebble phosphate of the Bone Valley formation, Polk and Hillsborough counties, Florida, is an unconsolidated uraniferous deposit. This deposit probably has been formed in part by the reworking of the underlying Hawthorne formation which includes layers of phosphatic limestone.

In this district a "leached zone" of aluminum phosphate minerals overlies the minable calcium phosphate deposits. The calcium phosphate has been altered to aluminum phosphate and partially leached from this layer, but the uranium has been enriched in this layer, either by leaching and reprecipitation or by enrichment by mineral and other constituents. The uranium content of both the calcium phosphate and the aluminum phosphate layers normally ranges from 50 to 200 ppm (J. A. Barr, Jr., unpublished address, September 29, 1953). In isolated spots the aluminum phosphate layer may contain as much as 1000 ppm of uranium.

An extensive suite of phosphate samples from all over the world was studied by Davidson and Atkin (1953). They report equivalent uranium contents from less than 10 ppm to 1500 ppm and find that the uranium is uniformly distributed in the rock.

Evaporites. Stratified deposits of salines are formed by partial or complete desiccation of large bodies of water. Evaporation of ground water and hydrothermal solutions in semiarid regions often leaves caliche-type deposits. Bodies of water undergoing desiccation are usually rather shallow, are subject to considerable turbulence, and therefore tend to be aerated and form oxidizing environments. These conditions are not favorable for the precipitation of uranium compounds or adsorption of uranium on sediments. Because of their low initial concentrations and high solubilities, uranium salts tend to be concentrated in the last residual mother-liquors during the desiccation of lakes and seas. The last-deposited salts are rarely preserved, being blown away by winds or carried into overlying clastic sediments by capillary action and subsequently leached. Limestones, gypsum, anhydrite, halite, and potassium and magnesium salts deposited during the intermediate stages of desiccation are practically free of uranium. These saline deposits commonly contain less than 1 ppm of uranium. Gentner et al. (1954) report a uranium content of the order of 0.1 ppm in sylvite from Baden, Germany.

Uraniferous caliche-type deposits are formed in semiarid regions where the small amounts of ground and surface waters present are able to leach soluble uranium compounds from slightly uraniferous formations exposed at the surface or lying at shallow depths. Such deposits appear and disappear with changing seasons or periods of precipitation. At times it is possible to collect grains, incrustations, and nodular masses of nearly pure uranium minerals such as schroeckingerite, the complex fluorocarbonate-sulfate of sodium, calcium, and uranium. When a large mass of material is considered it is probable that the total uranium content never exceeds some 400 or 500 ppm and reaches this value only when selected high-grade material is tested. The schroeckingerite occurrences of the Red Desert of Wyoming are examples of such deposits. Caliche-type deposits usually develop in soils and therefore are not strictly syngenetic. In some parts of the Colorado Plateaus yellow coatings of carnotite, or a carnotite-type mineral, appear on outcrops and on walls of mine workings where evaporation of ground water occurs. These incrustations obviously are not syngenetic, but the migration of slightly soluble uranyl salts is indicated.

Miscellaneous chemical sediments. Chemical sediments which are initially formed as gelatinous or colloidal precipitates occasionally are somewhat uraniferous. These sediments include siliceous, ferruginous, aluminous, and manganous precipitates. Chert and flint probably provide the greater number of specimens. Such materials are interesting because of their fluorescence. Uranium probably is incorporated into these sediments by adsorption. The uranium content is commonly less than 3 ppm.

2.3.d Epigenetic uranium deposits

Epigenetic deposits of uranium are found in all kinds of rocks, including sedimentary rocks, and in some unconsolidated sediments. Uranium is introduced by hydrothermal solutions, by ground waters, or by mixtures of the two types of waters. The depositional processes either are chemical or consist of evaporation of the aqueous solutions. Deposition occurs both in fractures and in porous formations. The kinds of uranium minerals deposited are determined by the chemical environments existing at the sites of deposition. When deposition occurs below the zone of oxidation in a reducing environment it is probable that uraninite is most commonly deposited. When deposition occurs in the zone of oxidation complex compounds such as torbernite-, autunite-, and carnotite-type minerals are deposited. The geochemistry involved in the deposition of the complex epigenetic uranium minerals has not been fully determined.

Epigenetic deposits of uranium minerals are common and include practically all the material mined as uranium ore throughout the world. Only a very small number of the known deposits meet the requirements of ore-grade material. It is probable that the uranium in most of these deposits was introduced below the zone of oxidation and deposited as uraninite, although much of the known material appears in the present zone of oxidation and has been altered to other minerals.

The best-known examples of epigenetic uranium deposits in sedimentary formations are those at Shinkolobwe in the Belgian Congo as described by Thoreau et al. (1933). The uranium deposits of the Colorado Plateaus are probably of epigenetic origin. The manner in which these deposits were emplaced is still a controversial subject. They are found in all sedimentary formations of the area, from Permian to Cretaceous in age. Until about 1952 all ore was mined from the zone of oxidation. Carnotite, or carnotite-type minerals, accounted for all uranium recovered. Deeper mining and exploration under impervious shale cappings have proved large tonnages of uraninite ores. The preponderance of evidence now appears to indicate an epigenetic origin with the uranium having been introduced by hydrothermal solutions and deposited below the zone of oxidation, probably as uraninite. The South African Rand conglomerate contains significant quantities of uranium, some of which occurs as uraninite (Davidson, 1953). The origin of this conglomerate and the metals contained in it also is a controversial subject.

2.3.e Thorium in sedimentary rocks

Thorium and thorium-bearing minerals are released from rocks by weathering processes. Inasmuch as some of the most abundant thorium-bearing minerals, such as monazite and zircon, are resistant to chemical decomposition, a large part of the thorium is retained in heavy-mineral resistates which accumulate in residual soils or are deposited with clastic sediments. These resistates also contain uranium, and their distribution is described in the section dealing with indigenous uranium in sediments (Section 2.3.b). The thorium contents of economically important placer deposits are well known, and some of these have already been presented with the data pertaining to uranium. It is probable that all clastic sediments which include radioactive resistates have a small thorium content.

Some of the thorium released from rocks during weathering dissolves in ground and surface waters and is removed in the run-off. This thorium is easily hydrolyzed and accumulates in the hydrolyzates (Rankama and Sahama, 1950). Some dissolved thorium is carried into the oceans where it is probably deposited with deep-sea sediments. Thorium in the oceans is discussed by Pettersson and Koczy in Section 2.4.

Determinations of the thorium contents of rocks are rather limited. Koczy (1949*a*) studied the Cambrian alum shales of Sweden and reports thorium contents between 0.6 and 2 ppm. The following data compiled by Rankama and Sahama (1950) from the sources indicated possibly represent very rough average contents for the principal groups of sedimentary rocks:

Rock	Approximate Th Content (ppm)
Rocks of arenaceous origin (Joly, 1910)	5
Rocks of argillaceous origin (Joly, 1910)	12
Shales (Minami, 1935)	10
Limestones (Evans and Goodman, 1941)	1

2.4 RADIOACTIVE ELEMENTS IN OCEAN WATERS AND SEDIMENTS

2.4.a Historical review and experimental results

HANS PETTERSSON *

Early investigations on samples of deep-sea deposits from the *Challenger* collection of 1873–1876 (Joly, 1908) proved that in some of them, especially in samples of red clay from great ocean depths, there was a surprisingly high content of radium, more than 10^{-11} g/g. Later measurements (Pettersson, 1930; Piggot, 1933) proved such high values to be real, but did not confirm Joly's assertion that there is a regular increase in radium content with increasing depth of water. Joly at first assumed that this deep-sea radium is chemically precipitated from the supernatant sea water and later that the radium present in the deep-sea sediments is supported by uranium, which he assumed to be present in relatively great concentrations in deep-sea deposits. Both of these assumptions have been disproved by later investigations (Urry, 1941*a;* Hecht, 1952; Kröll, 1953).

An investigation of ocean water, started 20 years ago by the present author together with a team of specialists from Vienna and Oslo, proved the content of radium, for which highly divergent values had been reported earlier to be very moderate, and also to be variable with locality and depth (Figure 2.6). From a few up to 10 or 12×10^{-17} gram of radium per milliliter of water were found, the average value being 8×10^{-17} g/ml.

An exact fluorimetric method for determining the amount of uranium dissolved in sea water was developed at the Institut für Radiumforschung in Vienna (Hernegger and Karlik, 1935), giving an average value of 1.3×10^{-9} gram per milliliter of sea water of normal salinity (35 permille). This value also displays variations with depth (G. Koczy, 1950; see Figure 2.7), although much less pronounced than those of the radium content. Lower figures for the uranium content of ocean water are given by Rona and Urry (1952), but are not confirmed by other workers.†

* Oceanografiska Institutet, Göteborg, Sweden.

† Erroneously low uranium analyses may be due to failure to acidify the water sample when taken. Experience in Sweden and in Vienna indicates that about 3 cc of concentrated hydrochloric acid should be added to each liter of water

Comparing the uranium values with those found for radium, one notices that there is a deficiency of radium in sea water. In equilibrium there should be about 5×10^{-16} gram of radium per milliliter of sea water, whereas only about one-sixth of that quantity is present, on the average.

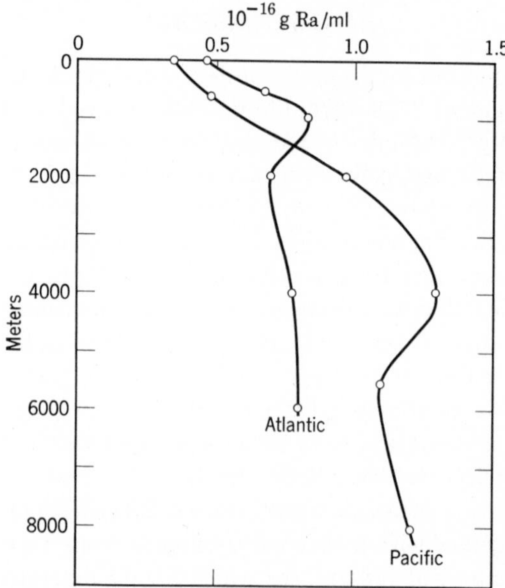

Figure 2.6 Radium content of sea water, plotted as a function of depth, in the Pacific (5° 10′ N, 127° 53′ E, off Mindanao) and in the Atlantic (28° 05′ N, 60° 49′ W, off Bermuda). After T. Bernert, 1951 and private communication.

To account for the lack of radium in sea water and the excess of the same element in the surface layers of the deep-sea deposits, it was suggested (Pettersson, 1937) that thorium^{230} (ionium) may be precipitated from sea water, probably with ferric hydroxide, and thus carry a potential supply of radium down to the sediment surface. There, in the course of time, the precipitated thorium^{230} would give rise to thorium^{230}-supported radium which, as long as it remained in contact with its mother element, would increase in the course of about 10,000 years until radioactive equilibrium between radium and thorium^{230} was established. Thereafter both elements should decrease regularly with the disintegration rate of thorium^{230}. Its halflife is 80,000 years.

sample. Without this precaution, a considerable part of the uranium present in the water will become adsorbed on the glass walls of the container, with a corresponding error in the analytical results.

On the assumption that such an accumulation actually takes place in the uppermost layers of deep-sea deposits like red clay, radium measurements would afford a means of determining the age of different layers of the deposit and hence of estimating the rate of deposition. This possibility is discussed in Section 9.3.

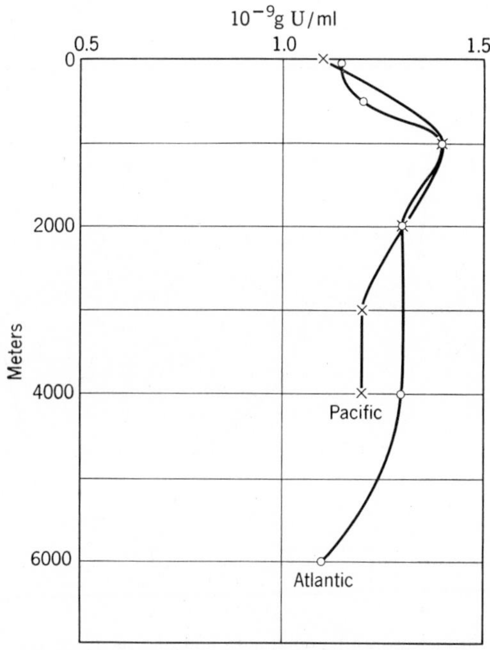

Figure 2.7 Uranium content of sea water, plotted as a function of depth, in the Pacific (13° 25′ S, 149° 30′ W. off Rangiroa, Tuamotu Archipelago) and in the Atlantic (28° 05′ N, 60° 49′ W, off Bermuda). After G. Koczy (1950).

Extensive measurements of the radium content in deep-sea deposits have been carried out in the Oceanographic Institute of Göteborg by Pettersson, Bernert, Kröll, and others, using material from sediment cores raised during the Swedish deep-sea expedition of the *Albatross* (1947–1948). Other measurements were made by Piggot, Urry, Sanderman, and Utterback (see Literature Cited), on samples from various localities. The results obtained may be summarized thus:

(*a*) In the very uppermost surface layers of red clay and of radiolarian ooze, a radium content of several units $\times 10^{-11}$ gram per gram of sediment is found.

(*b*) Instead of the regular fall-off in radium content in the sediment below the surface, to be expected from the thorium^{230} precipitation hypothesis, a more complicated behavior of the radium curve is found. Two or even more distinct maxima are observed, with a final decrease to very low radium values at depths of 40 to 80 cm below the surface. The results found by Kröll (1953) are given in Figure 2.8.

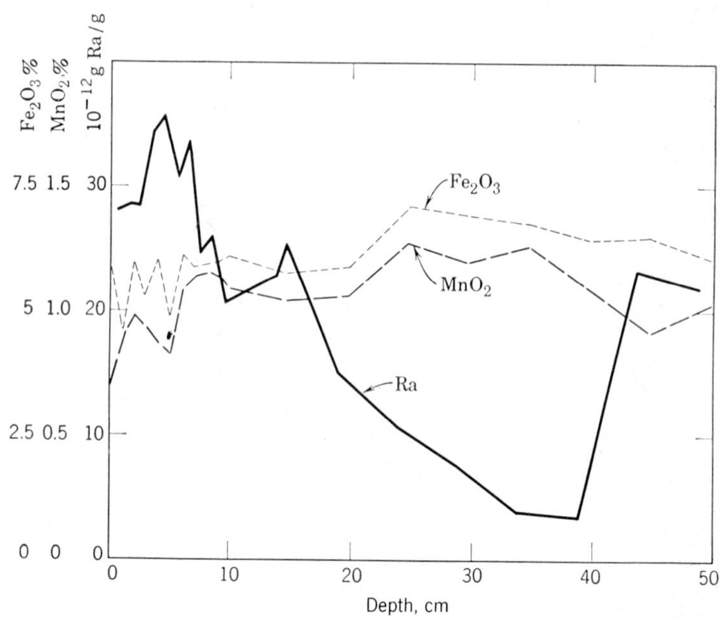

Figure 2.8 Radium, iron, and manganese content of a red clay core from the Central Pacific Ocean, plotted as a function of depth below the bottom. Core No. 85 B, 02° 23′ N, 173° 50′ W, depth of water 5560 m. Kröll (private communication).

(*c*) At still greater depths below the sediment surface one generally finds very low radium values of the order of 10^{-12} to 10^{-13} g/g. This radium may be assumed to be in radioactive equilibrium with the uranium content, as found by direct uranium determinations in the same layers.

The vertical distribution of radium in the upper parts of the cores probably does not follow the ionium precipitation hypothesis. One explanation for these irregularities would be that radium is not stationary in the sediment, but migrates from its mother substance, thorium^{230}, so that the radioactive equilibrium between the two elements is not maintained. In favor of this explanation one may quote the well-known tendency of radium to become concentrated with manganese, which explains the very high content of radium in the surface layers of the so-called *manganese nodules.* The decay with time of such "unsupported" radium has been used for measuring the rate of radial growth of the nodules (Pettersson, 1943).

In order to obtain confirmatory evidence for the supposed separation between radium and thorium^{230} in the sediment, a method for measuring the thorium^{230} present in deep-sea deposits directly has been developed in the Centre de Physique Nucléaire of Brussels by Isaac and Picciotto (1953). By means of an ion-exchange column and various elution processes, the thorium isotopes present in a solution made from the sample are separated from the other radioactive elements. A tracer isotope (thorium^{234}) serves as a control of the efficiency of the separation method. A drop containing the thorium isotopes is finally deposited on a nuclear photographic plate, and after exposure for 8 to 14 days the number of alpha tracks produced is counted under the microscope. Since the disintegrating atoms of thorium^{230} give rise to single tracks only, they are easy to distinguish from the 5-branched thorium stars. The method permits detecting a thorium^{230} concentration of 10^{-11} g/g in a sample weighing 0.5 gram.

The method is very laborious, and so far only a few of the samples from the *Albatross* expedition have been examined that way. The results indicate that radioactive equilibrium does exist between the thorium^{230} and the radium present in the same layers, which seems to negate differential migration of either element from the original layer. At present, therefore, the irregularities in the radium curves have to be explained as due to variations either in the rate of sedimentation or in the rate of thorium^{230} precipitation or as horizontal displacements by bottom currents of previously deposited layers.

2.4.b Summary

Of the radioactive elements present in ocean waters and recent marine sediments, radium alone has been accessible to direct measurements since the early years of the present century. The uranium content in sea water could be measured only after the development of the fluorescence method in the early thirties, and it is now fairly well known. The relative scarcity of radium in sea water and the excess of the same element in the surface layers of deep sea deposits led to the assumption that the intervening element, thorium^{230} precipitates on to the sea bottom, especially at great depths and there gives rise to thorium^{230}-supported radium.

Direct measurements of the uranium present in deep-sea deposits have proved the content to be very low, rarely exceeding 10^{-6} g/g. Hence "the uranium-supported part of the radium present is only a few units $\times 10^{-13}$ gram of radium per gram of sediment, i.e., a few percent of the thorium^{230}-supported radium present in the uppermost sediment layers" (Kröll, 1953; Hecht, 1952).

Apart from a preliminary value obtained by Koczy (1949*b*), direct measurements of the thorium and of the thorium^{230} present in deep-sea deposits have only recently been realized, thanks to the work of Isaac and Picciotto (1953). It should be mentioned, however, that the presence of thorium in manganese nodules from great depths has been proved by a photographic method (Poole and Matthews, 1951).

2.4.c Geochemical balance in the hydrosphere

FRIEDRICH F. KOCZY *

Uranium and thorium accompany each other in igneous rocks and are especially concentrated in granites (see Section 2.1). Both uranium and thorium are highly insoluble but there is an important difference between them. Uranium as the uranyl ion is able to form complex compounds, which are in general soluble. This means that uranium can be carried in an oxidizing environment which is not true of thorium and its isotope, thorium^{230}.

Basaltic rocks contain very little uranium and thorium (Senftle and Keevil, 1947). Ultrabasic rocks apparently hold a minimum of both elements. Measurements made by Davis (1947) have given a uranium content of only 0.03 ppm for ultrabasic rocks. Comparatively few analyses are available for thorium, but it may be assumed that ultrabasic rocks are very low in thorium as well as in uranium.

In regions rich in granitic rocks the uranium content in river water should be greater than in basaltic regions. Uranium measurements in river water were made by Hoffmann (1942). His average value is a few units $\times 10^{-8}$ g/ml and, in general, is considered too high. Rona and Urry (1952) report values from 1.6 to 4×10^{-11} g/ml, but these measurements are probably too low, as we shall see later. In the minor cycle (Rankama and Sahama, 1950) uranium is transportable both in solution and in suspension. Thorium, on the other hand, is chiefly contained in mineral resistates and is hardly transportable in the dissolved condition, owing to its tendency to hydrolyze.

* Oceanografiska Institutet, Göteborg, Sweden.

In this fashion the separation of uranium isotopes from thorium is realized. It is seldom complete, for traces of uranium are also present in mineral resistates. Such resistates are deposited within and outside river estuaries on the shelf and are practically insoluble in sea water. As thorium and uranium chiefly occur in these sediments as heavy minerals, they are difficult to transport and they remain stationary near the coast.

In certain regions of the shelf the environment displays low redox (reduction-oxidation) potential (reducing environment), which is the case specially where there is an intense biological sedimentation and reduced vertical water circulation. In such regions, the uranyl complexes become reduced and uranium is precipitated or adsorbed as a 4-valent ion (see Section 2.3.c).

The extent of the sapropelic regions has been very considerable during different geological periods. At present they are found mainly within fjords (especially in the Baltic) and in the Black Sea. There are, however, regions in the free oceans where sapropelic sediments are found as in areas of upwelling water with very strong biogenic sedimentation (Walfish Bay, for instance). But it is very probable that during certain geological periods large regions of the ocean were so poorly aerated that uranium could have been deposited (Strøm, 1939). In late Quaternary sediments from Norwegian jords, Strøm found uranium contents from 50 to 100 ppm (Strøm, 1948). In view of these variations in the extent of uranium-rich regions, it seems probable that the uranium content of sea water also may have varied with time.

Isotopes of thorium, on the other hand, are practically insoluble in sea water and easily coprecipitated (Pettersson, 1939), or adsorbed on colloids (Piggot and Urry, 1939, 1941, 1942; Piggot, 1944). In this manner the greater part of thorium^{230} which is in equilibrium with uranium becomes extracted.

Koczy (1949*a*) has shown that the content of thorium decreases in marine sapropels with increasing uranium content and explained this by the fact that thorium is attached to the clay fraction. An extrapolation to 100 percent clay gives a thorium content of about 3 ppm in the Swedish alum shales, which corresponds roughly to the thorium content of basalt.

Radium in its geochemistry mostly resembles the alkaline earths. It should be soluble in sea water to a greater extent than actually found. But its concentration is obviously limited by the low content of its immediate parent, thorium^{230}, in sea water. On the other hand, radium may be built into calcareous shells, and, according to Wiesner (1939), it is concentrated to some extent in algae like *Fucus*. The concentration in marine algae lies between 0.05 and 0.12×10^{-12} gram of radium per gram of material. In fresh-water algae the concentration may be still greater, for instance up to 8×10^{-12} gram of radium per gram in *Spirogyra*. This biological extraction may affect the radium content in the water, for up to 0.1 percent of radium present may be extracted annually. The annual extraction can be computed under the assumption that the production of organic matter is 50 grams of organic substance per square meter per year (Nielsen, 1952) in a productive layer 100 m thick. In this way a reduction of the radium content in the surface layer by 10 percent might be possible in the course of 100 years, i.e., a short time compared to the reproduction by the decay of the $thorium^{230}$. Complete circulation in the ocean being assumed to occur in the course of 100 to 1000 years, this would imply that the radium content in the surface layer becomes reduced to 50 percent of the limit given by the $thorium^{230}$ content.

We may try to compute the balance for the radioactive elements in river water, in sea water, and in sediments, following an attempt made by Holland and Kulp (1954*b*). Such a computation becomes difficult if we assume the uranium content of sea water to be variable. As a first approximation we therefore assume the uranium, the $thorium^{230}$, and the radium content to remain constant with time, which probably holds true for the period of at least a few thousand years. The second difficulty is that the number of measurements in river water is extremely limited.

The uranium content in the ocean is fairly well known from investigations by Hernegger and Karlik (1935), Føyn et al. (1939), and Koczy (1950). As an average value for sea water of normal salinity (35 percent) we may take 1.3×10^{-9} g/ml. The distribution of uranium with depth shows a marked high at a depth of about 1000 m (Figure 2.7). At this depth a reducing environment prevails. The uranium content of the water sharply decreases upward from this depth. In deeper waters, the uranium content seems fairly uniform, not only with depth but with geographic location as well.

The radium content is more variable and generally fluctuates between 0.5 and 1.5×10^{-16} g/ml. Measurements in this range have been made by Pettersson (1930), Evans et al. (1938), Rona (1943), and more recently by Pettersson and Bernert (unpublished). The radium content also varies with depth (Figure 2.6). The surface layer contains little radium, but the content increases downward with the contents of silica and phosphate. A slight increase is observed near the bottom and may indicate solution of radium from the sediment. Thorium^{230} is presumably in radioactive equilibrium with radium. The content of this isotope should be about 5×10^{-15} g/ml (Koczy, 1949*b*; Holland and Kulp, 1954*b*).

Kröll (1953) estimates the rate of total sedimentation and the precipitation intensity of thorium^{230}. The determination of the precipitated thorium is more difficult to carry out, as it must be assumed that thorium also is included in heavy-mineral residues, in quantities comparable with those precipitated. Koczy has determined the thorium soluble in acids in samples from the *Challenger* expedition and found the content to be about 10^{-7} g/g. Picciotto and Wilgain (1954) in determining the total content of thorium, arrive at a value of about 5 ppm in samples for which they have determined the thorium^{230} content. The rate of sedimentation for these samples is estimated at 0.8 mm per thousand years. Limits for the sedimentation intensity of total thorium are thus obtainable and will be expressed in relation to the intensity of thorium^{230} precipitation. The lowest ratio is found from the measurements of Koczy to lie between 200:1 and 500:1. Using Picciotto's values the ratio is found to be about 1000:1. This value obviously has to be corrected for the thorium contained in the heavy-mineral residues, but in the following calculation we assume a ratio of 1000:1. Assuming that no changes with time have occurred in this ratio, the following equation gives the geochemical balance:

Supply by decay from the mother element + Supply by river water = Decay to daughter element + Precipitation to ocean bottom.

The following abbreviations are used:

$R_{\mathrm{U}}, R_{\mathrm{Io}}, R_{\mathrm{Ra}}, R_{\mathrm{Th}}$	for the content in river water in g/ml
$O_{\mathrm{U}}, O_{\mathrm{Io}}, O_{\mathrm{Ra}}, O_{\mathrm{Th}}$	for the content in ocean water in g/ml
$s_{\mathrm{U}}, s_{\mathrm{Io}}, s_{\mathrm{Ra}}, s_{\mathrm{Th}}$	for the amounts of precipitation from sea water on the ocean floor in g/m^2-year
$\lambda_{\mathrm{U}}, \lambda_{\mathrm{Io}}, \lambda_{\mathrm{Th}}, \lambda_{\mathrm{Ra}}$	for the decay constants in years^{-1} (where U represents uranium^{238}; Io, Th^{230} (ionium); Ra, radium^{226}; and Th, thorium^{232})
α	for the supply by river water in grams per m^2 of ocean floor and year
β	for the volume of ocean water above 1 m^2 of ocean floor in ml/m^2

In Table 2.4.1 the values for the constants and for the known contents are given. The equations for the different radioactive elements are as follows:

Uranium $$\alpha R_U = \beta O_U \lambda_U + s_U \quad (1)$$

Th^{230} $$\beta O_U \lambda_U + \alpha R_{Io} = \beta O_{Io} \lambda_{Io} + s_{Io} \quad (2)$$

Radium $$\beta O_{Io} \lambda_{Io} + \alpha R_{Ra} = \beta O_{Ra} \lambda_{Ra} + s_{Ra} \quad (3)$$

Thorium $$\alpha R_{Th} = \beta O_{Th} \lambda_{Th} + s_{Th} \quad (4)$$

Table 2.4.1 Known and assumed constants for calculation of geochemical balance of uranium and its daughter products in sea water

Constants	Measured Concentrations
$\alpha = 8 \times 10^4$ ml/m²-year	$O_U = 1.3 \times 10^{-9}$ g/ml
$\beta = 4 \times 10^9$ ml/m²	$O_{Ra} = 0.6\text{–}1.0 \times 10^{-16}$ g/ml
$\lambda_U = 1.5 \times 10^{-10}$ years^{-1}	$R_{Ra} = 0.7 \times 10^{-16}$ g/ml
$\lambda_{Io} = 9 \times 10^{-6}$ years^{-1}	$s_{Io} = 1.8 \times 10^{-9}$ g Io/m²-year
$\lambda_{Ra} = 4.3 \times 10^{-4}$ years^{-1}	$s_{Th} = 1.8 \times 10^{-6}$ g Th/m²-year
$\lambda_{Th} = 4.2 \times 10^{-11}$ years^{-1}	

The ratio of total thorium content to $thorium^{230}$ content in ocean water is, of course, the same as the ratio of precipitated thorium to $thorium^{230}$ because we are dealing with isotopes of the same element:

$$\frac{O_{Io}}{O_{Th}} = \frac{s_{Io}}{s_{Th}} = p \quad (5)$$

In order to solve this system of equations with 12 variables in 5 equations where only 5 variables are known, it is necessary to make two assumptions. The fi'st is easily found, for

$$O_{Ra(max)} \lambda_{Ra} = O_{Io} \lambda_{Io} \quad (6)$$

The next assumption concerns the equilibrium of uranium and $thorium^{230}$ in river water and involves a new factor, m:

$$R_U \lambda_U = m R_{Io} \lambda_{Io} \quad (7)$$

The factor m is always greater than 1, for $thorium^{230}$ is less soluble than uranium. Here m is assumed to be about 2. $Thorium^{230}$ is more soluble than total thorium, for the chemical bonds are weakened by the disintegration of the mother elements.

The calculation is carried out as follows: By assumption 6, the $thorium^{230}$ of sea water has been found to equal about 5×10^{-15} g/ml with an uncertainty of $\pm 1 \times 10^{-15}$. Using this value, we get the thorium content of sea water from equation 5 as 5×10^{-12} gram of thorium per milliliter, a somewhat uncertain value since the relation of s_{Io} to s_{Th} is not well known. The supply of thorium^{230} by river water can be calculated from equation 2, and the thorium^{230} content of river water is found to be 1.5×10^{-14} grams of thorium^{230} per milliliter. From equation 4 in which the decay of thorium can be neglected in relation to supply and precipitation, the thorium content

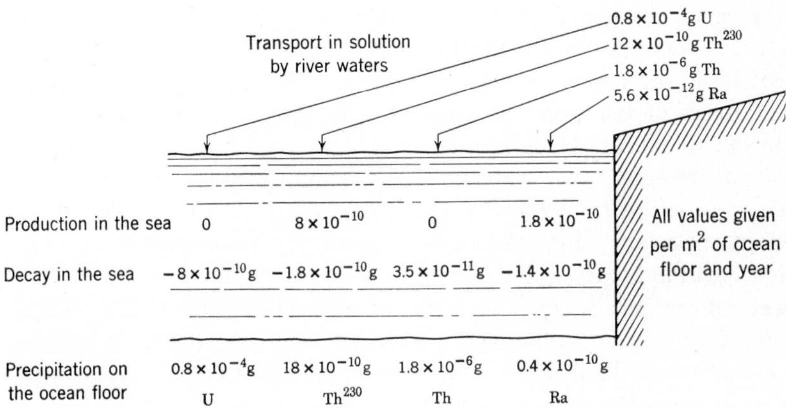

Figure 2.9 Geochemical balance of uranium, thorium^{230} (ionium), total thorium and radium in the sea.

of river water is calculated to be about 2×10^{-11} g/ml, another rather uncertain value in view of the uncertainty of the value of s_{Th}. The uranium content of river water is found from equation 7. We are thus able to calculate the precipitation of uranium from sea water by equation 1 as 1.4×10^{-4} g/m^2-year. From equation 3 the precipitation of radium is found to be 0.5×10^{-10} g/m^2-year. This value may also be regarded as doubtful.

Figure 2.9 gives the geochemical balance as calculated above. The content of the radioactive elements in sea water, in river water, and the precipitation on the ocean floor are shown in Table 2.4.2.

Table 2.4.2 Contents of radioactive elements in river water, ocean water, and the precipitation falling on the ocean bottom

	Ocean g/ml	River g/ml	Bottom g/m^2-year
Uranium	1.3×10^{-9}	1.0×10^{-9}	0.8×10^{-4}
Th^{230}	5×10^{-15}	1.5×10^{-14}	1.8×10^{-9}
Radium	$0.6–1.0 \times 10^{-16}$	0.7×10^{-16}	40×10^{-12}
Total thorium	5×10^{-12}	2×10^{-11}	1.8×10^{-6}

The uranium supplied by river water is found to be about 20 per cent of Hoffmann's (1942) mean value, which may well be the result of high uranium content of granite rocks from the area whence his river water was derived. The low uranium content in river water determined by Rona and Urry (1952) also seems improbable, for it would make the ratio m smaller than 1, indicating that more thorium^{230} is contained in river water than what would correspond to equilibrium with uranium. By the courtesy of the University of Wisconsin and the U. S. Geological Survey, the writer has received a large number of recent unpublished determinations of uranium content in spring and river waters from the United States and Canada. The mean of the values is about 1×10^{-9} g uranium per milliliter. Hecht (unpublished) obtained the values of 0.8 and 12×10^{-9} g/ml for two Swedish river waters. The uranium content of river waters seems to range from about 0.3 to 20 or more $\times$ 10^{-9} g/ml. If we adopt the mean value of 1×10^{-9} g/ml, the parameter m in equation 7 will approach unity. If we assume this figure, about 2×10^{-14} gram of uranium is annually added to each ml of ocean water. Therefore, if no uranium whatever is removed from sea water, its uranium content should be doubled in the course of about 60,000 years, which is an improbably short time from a geological point of view.

The deep-sea sediment (red clay) holds only 1 to 2 ppm of uranium (Urry and Piggott, 1942; Hecht, 1952; Kröll, 1953) which corresponds to a sedimentation rate of less than 1×10^{-6} g of uranium per m^2-year. It can be assumed that the main part is contained in heavy-mineral resistates, and it follows that about 1.5×10^{-3} g of uranium is precipitated per m^2 of the shelf. If we assume the rate of sedimentation to be about 500 g/m^2-year, the uranium content of shelf sediments could be about 3 ppm in addition to the uranium in the resistates deposited on the shelf (4 ppm). As stated above, the main part of uranium is concentrated in sapropels, but it is impossible to estimate their total area and no attempt can be made to determine the distribution of uranium in shelf sediment. The content of uranium in sapropels, is about 20 times higher than the mean value for shelf sediment calculated above. If only 5 percent of the total shelf area is sapropel, an amount of uranium equal to that transported to the ocean may become concentrated in the sapropel.

The estimated supply of thorium^{230} by river water has been worked out under the assumption that it precipitates uniformly over the whole ocean floor. The high content of thorium^{230} in deep-sea sediments is due to an extremely small dilution by other inactive sediments. The precipitation of thorium^{230} arrived at by two different methods appears well founded, and, consequently, the amount of this isotope supplied to the ocean may be considered as comparatively certain. The ratio of the thorium^{230} produced by decay of uranium in sea water to the amount of thorium^{230} transported to the sea comes out at 2:3. Consequently more thorium^{230} is found on the sea floor than might be expected from the uranium content of sea water alone.

The geochemical process affecting thorium^{230} also controls the distribution of all other thorium isotopes. For this reason the ratio of total thorium to thorium^{230} must be the same in the precipitate as in sea water. The ratio used in our calculations is an average value which may vary within very wide limits (viz., from 1:200 to 1:2000). Owing to this uncertainty, the thorium content in sea water can vary within the limits of 1 and 10×10^{-12} g/ml. Accordingly the thorium content of river water should fall within the limits of 4 and 50×10^{-12} g/ml.

So far we have discussed elements with a rate of decay much longer than the rate of oceanic circulation. When we consider radium, this is no longer the case. Therefore, it seems nearly impossible to draw up a balance sheet for radium with any certainty. The high amount of precipitated radium (45×10^{-12} g/m^2-year) found from our calculation is based on the assumption that thorium^{230} is in equilibrium with our higher values of radium content in ocean waters. The radium variations occurring in the sea may be caused by biogenic extraction and adsorption and may vary considerably both with time and space. It is likely also that radium is dissolved from the sediment. The adsorption mechanism is discussed by Holland and Kulp (1954*a*).

The geochemical balances set up above are obviously tentative in character, mainly for two reasons. First, we have assumed that contents of the radioactive elements in river water are constant with time. Results to date indicate that this assumption may not be generally valid. For instance, it is improbable that thorium^{230} is in equilibrium with uranium in river water. The second reason is the paucity and spotty distribution of reliable measurements of radioactive elements in river waters. More definite values may be expected in the near future through determinations of the thorium^{230} content and total thorium content in sea and river water and through new determinations of the uranium content in the water of major rivers. Measurements within enclosed basins like the Baltic Sea can be expected to yield interesting information.

Chapter 3

THE ABUNDANCE OF POTASSIUM

LOUIS H. AHRENS *

Potassium is the most common of the radioactive elements. As found in nature, it consists of three isotopes of mass 39, 40, and 41 with respective isotopic abundances of 93.08, 0.0119, and 6.9 percent (Nier, 1950). Potassium^{40}, by far the rarest isotope, is radioactive and has a particularly interesting decay scheme (Figure 3.1). It is

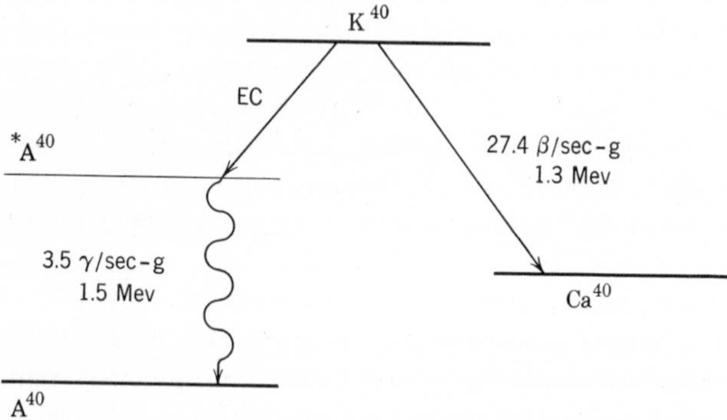

Figure 3.1 Decay scheme of potassium^{40}. Constants are weighted averages, after Burch (1953).

important in age determination (see Section 9.5) and as the source of argon^{40}, the most common isotope of argon (see Section 4.1). The halflife of potassium^{40} is very great, and the determination of the constants of decay is rather difficult. Therefore, the values are still uncertain. The beta-decay constant is the best known, about 27 or 28 1.3-Mev betas/second-gram of potassium. The values determined

* Department of Geology and Geophysics, Massachusetts Institute of Technology, Cambridge 39, Massachusetts. (Now at the Department of Geology and Mineralogy, Oxford University.)

for gamma-ray emission range from about 3 to about 3.6, and the evidence is good that the 1.5-Mev gamma ray follows each K-electron capture. The total halflife is about 1.3×10^9 years, and the various recent values for the branching ratio are listed in Table 9.5.1. Partly because of its geologic and biologic importance, potassium is of great interest to physicists, and it is likely that continued experiments in the next few years will narrow the limits of uncertainty of the decay constants.

The principal aim of this discussion is to provide some abundance data on potassium which may be of use for calculations on sources of radiogenic argon and of the Earth's heat. For our purpose we shall assume that the Earth consolidated from primary cosmic material which had a composition equivalent to that of the commonest stony meteorite, chondrite. In conformity with much current thought, it will be assumed further that fractional crystallization processes of one type or another led to the formation of the common igneous rocks; some of these appear abundantly at the earth's surface and others (or their chemical equivalents), although infrequently exposed, may comprise various inner shells or subshells. The rock types granite, basalt, dunite, and eclogite will be considered as well as the chondritic meteorites.

Ahrens (1954) has shown that the concentration of many elements is lognormally distributed in a specific rock type; consequently the geometric mean and not the arithmetic mean gives the most frequent concentration. For the purpose, however, of compiling an average abundance, the arithmetic mean (average) is used here, irrespective of whether distribution is normal, lognormal, or of some other type.

An abundance value of about 0.2 percent usually has been assigned to potassium in compilations of the cosmic abundances of the elements. Ahrens, Pinson, and Kearns (1952) give a value of 0.09 percent potassium, based on determinations of potassium in a suite of chondrites. They give evidence that indicates that several of the earlier determinations are seriously in error, and their value will be used here. The abundance of potassium and many other elements is remarkably uniform in chondrites, and there is very little difficulty in compiling an average. The potassium concentration appears to range from 0.05 to 0.15 percent, a factor of 3; it is quite probable, however, that actual dispersion is considerably smaller because of the presence of analytical error.

Dispersion of the potassium concentration is also comparatively small in granite. The concentrations of most specimens fall within the range of 2 percent to 6 percent potassium, again a factor of about 3. A satisfactory average abundance can be arrived at, without difficulty, and the value of 2.9 percent potassium given by Daly (1933) may be used. Other published averages do not differ significantly from this value.

Greater difficulty is encountered when attempting to compile averages for basalt, eclogite, and dunite. Concentrations vary much more widely, and a higher proportion of the available determinations are undoubtedly inferior because the potassium concentration is often so small and because it is difficult to decide sometimes which particular variety of rock should be chosen.

Daly (1933) gives 1.3 percent potassium as the average for all basalt. This seems high as the respective averages for the abundant varieties, oceanite and plateau basalt, are (Daly, 1933) 0.37 and 0.65 percent, respectively. Part of the difficulty in obtaining an average value which can be recommended with confidence is due to the well-known fact that potassium is very sensitive to fractionation. The potassium content can vary considerably even in successive flows of seemingly homogeneous basalt, as in Columbia River basalt, where Ahrens, Pinson, and Kearns (1952) found regular variations in concentration between limits of 0.65 percent and 1.4 percent. The range for all basalt is from about 0.15 percent to 2 percent or more. It may be feasible to assume that surface and near-surface (continental) basalt should, as a whole, have a composition equivalent to that of plateau basalt and that basalt existing at greater depths should have the composition of oceanite.

Whereas large numbers of analyses of granite and basalt have been made, only a few complete analyses of eclogite are available. The general problem of compiling an average is further complicated by the fact that eclogite is found in various environments; several types of eclogite are presumably of deep-seated origin, but others may have had a different mode of formation. Table 3.1 gives several reported determinations of potassium in eclogite. The arithmetic mean of the values in Table 3.1 is 0.24 percent potassium, but it is difficult to assess what significance should be attached to this figure as indicating an average for eclogite, or of material of eclogitic composition which may occur at depth.

Dunite and serpentine are remarkably pure rocks in some respects and are virtually free of each of the five alkali metals. Although the average potassium content of dunite was once thought to be about 0.033 percent potassium (Daly, 1933), more recent investigations

Table 3.1. Some examples of the abundance of potassium in eclogite (Chief sources: Eskola, 1921; Alderman, 1936, and Tilley, 1936)

Locality	Percent K
Vanelvsdalen, Norway	0.085
Søndmore, Norway	0.085
G12 } Glenelg, Scotland	0.05
A535 } Glenelg, Scotland	0.37
Fichtelgebirge, Bavaria	0.12
Nordfiord, Norway	0.13
Weissenstein, Bavaria	0.17
Holsenø, Norway	0.23
Fay, France	0.27
Nordfiord, Norway (Island of Silden)	0.33
Schutthalde, Tyrol	0.75
Average	0.24

(Holyk, unpublished thesis, M.I.T., 1952; Holyk and Ahrens, 1953) indicate a magnitude of 10 parts per million, or about $\frac{1}{30}$ of Daly's amount. The potassium concentration varies considerably in other ultramafic rocks. Pyroxenite has about the same abundance as dunite, and this holds in a rather general way for all mica and feldspar-free peridotites; those that contain visible mica and/or feldspar have far higher concentrations of potassium.

The average values for chondrites and for each of several rock types are given in Table 3.2. Comparison of the data in this table

Table 3.2 Abundance of potassium in chondritic meteorites and in some rocks

	Percent
Chondrite	0.09
Granite	2.9
Plateau basalt	0.65
Oceanite	0.37
Eclogite	(0.24)
Dunite	0.001

with the uranium contents of various rock types, given in Table 2.1.1 and discussed in Sections 2.1, 2.2, and in Chapter 5, suggests a definite relationship between the potassium and uranium contents of rocks. The relationship is almost linear in some volcanic rocks (Figure 2.3).

Calculations of exact mean potassium contents of sedimentary rocks would be almost meaningless because of the great dispersion in the potassium content in rocks even from the same formation. Suffice it to say that the average potassium content of shales and other argillaceous sediments is about 3 percent, of sandstones a little over 1 percent, and of limestones a few tenths of 1 percent. The potassium content of some sedimentary rocks is given in Table 7.2. Various aspects of potassium content in some marine sediments are discussed by Whitehead (Chapter 7). The potassium content of sea water generally is given as 0.035 percent, or slightly less than the calcium content (0.041 percent). The sodium content, for comparison, is 1.045 percent.

Chapter 4

RARE GASES AND FISSION IN NATURE

4.1 HELIUM, ARGON, AND RADON

HENRY FAUL *

The electronic structure of the noble gases endows them with remarkable physical properties. Their chemical inertness is perhaps their most important characteristic from a geological point of view. A molecule of a noble gas, once trapped in a geological reservoir, remains intact through geologic time. Helium and argon, the two lightest of these gases, are prominent in geochronology because they are produced in significant quantities by nuclear reactions in nature. (A remarkably complete bibliography on helium was prepared by Wheeler and Swenarton, 1952.) The heaviest noble gas, radon, is the only gaseous element in the heavy radioactive series and enters into a number of geologically important processes. Being easily measured, it is studied by many investigators. (The intermediate gases, krypton and xenon, are discussed in Section 4.2.)

4.1.a Helium

The two natural isotopes of helium, helium^3 and helium^4, are present in minerals, rocks, natural gases, and the atmosphere in highly variable proportions. Some of the helium^4 may be primordial, but most of it (see Chapter 10) must be the product of alpha decay, the remains of dead alpha particles, so to speak. Helium^3, on the other hand, is a daughter of tritium (hydrogen^3), and is thought to be produced in rocks, largely by the reactions (Hill, 1941):

$$Li^6(n, \alpha)H^3$$

$$H^3(\beta^-)He^3$$

and in the atmosphere by the reactions (Libby, 1946):

* U. S. Geological Survey, Denver, Colorado.

$$N^{14}(n, C^{12})H^3$$

$$N^{14}(n, 3\alpha)H^3$$

followed by

$$H^3(\beta^-)He^3$$

Both processes of helium^3 generation require 1 neutron for each helium atom produced. An ample supply of neutrons is produced by cosmic rays in the atmosphere, and all the atmospheric helium^3 can be explained in this way, in spite of the uncertainty that arises from the probable continued loss of helium into space. In the earth, however, the cosmic neutron density diminishes very rapidly below the surface, and other sources of neutrons are relatively small. Some neutrons are produced in spontaneous fission of uranium (see Section 4.2), and others by (α, n) reactions on light elements. Of the two samples of spodumene analyzed by Aldrich and Nier (1948*a*), the one with a higher helium^3/helium^4 ratio came from the surface and the other from a shallow mine (see Table 4.1).

The plausibility of the reaction of neutrons on lithium was tentatively confirmed by Aldrich and Nier (1948*a*), who found that spodumene ($LiAlSi_2O_6$) has a relatively high helium^3/helium^4 ratio (see Table 4.1), although the total content of helium^3 in the mineral is roughly the same as in beryl [$Be_3Al_2(SiO_3)_6$]. In addition to the high helium content, some beryls also contain anomalous amounts of argon. No mechanism has been proposed for the generation of these gases in the crystal, and Aldrich suggests that they may have been generated in the magma and trapped when the crystal was formed. The helium content of common rocks is very low, compared to beryl and spodumene, and the retention of helium in rock-forming minerals varies (see Hurley, Section 9.2).

A metric ton of granite containing 2 parts of uranium and 10 parts of thorium per million will produce $0.22 + 0.29 = 0.51$ milliliter of helium (at standard temperature and pressure) per million years. Most of that helium will be trapped in the crystals of the rock, but some may be released by recrystallization and migrate into whatever porous formations are available. The mechanism of helium release from igneous rocks is discussed in detail by Hurley in Section 9.2.

Almost all commercially significant deposits of helium are in the southwestern United States, in Kansas, Oklahoma, the Texas Panhandle, and New Mexico, and most are being actively exploited. Helium can be separated from the natural gas and commercially re-

Table 4.1 Helium and argon content of some natural gases, minerals, and rocks

Locality	Material	$\frac{He^3}{He^4} \times 10^7$	He	A
	Gases *			
			(percent)	(percent)
Stamford, Connecticut	Air	12.0	0.004	0.94
	"	13.0		
Rattlesnake field, Shiprock, New Mexico	Natural gas	0.5	7.7	
Otis field, Kansas	" "	2.0	1.6	
Panhandle field, Amarillo, Texas	" "	1.5	1	0.1
Cliffside field, Amarillo, Texas	" "	1.5	1.8	<0.1
Amarillo, Texas	"Well" helium	1.73		
	Radioactive Minerals †			
Hittero, Norway	Blomstrandite	0.2		
Bahai, Brazil	Monazite	0.2		
Great Bear Lake, Canada	Pitchblende	0.3		
Joachimsthal, Czechoslovakia	Uraninite	0.3		
	Non-Radioactive Minerals †			
			(cc/g)	
Lemnäs, Kimito, Finland	Beryl	0.5	0.011	
Eräpyhä, Eräjärvi, Finland	"	0.6	0.018	
Keystone, South Dakota	"	1.2	0.022	
Spruce Pine, S. Carolina	"	1.7		
Jokkmokk, Lapland, Sweden	"	1.8	0.023	
Audubon, Maine	"	3.0		
West Rumney, New Hampshire	"	12	0.004	
Cat Lake, Manitoba, Canada	Spodumene	24	0.01	
Edison mine, So. Dakota	"	120	0.01	
	Common Rocks ‡			
Guttenberg, N. J.	Palisade diabase	...	7.5×10^{-6}	
Sudbury, Ontario, Canada	Gabbro	...	33×10^{-6}	
Sudbury, Ontario, Canada	Murray granite	...	165×10^{-6}	

* Aldrich and Nier, 1948*a*; Coon, 1949; Anderson and Hinson, 1951; Anderson (private communication).

† Aldrich and Nier, 1948*a*.

‡ Hurley and Goodman, 1941.

fined to a very high purity (up to about 99.995 percent pure). It has been a strategic material from the time it was first commercially separated (in Canada, 1918), although its original use for lighter-than-air craft has been overshadowed by the more recent application in shielded arc welding of aluminum and alloy steels. Helium is available in quantity only in the United States, where it is separated from natural gas by the Bureau of Mines.

Under commercial impetus, helium occurrences have been studied extensively, and their distribution is well known. The helium content of natural gases ranges up to about 10 percent, and the known deposits are enormous, but the geological origin of the gas remains obscure in most fields. It is generally accepted that helium is radiogenic (Aldrich and Nier, 1948*a*), and radioactive material has been found in association with the vast helium deposit in the Texas Panhandle and elsewhere (Satterly and McLellan, 1918; Faul et al., 1954). The amount of radioactive material, unusually great as it may be, does not seem sufficient to account for all the helium, even in the Panhandle, where the helium concentration is relatively low (on the average about 0.5 percent). There is no clear correlation between helium content and radioactivity. The helium in the Panhandle field is concentrated in a fairly small area along the postulated fault that forms the southwestern boundary of the field. The area of high helium content roughly coincides with local structural features (now under study). The widely disseminated uraniferous petroleum residues found here (Faul et al., 1954) possibly may be sufficient to account for all the helium in the Panhandle field.

The Rattlesnake field near Shiprock, New Mexico, contains about 8 percent helium in a gas composed largely of nitrogen. No significant radioactivity is observed in this field, and other helium fields fall between the extremes of the Panhandle and the Rattlesnake fields in this respect (see Table 4.5). It is likely that the helium has been introduced into many of these fields from some fairly remote source, but to assume that the source must be intensely radioactive is not justified (see page 327).

4.1.b Argon

The most common naturally radioactive isotope is potassium^{40}, which decays by beta emission into calcium^{40}, and by electron capture into argon^{40}. The disintegration scheme is shown in Figure 3.1, and potassium itself is discussed by Ahrens in Chapter 3. The decay of potassium into argon suggests a method of age measurement, and attempts to perfect such a method are detailed in Section 9.5. The presence of both radiogenic and non-radiogenic argon in potassium-bearing minerals was first shown by Aldrich and Nier (1948*b*). Their results are shown in Table 4.2. Four samples of microcline were examined by Mousuf (1952), who found that 92 to 100 percent of their argon was radiogenic (Table 4.3).

Unlike helium, argon is found only in very small concentrations in natural gas, and it is likely that most of it is derived from potassium decay. Two analyses are given in Table 4.1. It will be noted that the average concentration in the natural gases is much lower than the concentration in air. The isotopic composition of

Table 4.2 Argon content of potassium-bearing minerals *

Age (10^6 y)	Mineral	Argon (10^{-3} cc/g)	Potassium † (percent)	Radiogenic Argon ‡ (percent)
1400	Orthoclase, $KALSi_3O_8$	0.69	14	79.7
350	Microcline, $KAlSi_3O_8$	0.22	16	35.5
200	Sylvite, KCl	0.32	54	13.8
200	Langbeinite, $K_2Mg_2(SO_4)_3$	0.16	20	68.8

* Aldrich and Nier, 1948*b*.

† Estimated from accepted composition of mineral.

‡ Assuming that non-radiogenic argon has the same composition as argon in present-day air.

Table 4.3 Isotopic analyses of argon from microcline *

Age (10^6 y)	Locality	Argon (10^{-3} cc/g)	K (percent)	Radiogenic Argon (percent)
1030	Hybla, Ontario	0.328	10.5	99.4 ± 0.1
850–1050	Frontenac Co., Ontario	0.307	10.4	92.7 ± 0.5
850–1050	Monteagle Twp., Ontario	0.272	10.4	100 ± 0.1
850–1050	Leeds Co., Ontario	0.272	10.1	95.3 ± 0.4

* After Mousuf, 1952.

argon in air was determined by Nier (1950) as follows: 0.337 percent $argon^{36}$, 0.063 percent $argon^{38}$, 99.600 percent $argon^{40}$ (where the experimental error for all isotopes is ±0.001 percent).

The isotopic composition of argon in Italian fumaroles and soffioni (steam vents) has been measured by Boato et al. (1952). They find "a remarkable enrichment of $argon^{40}$, certainly due to the $potassium^{40}$ decay in the interior of the earth." Their results are summarized in Table 4.4. The gases studied consisted almost entirely of carbon dioxide (90 to 99 percent) with small amounts of nitrogen, noble gases, hydrogen, hydrogen sulfide, and methane. They calculate that the soffioni of Larderello (12 miles south of Volterra, near Pisa) alone contribute to the atmosphere about 4.4×10^6 grams of $argon^{40}$ per year as compared with the total $argon^{40}$ content of the atmosphere estimated by Brown (1952) as 6.6×10^{19} grams.

Fleming and Thode (1953) have studied the $argon^{38}$ content of pitchblende minerals. They found that the $argon^{36}/argon^{38}$ ratio ranges from 1.69 to 5.18 in four pitchblende samples, as compared to the value of 5.35 for atmospheric argon (Nier, 1950). The $argon^{36}/argon^{38}$ ratio appears to have no relation to the ages of the pitch-

Table 4.4 Enrichment factor μ $[(A^{40}/A^{36})gas/(A^{40}/A^{36})air]$ for argon^{40} in some Italian fumaroles and soffioni *

(The experimental error is ±4 percent.)

Source	μ
Fumaroles	
Bullicame (Viterbo)	1.00
Pozzuoli (Naples)	1.12
Agnano (Naples)	1.15
Rapolano (Siena)	1.26
Montemicciolli (Volterra)	1.99
Soffioni (all in Pisa province)	
Travale	1.21
Larderello (average of five)	1.22
Lago Tassinaie	1.25
Sasso	1.25
Castelnuovo (average of two)	1.26
Lagoni Rossi	1.45
Monterotondo	1.45
Serrazzano (average of two)	1.66

* After Boato, Careri, and Santangelo (1952).

blendes. They believe that this variation can be produced only by some nuclear reaction, and they tentatively propose reactions on chlorine (present as an impurity) as the most likely sources for the argon^{38}:

$$Cl^{35}(\alpha, p)A^{38}$$

or

$$Cl^{35}(\alpha, n)K^{38}$$

$$K^{38}(\beta^{+})A^{38}$$

4.1.c Radon

Among all the elements of the earth's crust, radon is unique. It is the only naturally radioactive noble gas. It has three naturally occurring isotopes, all of them radioactive: radon^{219} (actinon), radon^{220} (thoron), and radon^{222} (emanation). All have short halflives: radon^{222}, 3.825 days; radon^{219}, 3.92 seconds; radon^{220}, 54.5 seconds. The three isotopes are produced in the decay series of uranium^{238}, uranium^{235}, and thorium. It will be noted that the halflife of the longest-lived isotope, radon^{222}, is very convenient for measurement, and concentrations of 10^{-14} curie per liter can be detected without much difficulty. All precise radium determinations are made by removing the radon from a sample that has been stored for a few weeks to reach equilibrium, and measuring it in an ionization chamber. The method is discussed in greater detail in Section 1.14.

In nature, $radon^{222}$ accompanies radium but frequently migrates a considerable distance from its parent. Relatively impervious radioactive minerals such as zircon lose very little of the radon generated in them, but open-lattice structures such as carnotite may lose most of their radon under natural conditions. The degree to which a mineral loses radon is called the *emanating power*. It is defined as the fractional amount of radon that is missing from the mineral and is usually expressed in percent. Emanating powers in the neighborhood of 70 percent are not uncommon for carnotites. It is sometimes desirable to reduce the emanating power of a mineral sample. This can be done by sintering the mineral or by molding it into a pellet with a plastic resin (Faul, 1948). The sintering method is simpler and involves merely heating the powdered mineral to about 1000° C for a few minutes. The mineral is then stored to allow the radium-radon equilibrium to reestablish itself.

Radon migrates from its parent as a gas or is carried by water. The solubility of radon in water is a steep inverse function of temperature. The phase distribution ratio for radon in water and air, nitrogen, and a natural gas (mostly methane) was investigated by Rogers (private communication). His results, with selected earlier data, are shown in Figure 4.1. At a temperature near freezing, water will pick up roughly twice as much radon as at room temperature.

The migration of radon and deposition of its solid daughter products along fissures or other permeable passages makes it possible to detect these features where the soil cover is not too thick. A radioactivity high is observed on some faults that are otherwise concealed.

In view of the very short range of gamma rays in rocks, radon migration offers an effective long-range method of detecting concealed uranium ore deposits. The technique was first used by Ridland (1945), who was able to pick up a fissure at La Bine Point, N.W.T., where a vein of pitchblende comes within 60 feet of the surface. In the carnotite fields of the Colorado Plateau, radon from the ore is carried down dip by ground waters along impermeable mudstone lenses in the ore-bearing sandstone and is detected by gamma-ray logging of exploratory drill holes. The engineering applications of this phenomenon are discussed briefly in Section 8.3.

The radon content of soil air is highly variable and is affected primarily by atmospheric pressure variations, wind, and moisture content of the soil. A series of observations at depths of 25, 75, 150, and 200 centimeters was made in residual soil overlying a bedrock of Manhattan schist and Fordham gneiss at Fordham University (Kovach, 1944, 1945, 1946). Frequent readings over a period of more than 2 years show enormous fluctuations, particularly at the shallower levels. A portion of the record obtained there is shown in Figure 4.2. There is a qualitative correspondence between the radon content of

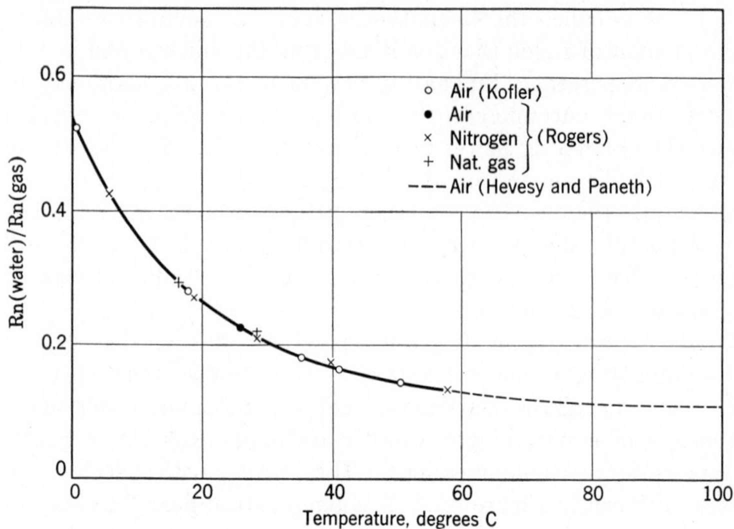

Figure 4.1 Phase distribution ratio of radon in water and various gases, plotted as a function of temperature. After Rogers (unpublished thesis, Univ. of Utah, 1954).

soil air and a combination of meteorological factors. A falling barometer generally causes the radon content to rise, and vice versa. High wind velocities, sustained for several hours, will reduce the radon content in the upper foot or two of the soil. Frozen, snow-covered soil accumulates radon (Kovach, 1945; Norinder et al., 1952), and very high concentrations have been observed under extensive, thick snow covers. Garrigue (1935) found intensities up to 0.74×10^{-9} curie per liter (at 540 mm pressure and 15° C) under the snow covering the rocky slopes of the Pic du Midi in the Pyrénées.

The uranium minerals disseminated in soils and porous rocks have very high emanating powers, as a rule, so that most of the radon can be removed from the upper foot or so of soil when the weather is windy and dry. More than half the gamma activity of uranium

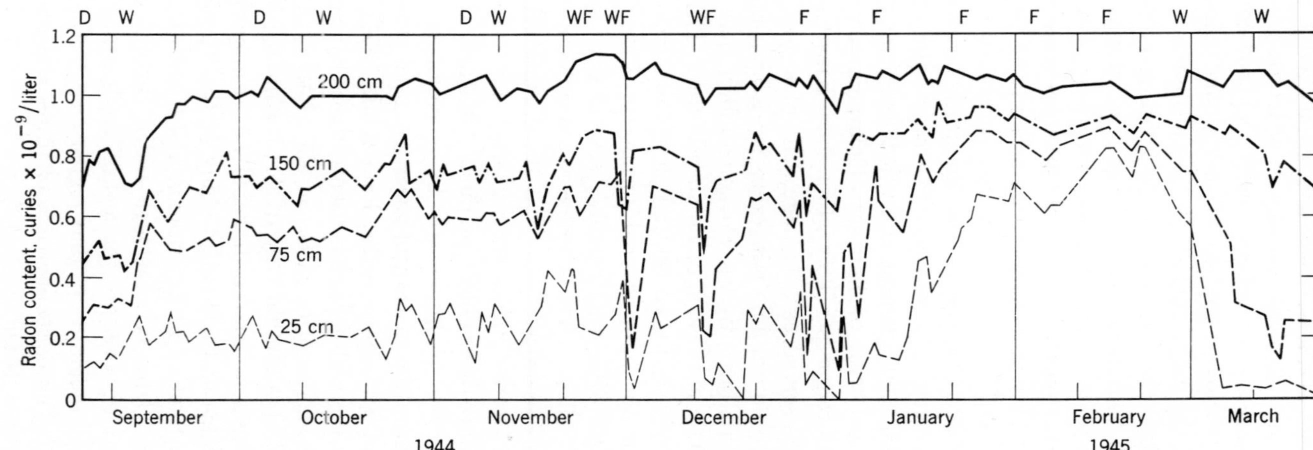

Figure 4.2 Record of radon content in undisturbed residual soil at depths of 25, 75, 150, and 200 cm at Fordham University, New York. The letters indicate soil conditions: D = dry, F = frozen, W = wet. Note the enormous fluctuations in radon content at shallow depths and particularly the great increase in February, when the ground was frozen. After Kovach (1945).

minerals comes from trapped radon and its daughter products, so that the variable radon content profoundly affects the total gamma-ray intensity observed over porous rocks and soil-covered areas. This rapid and capricious variation in background gamma activity thus sets a limit to the useful sensitivity of scintillation counters used in prospecting. This effect is discussed by Johnson in Section 8.1.

Very high radon concentrations are found in unventilated mines, including some with no visible uranium mineralization. Faul and Hunt (unpublished) found a mean radon concentration of about 5×10^{-9} curie per liter in a snow-sealed adit in the La Sal Mountains, Grand County, Utah. The adit has been driven about 1200 feet along a fissure into the west side of the north La Sal stock composed of soda-rich syenite porphyry. The most radioactive sample of this rock assayed 0.009 percent equivalent uranium. Sections of another sealed tunnel west of Fairplay, Colorado, contained up to 25×10^{-9} curie of radon per liter (Faul and King, unpublished). The tunnel formerly served as a haulage drift of a gold-silver mine, now abandoned, and no uranium mineralization is known there. It is said that some small unventilated carnotite mines may contain up to the order of 100×10^{-9} curie of radon per liter. The radon content is reduced sharply by forced ventilation of the mines. The radon content of the air in the snow-covered dormitory of the Pic du Midi Observatory (altitude 8703 feet) reached "several tens" $\times 10^{-9}$ curie per liter (Garrigue, 1934). The average radon content of mountain air in summer is of the order of 10^{-14} to 10^{-13} curie per liter (Garrigue, 1950, 1951). Radon in the atmosphere is not usually in equilibrium with its short-lived decay products (Blifford, et al., 1952). They are removed from the air, mostly by precipitation.

The radon concentration in natural gases has been studied in some detail (Satterly and McLennan, 1918; Faul et al., 1954) in attempts to find a source for the high helium concentrations that occur in some natural gases. Some helium-rich gases contain relatively high amounts of radon, whereas others contain very little. Radon and helium analyses from several fields are shown in Table 4.5. Comparison of data from the various fields and a detailed study of the Texas Panhandle field indicate no correlation between radon and helium content of the gas (Section 4.1.a). However, the high radon content of the Panhandle gas led to the discovery of the metalliferous asphaltic residues in the limestones and dolomites of that region (see Section 2.3.c, Carbonate sediments). The disseminated asphaltites contain up to several percent of uranium (Faul et al., 1954).

Table 4.5 Radon content of some helium-rich natural gases

Gas Field	Radon (curies × 10^{-12} per liter-STP)	Helium (percent)
Panhandle, Texas *	11–700	0.1–1.3
Hugoton, Texas, Oklahoma, Kansas *	10–280	0.36–0.81
Cliffside, Texas *	10–31	1.7–1.9
Table Mesa, Shiprock, New Mexico *	5.1	6
Rattlesnake, Shiprock, New Mexico *	<1	7.3–7.8
Pitt Meadows, British Columbia †	540	0.003
Welland, Ontario †	51–172	0.11–0.28
Medicine Hat, Alberta †	57–69	0.11–0.13
Oil Springs and Petrolia, Ontario †	4–22	0.14
Brant-Onondaga, Ontario †	131–800	0.25–0.33

* Anderson and Hinson, 1951; Faul et al., 1954.
† Satterly and McLennan, 1918.

4.2 SPONTANEOUS AND NEUTRON FISSION IN NATURE

HARRY G. THODE *

Since the discovery of fission, it has been recognized that spontaneous fission of thorium and uranium was possible and that this process would be of interest to nuclear physicists and geologists. It was realized, however, that the halflife for such a process would be very long, even compared to the age of the earth (Libby, 1939). It has been demonstrated with ionization chambers and boron trifluoride counter tubes that uranium undergoes fission spontaneously and emits neutrons in the process (Flerov and Petrzhak, 1940; Pose, 1943; Scharff-Goldhaber and Klaiber, 1946). Originally it was thought that 1 neutron was emitted per fission. Later work has shown that about 2.5 neutrons are emitted for each neutron fission of uranium^{235} (Segrè, 1953, p. 506) and about 2.2 neutrons for each spontaneous fission of uranium^{238} (Segrè, 1952). Thus, the spontaneous fission of uranium^{238} is a major source of neutrons in the earth, roughly equal to the neutron output of the various (alpha, n) reactions on light elements.

The separated isotope uranium^{238} has been found to have a spontaneous fission rate of about 23 times that of uranium^{235}, the half-lives for spontaneous fission of uranium^{238} and uranium^{235} being

* McMaster University, Hamilton, Ontario.

8.04×10^{15} and 1.87×10^{17} years, respectively (Segrè, 1952). Since present-day uranium contains only 0.7 percent of uranium^{235}, very little spontaneous fission can be attributed to this isotope. The spontaneous fission halflife of thorium^{232} is 1.35×10^{18} years, about 170 times longer than the same constant for uranium^{238}. Fission makes a finite contribution to the heat of the earth, but the magnitude of this contribution is extremely small, compared to the energy released in alpha decay.

Macnamara and Thode (1950) and Thode (1951) showed that the rare gases, krypton and xenon, extracted from uranium minerals exhibited essentially the same pattern of isotopes as fission product gases from neutron fission of uranium^{235} (Figure 4.3). The fission product gases extracted from uranium irradiated with neutrons contain 4 stable isotopes of xenon, xenon^{131}, xenon^{132}, xenon^{134}, and xenon^{136}, and 3 stable isotopes of krypton, krypton^{83}, krypton^{84}, and krypton^{86}, as compared to 9 and 6 stable isotopes of these elements in normal atmospheric gases, respectively. In addition, a 10-year isomer of krypton^{85} also appears. The fission gases extracted from uranium minerals, however, contain xenon^{129}, and the 10-year krypton^{85} is absent. These differences are easily explained and are due to the very great ages of the minerals. Iodine^{129}, the precursor of xenon^{129}, has a halflife of about 1.7×10^{7} years (Katcoff et al., 1951). This means that xenon^{129} will not appear in detectable quantities in fission gases from irradiated material, whereas well over 99 percent of the 129 mass chain of fission gases extracted from old uranium minerals (0.5 to 2.0×10^{9} years) will be present as xenon^{129}. The 10-year krypton^{85} will, of course, be absent from these very old samples.

There are other marked differences between the isotope patterns of xenon and krypton obtained from neutron fission of uranium^{235} and from fission in nature. First, the mass-yield curves in the xenon and krypton mass ranges are steeper for natural fission. Since there is much less energy available for spontaneous fission than for neutron fission, the process is expected to be more selective (steeper curves). This is strong evidence that spontaneous fission of uranium^{238} is involved in natural fission. Second, the abnormally high yields at masses 133 and 134 (fine structure in mass-yield curve) found for neutron fission of uranium^{235} is shifted toward the lower masses in the case of natural fission. This is the same direction of shift found between neutron fission of uranium^{235} and uranium^{238}. Again the evidence suggests that some form of uranium^{238} fission is taking place in uranium minerals. Finally, the xenon-to-krypton ratio is much higher

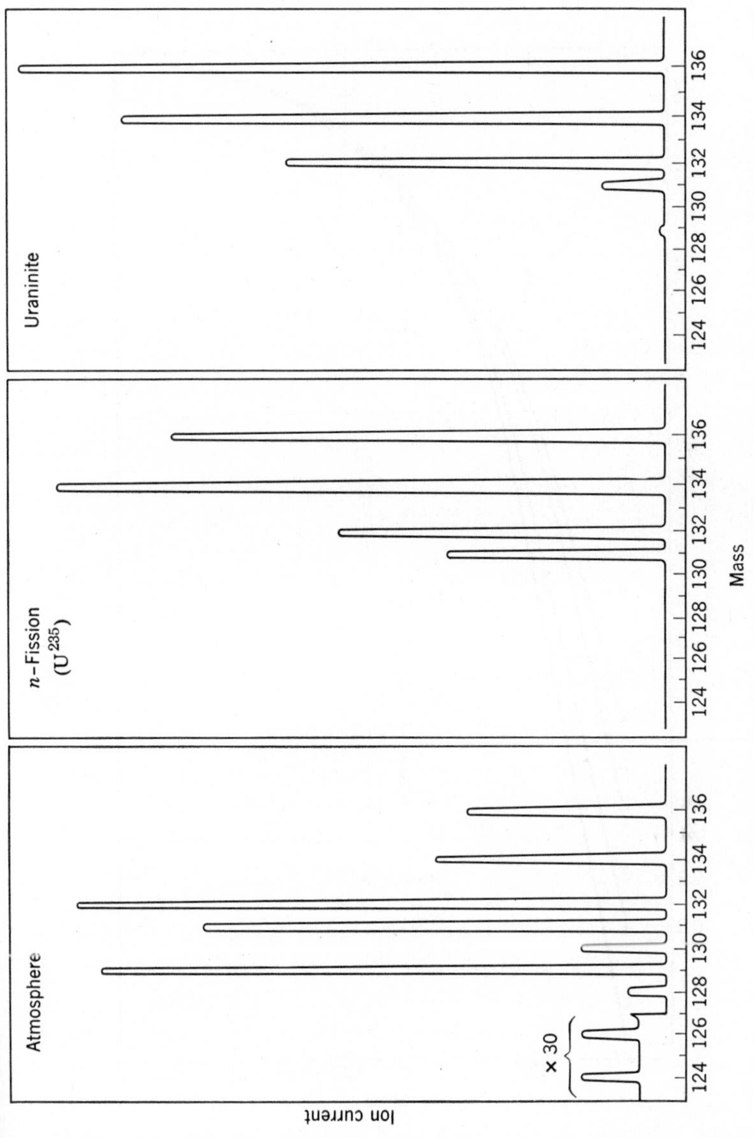

Figure 4.3 Isotope patterns of atmospheric xenon, of xenon produced in neutron fission of uranium^{235}, and of xenon extracted from uraninite from Cardiff Township, Ontario. After Macnamara and Thode (1950), Fleming and Thode (1953).

in the natural fission gases. This is due to the fact that the whole fission-yield curve must be shifted toward the higher masses for

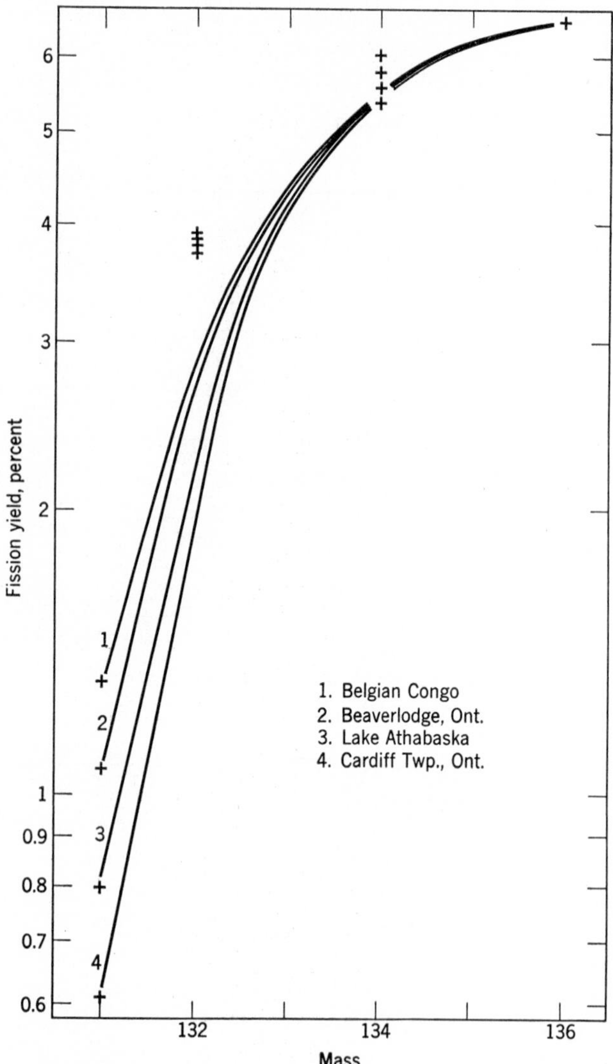

Figure 4.4 Variation in the fission yield of xenon isotopes extracted from uranium minerals from four localities

uranium[238] fission (see Figure 1.4). The result is lower krypton yields and higher xenon yields.

Fleming and Thode (1953) have shown that both neutron fission of uranium^{235} and spontaneous fission of uranium^{238} occur in nature. They found that the fission isotope patterns of xenon and krypton varied from one uranium ore to another, depending on the proportion of the two fission processes which have taken place (Figure 4.4). The variations that occurred (1) in the steepness of the fission-yield curve, (2) "fine structure of the fission-yield curve," and (3) in the ratio of xenon to krypton were all consistent with this picture. The proportions of neutron fission of uranium^{235} and spontaneous fission of uranium^{238} seem to depend on the age of the mineral, its uranium content, and the kind of impurities present in the uranium ore. Wetherill (1953) confirmed the existence of neutron and spontaneous fission in uranium ores.

Since the mass^{129} chain yield is about 1 percent for neutron fission of uranium^{235} and very nearly zero for spontaneous fission of uranium^{238} (curve for spontaneous fission is much steeper at this point), the yield of this isotope may be taken as an index of the proportion of neutron fission of uranium^{235} and spontaneous fission of uranium^{238} which has occurred in a given uranium mineral. Several samples of uranium with high concentrations of rare earths were found to contain less than 0.02 percent of xenon^{129}, indicating that at least 98 percent of the fission gas was due to spontaneous fission of uranium^{238}. Other samples showed up to 25 percent neutron fission of uranium^{235}. This is consistent with the fact that these minerals have appreciable quantities of plutonium (about 10^{-11} gram of plutonium per gram of uranium—see Levine and Seaborg, 1951). Since plutonium results from neutron capture by uranium^{238}, some neutron fission of uranium^{235} can also be expected. The sources of neutrons for these two processes are spontaneous fission and (α, n) reactions on the light elements.

Because the spontaneous fission rate of uranium^{238} is known and the proportion of xenon and krypton from spontaneous fission can now be determined, a new age determination method is possible. The method will involve an accurate determination of the amounts of fission gas present per gram of uranium in the ore. This can be done most readily by the isotope dilution technique (see Section 1.17).

Chapter 5

HEAT FROM RADIOACTIVITY

FRANCIS BIRCH *

Nineteenth-century geology and geophysics were dominated by the concept of an Earth slowly cooling from an initial high temperature. The best-known theory, that of Kelvin, led to the conclusion that the Earth could have been cooling by conduction for no greater period than some 10^7 to 10^8 years. The discovery of radioactivity provided not only age determinations showing a vastly longer time scale but also sources of heat which might be adequate to make good all of the Earth's thermal loss with no cooling whatever. The earliest measurements of the radioactivity of rocks showed that the Earth's loss of heat could be supplied by the generation of heat in a layer some tens of miles thick having a mean radioactivity equal to that of common surface rocks. This conclusion has been confirmed by the subsequent accumulation of data concerning the flow of heat from the interior and the radioactivity of rocks. Heat arising from radioactive decay cannot be distinguished experimentally from heat derived from other sources so that the question of the role of radioactive heat generation is inseparable from a complex of questions concerning the constitution, evolution, even the origin of the Earth. A brief sketch of some of the principal theoretical considerations will be given below, but it is well to understand at the beginning that this subject is still beset with uncertainty as to the total quantity and the location of the radioactive elements.

The disintegration constants of the most important naturally radioactive isotopes are probably known with sufficient precision for geophysical purposes. Many determinations of the uranium and thorium contents of rocks are as accurate as they need be, in view of the great variability of these quantities; some hundreds of determinations have been published and thousands await publication. On the

* Harvard University, Cambridge 38, Massachusetts.

other hand, we have little positive knowledge about the variation of radioactive content with depth in the Earth, and this is a serious, if not fatal, difficulty in the way of thermal theory. It is possible to place limits upon the total quantity of radioactive material present with the aid of reasonably tenable assumptions. Nevertheless, the differences between the maximum and the minimum allowable quantities, and the possible differences of distribution, are such as to lead to widely different consequences.

With the rapid development of nuclear physics, it has become possible to discuss more confidently some of the doubts and reservations that have been expressed concerning the invariability of the decay process with respect to time, depth in the Earth, and the like (see Section 1.6). At the same time, the continual discovery of new "particles," new isotopes, and natural nuclear reactions should give warning that some further revision of our views on these topics eventually may be required.

5.1 HEAT PRODUCTION BY RADIOACTIVE DECAY

The process of radioactive decay is one of conversion of mass to energy, according to the Einstein relation, $\Delta E = c^2 \Delta m$. This energy is first exhibited as kinetic energy of alpha and beta particles and of the recoiling parent nuclei, as radiation quanta of X-rays and gamma rays, and as neutrinos (see Section 1.6.c).

The ranges of the natural alpha, beta, and gamma rays in solids are all extremely short by comparison with terrestrial dimensions. Most of the gamma radiation observed with Geiger and scintillation counters by the prospector (aside from cosmic radiation) originates within a few inches of the surface; it is little absorbed in air and may be detected hundreds of feet above the ground. Neutrinos are not absorbed even by the whole diameter of the Earth (Benfield, 1948; Saxon, 1949; Barrett, 1950).

These particles and radiations are absorbed primarily by ionization, with production of new beta particles and radiations; chemical changes may be produced under special conditions (see Chapter 7); some energy may be stored in lattice distortions (see Chapter 6. For general reviews of radiation effects in solids, see Slater, 1951; Dienes, 1953). In the end, very nearly all of the energy is converted to heat in the immediate neighborhood of the source. This has been demonstrated by calorimetric measurements of the rate of heat generation by known amounts of bismuth^{210} (Ellis and Wooster, 1927; Meitner and Orthmann, 1930), though the uncertainty of such measurements might easily permit a small discrepancy to pass unobserved. The small amount of energy represented by such phenomena as the pleochroic haloes, thermoluminescence, and metamict mineralization, which can remain in storage only at relatively low temperatures (see Chapter 6), is unlikely to be of importance for geothermal problems involving the whole Earth (Morehead and Daniels, 1952; Hurley and Fairbairn, 1953).

In principle, there are two ways of finding the energy release associated with radioactive series: (1) by determination of the energy of all of the individual particles and quanta; (2) by mass-spectrometric determination of the mass difference between parent and end products. Except for closely spaced mass doublets, however, the direct determination of masses has not yet reached the required precision, and, in practice, the mass differences in radioactive series are best found by adding up the energies of the individual radiations. This has been done with care in a number of compilations. If it were not for the neutrino, heat production would be simply the energy equivalent of the mass difference between parent and end products; as it is, we must make a correction for the energy carried away by the neutrinos and not absorbed in the Earth.

The isotopes of importance for radioactive heat generation are uranium^{238}, uranium^{235}, thorium^{232}, and potassium^{40}, all having halflives of the order of 10^9 years or more. Several other naturally radioactive isotopes of long period have been discovered: rubidium ^{87}, indium^{115}, lanthanum^{138}, samarium^{147}, lutecium^{176}, rhenium^{187}; these elements appear to be too rare to be of significance for heat generation. A large number of short-lived radioactive elements which have been produced artificially may have existed and perhaps may have had some importance in the early history of the Earth, but all isotopes with halflives of the order of 10^8 years or less have been reduced to immeasurably small fractions of their original amounts except for members of radioactive series and those which are replenished by cosmic-ray (carbon^{14}) or natural neutron (plutonium^{239}) bombardment.

The uranium^{238}, uranium^{235}, and thorium^{232} series produce alpha particles, beta particles, and gamma radiation; the alpha particles account for roughly 90 percent of the energy in these series, and, as the mean alpha energy is not greatly different for the three series, a good determination of energy production for these elements may be obtained from alpha counts alone (see below). Potassium^{40} produces beta and gamma radiation, the latter being especialy significant; of the total gamma radiation from a typical granite, for example, as much as one-half may originate from the decay of potassium. Rubidium^{87} decays by beta emission, with a rare soft gamma component.

Values of the mass differences of the uranium and thorium series (after Stern, 1949 and unpublished) are shown in Table 5.1. The

Table 5.1 Mass differences expressed in energy units (Mev)

After Stern (1949 and unpublished)

Parent	End Product	1949	1952 (unpublished)
U^{238}	$Pb^{206} + 8He^4$	52.2	51.6
U^{235}	$Pb^{207} + 7He^4$	47.2	46.2
Th^{232}	$Pb^{208} + 6He^4$	44.4	42.6

mass differences have been converted to units of Mev; the conversion factors are: 1 mass unit = 931.15 Mev = 1.49158×10^{-3} erg; 1 Mev = 1.60186×10^{-6} erg (DuMond and Cohen, 1953). The two sets of values (Table 5.1) are of interest as indicating the present uncertainties, approximately 1 Mev for the total energy release from parent to end product.

The values of Table 5.1 must be corrected, for our purpose, for the energy carried away by the neutrinos; this has been taken as two-thirds of the maximum beta energy for each beta spectrum, with the results shown in Table 5.2. In the uranium^{238} decay, for example, the

Table 5.2 Disintegration constants and heat generation

Isotope	Half-life * in 10^9 years	λ in 10^{-9} per year	Heat Generation: Mev per atom	Heat Generation: Cal per g-year
U^{238}	4.50	0.154	47.4	0.71
U^{235}	0.71	0.98	45.2	4.3
U (ordinary)	...	...	...	0.73
Th^{232}	13.9	0.05	39.8	0.20
K^{40}	1.3	0.55	0.71	0.22
K (ordinary)	...	...	...	27×10^{-6}
Rb^{87}	60	0.011	0.044	130×10^{-6}
Rb (ordinary)	...	...	...	36×10^{-6}

* From Hollander, Perlman, and Seaborg, 1953.

total energy associated with beta decay is 6.3 Mev, of which the neutrinos are assumed to carry away 4.2 Mev; there remains to be absorbed 47.4 Mev. It is clear that the exact proportion attributed to the neutrinos is not of great importance for this calculation. Stern's values (unpublished) have been corrected in this way and converted to calories per year per gram of isotope in Table 5.2. Some of the older computations are collected in Table 5.3. No important changes

Table 5.3 Estimates of heat generation (cal/gram-year)

Author	Date	U	Th	K
Holmes and Lawson	1926	0.79	0.23	124×10^{-6}
Urry	1941*b*	0.704	0.20	5×10^{-6}
Evans and Goodman	1941	0.741	0.203	5×10^{-6}
Bullard	1942	0.723	0.200	8×10^{-6}
Present author	1953	0.73	0.20	27×10^{-6}

have taken place in the values for the uranium and thorium series in the last 10 years or so; the constants for potassium^{40} have changed appreciably. (For a review of work up to 1951, see Birch, 1951.) The values for rubidium^{87} are included, but as rubidium is approximately 100 times less abundant than potassium (Ahrens et al., 1952), its contribution to the heat production is negligible. The rates of heat generation are given in terms of the amount of parent isotope, but it is assumed that all the daughter elements are present in the equilibrium proportions.

The calculation of rate of heat generation per g-year for uranium^{238} is made as follows: the heat generation for the decay of 1 uranium^{238} atom to 1 lead^{206} atom plus 8 helium^{4} atoms is 47.4 Mev or 1.85×10^{-12} calorie. In 1 gram of uranium^{238} there are $6.025 \times 10^{23}/238$ atoms; in 1 year, 0.154×10^{-9} times this number of atoms decay. On multiplying the number of disintegrations by the yield per disintegration, we obtain 0.71 calorie per year and per gram of uranium^{238}.

5.2 RADIOACTIVE HEAT GENERATION IN ROCKS

There is hardly a more perplexing problem than the distribution of the radioactive elements; fifty years of study have left the principal questions not only unsolved but perhaps more baffling than they originally appeared. The demands for uranium ores have stimulated unprecedented activity in this field, but so far this work has had little effect upon general scientific thought, partly because of restrictions upon publication, and partly because the pressures of the moment have left insufficient time for analysis of the great masses of new data.

For the present, it is necessary to rely upon published data representing an uncomfortably small fraction of the total accumulation.

In the following discussion, it is assumed that in total quantity the uranium and thorium of ordinary rocks far outweigh the concentrated deposits which are of interest as ores, though the distinction between ores and non-ores is not very clean-cut for these elements. Although nearly all of the most common rocks contain a few parts per million of uranium and perhaps several times as much thorium, certain sediments, particularly black marine shales and phosphates (see Section 2.3), have as much as several hundred parts per million of uranium and may be considered low-grade ores; such common sedimentary rocks as sandstones and limestones are sometimes so poor in uranium, at least locally, as to approach the limit of reliable detection. The sedimentary rocks have been studied, for the most part, *in situ* by gamma-ray logging of drill holes; relative measurements of this kind have proved of value for correlation, but they seldom provide absolute values of uranium content. As the sedimentary column rarely exceeds a thickness of a few kilometers, we usually neglect the radioactivity of the sediments in comparison with that of the crust; this may not be warranted for thick sediments or for areas of exceptionally high radioactivity. A greatly neglected subdivision is the radioactivity of the metamorphic rocks, which conceivably constitute a considerable fraction of the crust. Most of the presently available measurements have been made on igneous rocks, with a usual preference for "fresh" unaltered material.

Since the earliest work, attention has been directed to the association of the radioactive elements with petrologic groups (granitic, basaltic, ultramafic, and so on) and with the individual minerals composing these rocks. With the improvement of techniques of measurements, the information on these subjects has become much more precise, and a number of detailed studies are now available which, on the whole, confirm and amplify certain generalizations that were made almost at the beginning on the basis of much less convincing evidence. Though exceptions to nearly every general statement are numerous in this subject, the following generalizations are reasonably valid:

1. Uranium and thorium are irregularly distributed, with relatively high concentrations occurring in accessory minerals that constitute a small fraction of the rock. The most common minerals, quartz, feldspars, pyroxenes, and olivines, have notably small uranium and tho-

rium contents (see Section 2.1 and Piggot and Merwin, 1932; Keevil, 1938*b;* Davis and Hess, 1949; Picciotto, 1950).

2. Uranium and thorium tend to be most concentrated in the granites and least abundant in the ultramafics; there is a marked tendency for uranium and thorium, as well as potassium, to increase with silica content. For any type of rock, and even in a well-defined rock unit, a more or less broad distribution is found among samples of moderate size (the usual hand sample, or even large samples), and the distributions for different kinds of rock generally overlap: individual samples of granite may show as little uranium as samples of basalt, for example (Poole and Joly, 1924; Holmes, 1933; Evans and Goodman, 1941; Keevil, 1943*b;* Davis and Hess, 1949).

3. Thorium is usually more abundant than uranium, the thorium: uranium ratio most frequently falling between 3 and 4, though the range of measured ratios is much greater (Poole, 1915; Jeffreys, 1936; Keevil, 1938*b,* 1944; Evans and Goodman, 1941; Senftle and Keevil, 1947; Davidson, 1951).

The early work on the radioactivity of rocks consisted largely of radium and thorium determinations on small numbers of samples, selected more or less at random from convenient localities, often quarries or road-cuts, without any clear geological significance. In the more recent work, especially that of Keevil and his collaborators, there has been an effort to study the variations within individual batholiths, among the different rocks of single magmatic units, and even among large geographical units. In much of this work, only the rate of alpha emission of small powdered samples has been measured; the alpha "activity," expressed as alphas per milligram-hour, can be converted to "radium equivalent," or to uranium and thorium content with the aid of an assumption concerning the thorium: uranium ratio, and so long as the samples fall in the most common range of values of this ratio the error is not ordinarily of importance. Measurements of this kind (see Section 8.1) are distinguished in the tables from measurements of radium by the usual radon method (see Section 1.14).

Some studies have been made on the basis of composites of large numbers of individual hand samples; in this way, a single determination gives a mean value for some tens or hundreds of samples, with an obvious economy of time and labor. This technique can evidently give no information concerning the distribution of values among the individual samples, nor can the grouping be rearranged.

Most of the available information concerning radium content has been collected in Tables 5.4 and 5.5. A number of the older measurements are shown, partly for comparison with later ones, partly because they have been so thoroughly analyzed statistically by Jeffreys (1936, 1942, 1952). He has called attention to the "proportional scatter," or the ratio of standard deviation σ to mean value m and has concluded that this ratio is characteristic of rock type, being largest for granites, smaller for basalts, lowest for ultrabasic rocks. The more recent work seems not to support this thesis. Small values of σ/m are found for groups of samples of granite drawn from restricted localities (for example, the Quincy granite of Keevil, or the Hiei granite of Asayama); relatively large values of σ/m are found for groups of basaltic rocks (San Marcos gabbro of Larsen and Keevil, Keweenaw basalt of Urry). As more diverse groups are combined the ratio σ/m increases. But diversity may exist on a small geographic scale; thus Ingham and Keevil (1951) find pronounced differences between the inner and outer zones of the Bourlamaque batholith, and of the Cheddar batholith; more complicated short-range variations are found in the Elzevir batholith and the Round Lake batholith (Slack, 1949; Slack and Whitham, 1951). The variation among the different rocks of single magma series is discussed in Section 2.1.

These relatively complicated variations within small areas make it difficult to formulate the concept of regional variation, though the impression is current that certain "regions" are generally more radioactive than others (Davidson, 1951). The problem of sampling a "region" within which large variations may take place on a small spatial scale, and in which the basement rocks may be only accidentally accessible at scattered outcrops, is a forbidding one. The closest approach that we have at present is represented by the composite samples of Senftle and Keevil (Table 5.5). These were grouped according to contiguous geographical areas, but, aside from being "simply connected," these areas have little geological significance. If we combine groups to represent, as nearly as possible, the main geological provinces of North America, we find relatively little variation, either for the granitic or the intermediate classification, though there is an indication of lower activity in the "Central lowlands" than in either of the mountain provinces. On purely statistical grounds, one might easily conclude that real regional differences are indicated, but, in view of the other sources of variation already discussed, it appears that a more careful examination of the distribution of the original samples with regard to all the relevant circumstances will be required before significant differences can be claimed.

Table 5.4 Radium content of granitic, intermediate, and basaltic rocks

(n = number of samples; m = mean radium content; σ = standard deviation of individual determination.)

(a) Radium Content of Granitic Rocks

Reference	Region	n	m 10^{-12} g/g	σ 10^{-12} g/g	σ/m
Jeffreys (1936)	"All granite"	122	2.38	1.78	0.75
Jeffreys (1936, 1952)	"North America, etc."	53	1.59	0.88	0.55
Strutt (1906) *	England	6	3.38	1.06	0.31
Joly and Poole (1924) *	Scotland	7	1.69	0.37	0.22
Joly and Poole (1924) *	Finland	15	4.40	1.56	0.35
Piggot (1938) †	Finland	24	1.74	1.13	0.65
Fletcher (1911) *	Ireland	23	1.73	1.00	0.58
deFinaly (1932) *	Hungary	10	2.40	0.72	0.30
Hatsuda (1934) *	Japan	7	1.60	0.59	0.37
Asayama (1936)	Japan	13	1.28	0.28	0.22
Smeeth and Watson (1918) *	India	14	1.15	0.62	0.60
Immelman (1934)	So. Africa	18	2.36	0.68	0.29
Føyn et al. (1941)	Norway	2	0.94		
Piggot (1931) *	East coast, North America	13	1.40	1.11	0.79
Evans and Goodman (1941)	North America	26	1.02	0.80	0.78
Keevil (1943) †	Quincy, Mass.	30	0.88 ‡	0.17	0.20
Billings and Keevil (1946) †	New Hampshire	45	1.79 ‡	0.81	0.45
Senftle and Keevil (1947) †	North America	1257	1.40		
Ingham and Keevil (1951)	Ontario				
	Elzevir batholith "gray granite"	94	0.62 ‡	0.34	0.55
Pinson (unpublished)	Colorado				
	granites	17	1.5 §	0.53	0.35
	schist and gneiss	14	1.3 §	0.63	0.50
(b) Radium Content of Intermediate Rocks					
(Granodiorite, quartz diorite, quartz monzonite, syenite, etc.)					
Jeffreys (1936)	World	36	1.9		
Evans and Goodman (1941)		7	0.51		
Billings and Keevil (1946)	New Hampshire White Mt. series:				
	Syenite	9	1.17 ‡	0.71	0.61
	Quartz syenite	9	1.64 ‡	0.53	0.32
	N. H. series: Quartz monzonite	16	0.99 ‡	0.28	0.28
Larsen and Keevil (1947)	So. California				
	Woodson granodiorite	11	0.92 ‡	0.25	0.27
	Bonsall tonalite	13	0.37 ‡	0.17	0.45
	Green Valley tonalite	6	0.37 ‡	0.09	0.23
Senftle and Keevil (1947) †	North America	297	0.91		
Ingham and Keevil (1951)	Bourlamaque batholith:				
	inner	27	0.094 ‡	0.046	0.50
	outer	65	0.331 ‡	0.185	0.56
	all	92	0.26	0.19	0.74
(c) Radium Content of Basaltic Rocks					
Jeffreys (1936)	World	106	0.95		
Evans and Goodman (1941)		54	0.38		
Keevil, et al. (1943)		182	0.29 ‡		
Urry (1936*a*)	Keweenaw				
	basalt	16	0.16	0.10	0.63
Larsen and Keevil (1947)	San Marcos				
	gabbro	16	0.19 ‡	0.12	0.63

Table 5.4 Radium content of granitic, intermediate, and basaltic rocks (Cont.)

Reference	Region	n	m 10^{-12} g/g	σ 10^{-12} g/g	σ/m
Hurley (1952*a*)	Palisades diabase	5	0.18 ‡	0.03	0.19
Pinson (unpublished)	Samoa	7	0.34 §		
	Hawaii	10	0.29 §	(surface)	
		8	0.50 §	(drill cores)	

* Included in Jeffreys' 1936 Summary.
† See Table 5.5.
‡ From α-count.
§ Fluorimetric determination of uranium.

Table 5.5 Radium content of certain groups of rocks

Reference	Region	n	m 10^{-12} g/g	σ 10^{-12} g/g	σ/m
Piggot (1938)	Finland, Precambrian granites				
	Rapakivi	9	1.53	0.60	0.39
	Post-Jatulian	3	1.38		
	Post-Bothnian	8	2.52	1.45	0.57
	Post-Svionian	4	0.94	0.25	0.27
Billings and Keevil (1946)	New Hampshire, Paleozoic granites				
	White Mt. series	16	2.46	0.90	0.36
	N. H. magma series	18	1.38	0.40	0.29
	Oliverian series	11	1.45	0.47	0.32
		Granites		Intermediate	
		n	m	n	m
Senftle and Keevil (1947)	Ontario and Quebec	396	1.02	72	0.74
	New England, etc.	123	1.75	31	1.34
	Eastern states	143	1.20	20	0.46
	Central	76	1.24	17	0.77
	Southwest states, Mexico	50	1.48	10	0.89
	West coast states	52	1.09	23	0.91
	Rocky Mt. states	199	1.75	52	0.96
	Central Canada	126	1.65	23	1.30
	British Columbia, Alaska	92	1.24	49	0.90
	Means for Geological Provinces (weighted according to number of samples)				
	Appalachians	266	1.45	51	0.99
	Western Cordillera	393	1.51	134	0.92
	Central lowlands	598	1.18	112	0.86

The measurements of radioactivity of rocks have been subject to large experimental errors arising from a number of causes: in the early work, errors of standardization were doubtless frequent (see Evans and Goodman, 1941), and a tendency to report higher values than now seem probable was perhaps the most common fault. This is especially important for the rocks of low activity; none of the measurements on meteorites, dunites, peridotites, or eclogites made before 1941 can be relied on, and many of the later determinations are suspect. These rocks contain less radioactivity than any common material, and contamination is difficult to avoid. The measurements of Davis (1947), which give the lowest values, are probably the most reliable. Many more determinations on rocks in this category are needed because of their great importance to geothermal theory and geochemistry. The older measurements seem to be defective even for the basaltic rocks; Jeffreys' (1936) compilation gives the average radium content as 0.95×10^{-12} g/g, but the average values for all the later groups are scarcely more than half as large.

For the purpose of finding the rate of heat production by the uranium and thorium series, the method of alpha counting is especially suitable, since the mean energies of the alpha particles of the three series differ very little. If we divide the total energy for each series (Table 5.2) by the appropriate number of alpha particles, we obtain the following values: uranium^{238} series, 5.92 Mev; uranium^{235} series, 6.46 Mev; thorium^{232} series, 6.63 Mev. These figures include the energy of the beta and gamma radiation, and are, of course, slightly higher than the mean energies of the alpha particles alone. For a thorium:uranium ratio of 3.6, the weighted mean energy per alpha particle is 6.31 Mev. The error in using this figure for computing heat production from alpha activity will never exceed about 5 percent, even for pure uranium or pure thorium (Urry, 1941*b*; Keevil, 1943*a*), and this is smaller than most of the other uncertainties. Thus, for the purpose of estimating heat production, a discussion of the thorium:uranium ratio is unnecessary when we have direct measurements of total alpha activity. Alpha activity (denoted by A) is usually expressed as the number of alpha particles emitted per milligram of sample per hour. With the average value 6.31 Mev, this gives, for the energy release, $2.11A$, in calories per gram per million years. This relation is sometimes modified with a conventional allowance for the additional heat produced by the potassium decay, but it is preferable to determine the potassium content wherever possible.

In view of the variability of the data shown in Tables 5.4 and 5.5, and in view of the many sources of variation that have received only the most preliminary form of treatment, it seems hardly worthwhile to attempt more than a tentative selection of "typical values" for certain reasonably distinct groups of rocks. It should be clear that in using such values for theoretical purposes we are necessarily making tacit assumptions that are as yet unsupported by satisfactory evidence.

Table 5.6 Typical values of heat production in rocks

Rock	Concentration Ra 10^{-12} g/g	Concentration K g/g	Heat Production (cal/g-10^6 y) U	U + Th	K	Total
Granitic	1.4	0.035	3	6	1	7
Intermediate	0.7	0.02	1.5	3	0.5	3.5
Basaltic *	0.2	0.01	0.4	0.8	0.3	1.1
Ultramafic (Dunite)	0.005	0.00004	0.01	0.02	0.001	0.02
Stony meteorites	?	0.001	?	?	0.03	>0.03
Iron meteorites †	0.001?		0.002	0.004		0.004?

* See also Hurley, 1952*a*.
† Based on Davis, 1950; Arrol et al., 1942; Patterson et al; 1953*a*.

In forming the values of heat production of Table 5.6, it is assumed that as much heat is produced by the thorium series as by the two uranium series; this will be the case for a thorium:uranium ratio of about 3.6, which is near to the most frequently observed value (Senftle and Keevil, 1947). As mentioned above, however, we may obtain the heat production directly from the alpha activity without such an assumption, and the total heat production assigned to U + Th in Table 5.6 is consistent with the measurements of alpha activity, so far as they may be represented by "typical" values.

The values for heat production of Table 5.6 correspond, of course, to the presently assumed quantities of uranium, thorium, and potassium. The present amounts of the radioactive isotopes are smaller than those which existed in the past, and for calculations dealing with the whole lifetime of the Earth it may be important to take the decay into account (Urry, 1949*a*; Urey, 1952). The rate of heat production at a time t years ago was $e^{\lambda t}$ times the present rate, for a given present quantity of material, of disintegration constant λ. The ratio of the total heat produced over a time t, allowing for the decay, to the amount that would have been produced in the same time if the present quantity had always been present, is $(e^{\lambda t} - 1)/\lambda t$. This ratio is given in Table 5.7 for a few values of t for the important heat-pro-

Table 5.7 The function $(e^{\lambda t} - 1)/\lambda t$

(t in units of 10^9 years)

Isotope t =	1	2	3	4	5
U^{238}	1.08	1.17	1.27	1.38	1.51
U^{235}	1.70	3.11	6.09	12.60	27.20
U (ordinary) *	1.11	1.25	1.47	1.85	2.57
Th^{232}	1.03	1.05	1.08	1.11	1.14
K^{40}	1.33	1.82	2.55	3.65	5.33

* See text.

ducing series. Natural uranium is a mixture of uranium^{238} and uranium^{239} and has no single disintegration constant. The tabulated values are the desired ratios of true mean rate to present rate of heat production, allowing for the two series.

5.3 LOSS OF HEAT FROM THE INTERIOR OF THE EARTH

In discussing the flow of heat from the interior of the Earth, it is convenient to distinguish between regions that show evidence of recent or late Tertiary volcanic activity and other, or "normal," regions. Volcanism is characterized by the rapid transport to the surface of hot materials, ash, lava, and water, which bring with them impressive quantities of heat. Locally, and for relatively brief periods, the convective transport of heat by volcanic processes no doubt exceeds the outward flow of heat by conduction. For the Earth as a whole, and for the long periods of geological time, it seems probable that conduction accounts for by far the greater part of the Earth's heat loss; some estimates of the relative importance of these processes are given below. For the moment, we confine our attention to conducted heat in presently non-volcanic areas.

Below the relatively shallow layer affected by seasonal variations, the temperature everywhere increases as the depth increases. There must consequently be conduction of heat outward from the interior. The order of magnitude of the conducted heat has long been known. If the rate of increase of temperature vertically downward is dT/dz, where z is the vertical depth, at a place where the thermal conductivity of the rock is K, then the outward flux of heat by conduction per unit of area and per unit of time is $Q = K\ dT/dz$. From measurements of temperature in deep wells and mines, it has been found that dT/dz is commonly of the order of 20 to 40 degrees centigrade per kilometer. Laboratory measurements, as well as such measurements *in situ* as those of Lord Kelvin, lead to an order of magnitude for K of about 0.005 calories/cm-sec-degree. Thus Q is of the order of 10^{-6} calorie/cm^2-sec, or 30 cal/cm^2-year; or roughly 2×10^{20} cal/year for the whole Earth (see, for example, Joly, 1909, p. 76). This is very small by comparison with the average rate of absorption and reradiation of solar energy ($12{,}000 \times 10^{20}$ cal/year) which determines the mean surface temperature of the Earth. It cannot be repeated too often that the flow of heat from the Earth's interior has no measurable influence on the surface temperature. On the other hand, short-period variations of surface temperature (diurnal or annual) do not affect the temperature for more than 50 feet or so below the surface.

In the last decade or two, the emphasis in geothermal studies has shifted from more or less random collection of thermal gradients to determinations of conducted heat at particularly favorable places where it has been possible to obtain not only measurements of temperature but also samples of rock for the measurement of thermal conductivity. This combination of circumstances is much less common than might be supposed, but, thanks largely to the stimulus given by the Committee on Underground Temperatures of the British Association for the Advancement of Science, a number of such occasions have been recognized and exploited.

These studies show that the flow of heat is approximately uniform, the vertical thermal gradient being roughly proportional to the thermal resistivity of the local rock. The rate of increase of temperature with depth is low where the conductivity is high, as in quartzites, quartz-rich schists, or quartz-rich sandstones of low porosity; it is high in rocks of low conductivity, such as most shales. Nearly all the reasonably well-determined values are included within the limits, $Q = 1.2 \times 10^{-6}$ cal/cm^2-sec ± 50 percent, though the gradients vary from place to place by a factor of as much as 10.

The temperatures may be disturbed in many ways, both artificially and naturally. Among artificial disturbances are ventilation in mines, circulation of water or drilling mud in wells, the flow of oil or gas or water; among natural disturbances in non-volcanic areas are changes of surface temperature resulting from climatic change; erosion; deposition; uplift or subsidence; the flow of underground water; the effect of irregular topography; the effect of geological structure which may involve complicated geometric relationships between good and poor conductors, for which it may be difficult to correct. These factors usually have been recognized, but it is often impossible to avoid appreciable uncertainties.

The early measurements of thermal conductivity of rocks showed discrepancies which for a long time left the subject in some confusion; failure to study and record the petrography was perhaps as much to blame as experimental error. More systematic work has now established the principal factors determining the conductivity of rocks of low porosity (Bullard, 1939; Birch and Clark, 1940; Mossop and Gafner, 1951), but the systematic study of sedimentary rocks has only begun (Clark, 1941; for additional results, see Benfield, 1939, 1947; Coster, 1947; Bullard and Niblett, 1951; Birch, 1954).

In Table 5.8 have been collected the determinations of heat flow, with additional data that aid in appraising the significance of the results. In all determinations there may be systematic errors, arising from some of the possible disturbances already mentioned, far greater than the statistical ones. For example, the unusually high values found in Nottinghamshire, England, by Bullard and Niblett (1951) have been attributed to an underground flow of water which brings an abnormally large amount of heat to the area investigated. Such an explanation would lead to the corollary of a low apparent heat flow in the region from which this heat was derived. Disturbances of this kind are evidently to be expected in areas of high rainfall and porous rocks. Determinations depending on depths of less than 1000 feet have been omitted as well as estimates based on assumed values of conductivity. Corrections up to 50 percent sometimes applied for the supposed effects of deglaciation have been omitted from the tabulated values; a moderate correction may be required in certain regions, but the internal evidence is inconclusive (Birch, 1948, 1954).

The geographic distribution of these determinations leaves much to be desired. There appear to be no satisfactory measurements of heat flow for continental Europe, South America, or Australia; Asia is represented only by a group of values for the Masjid-i-Sulaiman oil field in southwest Iran; Africa only by the measurements in the Union of South Africa. (It is possible that Russian publications on this subject have escaped notice.) The mining areas of southeastern Canada have been very well studied, and there are several scattered measurements for the United States. It is remarkable that an area so intensively drilled as the United States should have furnished so few opportunities for studies of this kind.

The development of apparatus for measuring the thermal gradient in the mud covering the ocean floor may lead to a revolution in our ideas about the distribution of radioactivity, despite the preliminary nature of the oceanic studies. In this work, a probe equipped with temperature-sensitive elements is driven into the bottom mud by the same methods used for core sampling, and a temperature difference is found for points near the deep and the shallow ends of the probe; samples of the bottom are taken in the usual way for studies of conductivity. Two types of equipment have been employed: in the first, a temperature difference between two points about 10 meters apart was determined with a recording differential alcohol thermometer

Table 5.8 Summary of determinations of flow of conducted heat

Region	Max. Depth (feet)	No. of Samples	Mean K (conductivity) $\left(\frac{\text{millical}}{\text{cm-sec-°C}}\right)$	Mean Gradient (°C/km)	H (heat flux) $\left(\frac{\text{microcal}}{\text{cm}^2\text{-sec}}\right)$	Reference
Africa						
Orange Free State						
Dubbeldevlei	4900	4	6.8	22.3	1.52	Bullard (1939), Krige (1939)
Transvaal						
Doornhoutrivier	6000	...	7.4	13.1	0.97	Do.
Doornkloof	6300	...	13.5	8.9	1.20	Do.
Driefontein	...	...	10.8	7.0	0.75	Do.
Gerhardminnebron	10,000	30	13.5	9.5	1.28	Do.
Jacoba No. 3	7300	14	7.5	12.8	0.95	Do.
Reef Nigel	4700	...	10.0	10.3	1.03	Do.
Canada						
Ontario						
Toronto	1000	5	6.4	16	1.03	Misener et al., 1951
Sudbury	5000	6	6.4	15.8	1.01	Do.
Kirkland Lake *	7000	39	7	13.0	1.0	Do.
Larder Lake	2700	6	9.1	9.7	0.88	Do.
Timmins	5500	9	8.0	9.1	0.73	Do.
Quebec						
Thetford	1200	8	6.7	15.7	1.05	Do.
New Calumet	1400	4	8.5	15.6	1.32	Do.
Malartic	1500	8	6.8	10.1	0.69	Do.
United States						
Michigan						
Calumet	6000	89	5.0	18.6	0.93	Birch, 1954
California, Berry 1	9000	34	3.5	39	1.29	Benfield, 1947
Colorado,						
Adams Tunnel	4000	123	7.8	22	1.7	Birch, 1950
Texas, Big Lake 1-B	8300	4	8	24	2	Birch & Clark, 1945
Iran						
Masjid-i-Sulaiman (18 wells)	~3000	35	...	...	0.87 (Mean)	Coster, 1947
Great Britain						
Yorkshire						
Kirkleatham 1	3066	14 (Kirkleatham 1 and Tocketts 1)	5.5	20.9	1.15	Bullard & Niblett, 1951
Tocketts 1	2972		4.3	27.7	1.18	Do.
Nottinghamshire						
Kelham Hills 1	2190	41 (Kelham Hills 1, Caunton 11 and Eakring)	4.0	36.4	1.47	Do.
Caunton 11	2133		4.3	39.1	1.67	Do.
Eakring	2000		3.4–4.0	57–79	1.97–2.87	Do.
Holford	1300	4	6.2	13.3	0.74	Benfield, 1939
Balfour	3955	...	...	...	0.68	Do.
Oceanic						
Latitude Longitude	Water Depth (*m*)					
Pacific						
N20°48′ W159°42′	4500		1.8	70	1.3	Revelle & Maxwell, 1952
N18°18′ W173°23′	3900		2.2	40	0.9	Do.
N19°28′ W174°35′	4900		2.0	60	1.2	Do.
N16°45′ W176°24′	5040		1.8	70	1.3	Do.
N19°02′ W177°19′	4750		1.6	70	1.1	Do.
N32°35′ W132°30′	4000		1.8	70	1.3	Do.
N 0°04′ E169°17′	4310		(1.7) †	76	1.3	Revelle & Maxwell (unpublished)
S 9°04′ E174°51′	5000		1.6–2.1	73	1.3	Do.
S18°59′ E177°36′	2700		(1.7)	72	1.2	Do.
S21°56′ E178°33′	3900		1.9	125	2.4	Do.
S17°28′ W158°40′	4880		(1.7)	86	1.5	Do.
S12°48′ W143°33′	4400		(1.7)	26	0.4	Do.
S14°45′ W112°11′	3020		1.5	214	3.3	Do.
N 5°52′ W123°55′	4100		(1.7)	70	1.2	Do.
N14°59′ W124°12′	4350		(1.7)	123	2.1	Do.
Atlantic						
N49°46′ W 12°30′	2032		2.59	42.6	1.10	Bullard, 1954
N49°58′ W 18°33′	4017		2.58	54.8	1.42	Do.
N49°09′ W 17°38′	4532		2.43	23.7	0.58	Do.
N48°14′ W 16°58′	4670		2.28	25.4	0.58	Do.
N48°52′ W 15°00′	4710		2.64	45.5	1.20	Do.

* See also Leith, 1952.
† Conductivities in parentheses are estimated.

(Pettersson, 1949); in the second, two thermistors about 2 meters apart were arranged to record the temperature difference as function of time (Revelle and Maxwell, 1952; Bullard, in press); with this arrangement it is possible to correct for the failure to reach a steady temperature difference in the relatively short time during which the probe can be left in the bottom.

Since the difference of temperature over so small a depth is only of the order of 0.1° C, careful calibration is required for an accuracy of 10 percent and the possibility of systematic error requires close attention. It is clear that the method would be useless on land because of the large disturbance produced near the ground surface by annual and other fluctuations of temperature; its validity in the deep ocean floor depends upon the constancy of the temperature of the water in contact with the bottom. Even a rather small change of this temperature might produce an appreciable disturbance of gradient in the uppermost few meters of the bottom. There is evidence of a world-wide cooling since the "postglacial thermal maximum" (Flint, 1947, pp. 491 *et seq.*; Flint and Deevey, 1951), and, if the temperature of the water in contact with the bottom has gradually decreased by only 2° C in the last 3000 years, the surface gradient in the mud will be some 20° C/km too high. More recent disturbances of temperature can be even more important. It seems only prudent to accept the oceanic measurements with some reserve until there has been further investigation of the various uncertainties.

If, however, the oceanic technique proves reliable, the accumulation of data can evidently proceed rapidly, and we may soon possess more evidence concerning oceanic heat flow than concerning continental heat flow. The preliminary results now available suggest that the heat flow is approximately the same everywhere, aside from what may be regional or local variations. This is unexpected, since the higher radioactive content of typically continental rocks has led to an anticipation of greater heat flow in continental than in oceanic regions. If substantiated, the new findings must produce a drastic revision of current doctrine regarding the distribution of radioactivity.

Crude and sparse as are the determinations of loss of heat by conduction, they are much more precise than the estimates of the average loss of heat by the processes associated with volcanism, such as the production of steam, hot water, ash, lava, and intrusives. Attempts have been made to calculate the loss of heat from volcanoes and from warm and hot springs in particular areas at the present time, but it is evidently difficult to integrate such results for what are probably always exceptional circumstances over the whole surface and over geological time.

The rate of loss of heat by conduction at present is of the order of 2×10^{20} calories per year for the whole Earth. According to Einarsson (1949), the 1947 eruption of Hecla in Iceland produced a total of 0.4 km^3 of ash and lava, reduced to a density of 3. If we assume a heat content of 500 cal/g, this leads to 6×10^{17} calories brought to the surface in a few days and in a small region. Several hundred Heclas each year would be needed to equal the total heat loss by conduction; the actual period of Hecla itself is about 50 years.

Allen and Day (1935) estimate the heat carried away by the hot springs of Yellowstone National Park as 2×10^8 cal/sec. The area of the region in which these springs are abundant may be taken as roughly 50 by 100 km, or 5×10^{13} cm^2. Thus the average loss is 4×10^{-6} cal/cm^2-sec, or several times the normal loss by conduction, though perhaps not more than the loss of heat by conduction in Yellowstone Park itself. On the other hand, Yellowstone, though by far the largest thermal area at the present time, is evidently of trivial extent on the planetary scale.

Rubey (1951) has used data on the hot springs of the United States for an estimate of the world total, obtaining 66×10^{15} g/year. The average difference of temperature from mean surface temperature was about 20° C; the net transport of heat would then be 10^{18} cal/year, still negligible by comparison with the total conducted heat.

Verhoogen (1946) estimates the average rate of loss of heat by volcanic eruptions, since the close of the pre-Cambrian, as about one-thousandth of the rate of loss by normal conduction. A somewhat higher figure is given by Lotze (1928), who obtains a total loss of 2×10^{20} cal from known volcanic action since the year 1600; this would thus be at an average rate of about 1/350 of the loss by conduction and is considered to be a lower limit because of the neglect of unobserved eruptions.

Still cruder estimates, based on the idea of the gradual production of the whole ocean as steam from the interior, and of the crust as lava, distributed over a period of 3×10^9 years give mean values of 3×10^{17} cal/year for the water, 7×10^{18} cal/year for the lava (Birch, 1951, p. 119).

Rough as these estimates certainly are, it seems likely that the average rate of loss of heat by volcanic activity is at least an order of magnitude smaller than the rate of loss by conduction for the Earth as a whole.

5.4 THEORETICAL CONSIDERATIONS AND CONCLUSIONS

The geothermal measurements show that the Earth is losing heat at a rate of about 1.2×10^{-6} cal/cm^2-sec, or roughly 2×10^{20} cal/year if this rate is taken as the mean for the whole surface. These measurements cannot distinguish between radioactive heat and heat from other sources. This division depends upon theory, and, since a satisfactory solution must be consistent with other than purely thermal evidence, various writers have drawn upon additional information furnished by geology, geophysics, and geochemistry. We can consider only a few of these theories, with special reference to the question of radioactive heat.

A simple comparison with the rates of heat production of typical rocks shows at once that relatively thin layers having the mean radioactive contents assigned to common rocks in Table 5.6 would suffice to produce all the observed heat loss. The required thicknesses are 20 km of granite, or 40 km of intermediate rock, or 120 km of basalt, of the assumed average compositions. Such small values show that these rocks must be greatly enriched in the radioactive elements by comparison with the Earth as a whole; for example, if the whole mantle had the average radioactivity of basalt, the rate of heat production would be about 15 times the rate of heat loss, and the flow of heat at the surface would be roughly 4 times as great as the observed value. The discrepancies would be, of course, much greater if the value for granite were assumed to be typical of the whole mantle.

In arriving at estimates for the effect of deep-lying heat sources, we encounter one of the fundamental limitations of geothermal observations. Rocks as we know them at the Earth's surface are poor conductors of heat, characterized by values of *thermal diffusivity* in the range, 0.005 to 0.02 cm^2/sec. We have no direct information about this property for the deep interior of the Earth, but there are reasons for thinking that the order of magnitude is still about 0.01 cm^2/sec; this is based upon the distinction between electrical conductors (metals) and electrical insulators or semiconductors. We have evidence that the electrical conductivity of the mantle is considerably below that of typical metals, and we infer that the thermal conductivity must also be of non-metallic character, and hence of the order stated above (for typical metals, the range is 0.1 to 1.0 cm^2/sec). The thermal diffusivity of the mantle may be expected to vary with temperature, pressure, chemical composition, and phase, but, in the absence of detailed information, and in the interest of simplicity, it will be taken as uniform, and equal to 0.01 cm^2/sec, or in more practical units, 32 $km^2/10^6$ years. Some consequences of other values will be considered below.

With this low diffusivity, very little of any heat generated at depths greater than about 700 km can reach the surface by conduction even in times of the order of several thousand million years. For this reason the surface heat flow does not give a definite answer to the question of the total amount of radioactivity (Slichter, 1941). It does, however, definitely limit the amount of radioactivity in the surface layer, several hundred kilometers thick, from which the heat flow to the surface is nearly equal to the rate of heat generation. We cannot have at the surface, for example, 200 km of material with the mean radioactivity of the typical basalt of Table 5.6.

Another argument to the same effect may be drawn from the integrated heat generation. Because of low conductivity, almost no heat is lost from depths below about 700 km; but in 3000 million years the heat generation per gram from the radioactivity of basalt (1 cal/10^6 years) becomes 3000 cal/g, without allowance for radioactive decay, or nearly 5000 cal/g, allowing for decay. Now the total heat of melting of silicates from low temperature is of the order of 500 cal/g; but the seismological and tidal rigidity shows that the mantle is solid; thus either the average radioactivity must be much less than that of basalt, say one-tenth, or else the rate of escape of heat must have been much more rapid than has been supposed; in the latter event, the surface heat loss includes the heat generation at deep levels, and thus limits the total amount of radioactivity more drastically. We notice that the present rate of heat loss divided by the mass of the mantle gives a figure of 0.05 cal/g-10^6 years, about one-twentieth of the rate of heat generation in typical basalt. This would be the upper limit for the average rate for the whole Earth if the conductivity were very high, say about equal to that of copper, or if convection currents were sufficiently active to produce an equivalent heat transport.

It is generally considered that the seismological boundary known as the Mohorovičić discontinuity is also a chemical boundary, which divides the silica-, alkali-, and alumina-rich rocks of the crust from the magnesia-rich, "ultramafic" silicates of the mantle. This boundary lies at a mean depth of some 30 to 40 km under the continents and perhaps 5 to 10 km under the oceans (Raitt, 1949; Hersey et al., 1952; Officer et al., 1952). The continental crust is sometimes further divided into "granitic," "intermediate," and "basaltic" layers, though the reality of such layering is in question. Whatever the details, however, there is little reason to doubt that the granitic and intermediate rocks constitute a considerable fraction of the continental crust, and it is noteworthy that the seismological thickness of this crust is just about what is needed to account for the whole surface heat flow in terms of the observed radioactivity of granitic and intermediate rocks. All this evidence points to a relatively extreme concentration of radioactivity in the typically continental rocks, with much lower concentrations below the crust. This conclusion is supported by the discovery of the low, nearly vanishing, activity of such rocks as dunite, which many believe to be the principal component of the mantle; whether this is true or not, the extreme poverty of these rocks with respect to all the radioactive elements shows that a fractionation of remarkable completeness can occur in nature.

This line of reasoning has been followed by Jeffreys as part of a completely developed thermal history of the Earth (Jeffreys, 1952, Chapter 10). Jeffreys supposes that the mantle of the Earth passed through a molten stage, that it crystallized from the base upward, and that the surface temperature fell, as soon as the early stage of rapid convection was over, to essentially the present temperature which is determined by solar radiation. In the process of crystallization, the radioactive elements were segregated toward the top of the mantle. The subsequent history was one of cooling by conduction toward the fixed surface temperature, the initial temperature at all depths being practically the freezing temperature, plus warming by radioactive heating. If the diffusivity is taken as independent of the temperature, then the cooling and heating processes may be considered separately, each going on independently of the other.

The contribution from initial heat is found just as in Kelvin's theory. Kelvin took the freezing point as constant, T_0, and used the solution for the cooling of a uniform, semi-infinite conductor with zero surface temperature. This solution (Carslaw and Jaeger, 1947, pp. 66–69), gives the temperature T at depth x and time t as:

$$T = T_0 \operatorname{erf}\left(\frac{x}{\sqrt{4kt}}\right)$$

where k is the thermal diffusivity. The gradient of temperature is then

$$\frac{\partial T}{\partial x} = \frac{T_0 \exp\left(-\frac{x^2}{4kt}\right)}{\sqrt{\pi kt}}$$

and at $x = 0$, this is simply

$$\left(\frac{\partial T}{\partial x}\right)_0 = \frac{T_0}{\sqrt{\pi k t}}$$

This result was used by Kelvin to find the time t for reaching a given surface gradient; with $(\partial T/\partial x)_0 = 20°$ C/km, $T_0 = 1400°$ C and $k = 32$ km^2/10^6 years, we obtain $t = 50 \times 10^6$ years. Since we now take t to be roughly 5×10^9 years, the corresponding surface gradient can be only $20/\sqrt{100}$ or so, or about 2° C/km.

Jeffreys has extended this theory by allowing for a difference of conductivity between crust and mantle, for a rise of freezing point with depth, and for radioactivity. If the initial temperature is taken to be $T_0 + mx$, where m gives the rise of freezing point with depth, then the surface gradient is

$$\left(\frac{\partial T}{\partial x}\right)_0 = \frac{T_0}{\sqrt{\pi k t}} + m$$

The value of m is of the order of a few degrees per kilometer, and thus the initial temperature accounts for about one-quarter of the actual surface gradient. In order to account for the whole gradient in these terms, it would be necessary to take k some 60-fold smaller than the adopted value, or T_0 some four times as high; both of these alternatives are inacceptable. Jeffreys thus takes the difference between the whole heat loss and the fraction, roughly one-quarter, arising from the initial temperature, as a measure of the radioactive heat generation, and supposes that the radioactive elements are concentrated so close to the surface (within about 200 km) that this difference determines the total quantity present. As we have seen, this is consistent both with what is known of the radioactivity of continental rocks and with the seismological thickness of the continental crust.

This theory has the great advantage of leading to definite calculations and expectations. For example, if most of the radioactivity is concentrated in the continental crust, then in mountainous regions where the continental crust is conceived to be thicker than normal, an abnormally high flow of heat should be found, and this appears to be true (Birch, 1950). On the other hand, the new measurements of oceanic heat flow suggest that a more complicated pattern of distribution of radioactivity may have to be considered. As perhaps half of the continental heat flow might arise from the "granitic" layer, and as granitic rocks are not found in the deep ocean basins, the oceanic heat flow ought not to exceed about one-half of the continental value. The oceanic observations of heat flow, if taken at face value, show no significant difference from the continental values. This unexpected result might be interpreted by assuming (Bullard, 1952) that the total quantity of radioactive material, per square kilometer of surface, is roughly the same everywhere, but that in continental regions it is largely concentrated in the crust, whereas under the oceans it is distributed through some as yet indeterminate depth below the crust. Evidently this would imply a higher radioactive content for the suboceanic rocks than for the subcontinental rocks below the Mohorovičić discontinuity. But this reopens the question of the degree of concentration in the continental crust, and it is possible that more radioactive material lies below the Mohorovičić discontinuity than is suggested by Jeffreys' theory in its most definite form.

That this may be a part of the answer may also be inferred from certain geochemical speculations. A widely adopted assumption regarding the chemical composition of the primitive Earth is that the relative abundances correspond more or less closely to the distribution in the stony meteorites. The older determinations gave about 0.2 percent for the potassium content (Goldschmidt, 1937; Brown, 1949); more recent work (Ahrens, et al., 1952, see Chapter 3) leads to about 0.1 percent. With the lower value, the original potassium content of the Earth (ignoring the core) would be 4×10^{24} g. The total mass of the continental crust is about 14×10^{24} g, and its potassium content can hardly exceed that of true granites, about 4 percent. Thus the crust would contain only about 0.6×10^{24} g of potassium; most of the potassium would still lie below the crust and would be capable of producing about 10^{20} cal/year, or half of the total heat loss. The original potassium content of the mantle is, of course, highly uncertain. There is not enough reliable information about the uranium and thorium content of stony meteorites to permit a similar calculation for these elements; they may be more completely segregated toward and within the crust than is the potassium. There is evidence, however, that uranium follows potassium, at least in some rocks (Figure 2.3).

It should also be recognized that we are ignorant of the proportion of true granite, in the petrological or chemical sense, in the "granitic" layer of seismology. For the seismologist, "granite" is a rock in which the velocity of the compressional wave (P) lies somewhere between 5.5 and 6.2 km/sec. The comparable velocity for gabbro is about 7 km/sec. The velocities in the crust lie generally between about 5.5 and 7 km/sec. A wide variety of sedimentary and metamorphic rocks can also have velocities in this range; but a quartzite or a marble with velocities in the "granitic" range ordinarily contains very much less radioactivity than "average granite." Thus, even if we knew the correct mean value for true granite, we should still be faced with the problem of deciding how much of such material is present in the crust. It seems likely that the proportion has been overestimated, and that the average radioactivity of the crust as a whole is lower, and of the subcrust, higher, than is usually supposed.

This uncertainty regarding the vertical distribution of the radioactive elements makes it impossible to calculate internal temperatures with confidence, and leads to the often repeated statement, "The Earth may be either cooling or heating." The problem is not beyond resolution, at least in principle, since the possibility exists of a rough determination of thermal gradient at considerable depth, either by the use of the rate of change of seismic velocities with depth (Birch, 1952) or of the rate of increase of electrical conductivity with depth (Hughes, unpublished). It is still too soon to place much confidence in the preliminary results obtained by these methods.

Certain astronomical theories propose the formation of planets by a slow accretion of cosmic dust, which might result in an initial condition of relatively low temperature, but with the radioactive elements approximately uniformly distributed throughout the body. A period of radioactive heating then raises the temperature to a point at which differentiation of the interior becomes possible, with formation of a crust substantially different from the underlying mantle. In such theories, it is important to remember that the "initial temperature," from the point of view of heat conduction, is the temperature at a certain moment after which the transport of heat is predominantly by conduction and may have nothing to do with the temperature of the original accumulation of material; it may be necessary to consider a pregeological era of relatively rapid heating because of the greater abundance of the active isotopes. This era would reach a climax of mobility essentially like the primitive molten globe of Kelvin and Jeffreys, and, if the active elements were then segregated toward the surface, the subsequent history would be as describd by Jeffreys. This would mean that the date of origin might be as far back as 5000 million years or so (Urry, 1949*a*; Birch, 1951). The age of the crust is possibly more than 4000 million years (see Section 9.1), and, since a stable crust could hardly be formed until at least a partial differentiation of the radioactive elements was effected, solidification may date from about this epoch.

In another modification of the accretion theory (Urey, 1952) the initial temperature is taken to be lower than the freezing point (927° C, Urey, 1952, p. 170), and the stage of general fusion has not yet taken place. In this case, the contribution of the initial heat to the surface gradient is about 2° C/km. Urey considers the effect of a uniform distribution of radioactivity, with values based on the analyses of stony meteorites and dunites, and calculates the temperatures at later times according to various assumptions regarding the presence or absence of convection, including a special kind of convection consisting of settling-out of free iron from the mantle to the core. No direct use is made of the observed heat loss from the surface, which is in conflict with the results of most of these calculations. We may remark also that with Urey's value of the potassium content, 0.2 percent, the heat generation would be 800 cal/g in 4000 million years, probably more than enough to produce melting at the deeper levels by potassium decay alone, and a consequent transformation of the problem to one of convection rather than conduction, and of a closer balance between heat loss and heat generation. These figures suggest that an upper limit for the potassium content of the deep mantle might be about 0.1 percent, even if the initial temperature were low; if the initial temperature approached the melting point, then still less would be permissible. A further reduction, to allow for the heating by uranium and thorium, is, of course, required but uncertain.

It is interesting to see that the upper limit on a uniform distribution, imposed by the requirement that the total heat generation must not exceed the melting heat, is considerably lower than the limit imposed by the heat flow at the surface. For this calculation, we neglect the fact that the core has different thermal and radioactive properties from the mantle, and suppose that diffusivity and heat generation are uniform throughout the sphere. We are interested only in the thermal gradient, or the heat flow, at the surface. The solution for a constant rate of heating, say A cal/cm^3-sec, is given in the standard texts (Carslaw and Jaeger, 1947, p. 207; Slichter, 1941):

$$-K\left(\frac{\partial T}{\partial r}\right)_{r=a} = \frac{Aa}{3}\left\{1 - \frac{6}{\pi^2}\sum_{n=1}^{\infty}\frac{1}{n^2}\exp\left(-\frac{n^2\pi^2kt}{a^2}\right)\right\}$$

$Aa/3$ is the rate of heat production per unit surface area, and the numerical factor in brackets is the ratio of the rate of loss of heat by conduction at the surface to the rate of heat generation. For $k = 32$ km^2/10^6 years, and $t = 4000 \times 10^6$ years, this ratio is 0.18; that is to say, with these values, only 18 percent of the total heat currently generated by a uniform distribution is represented in the surface heat flow. With $k = 320$ km^2/10^6 years, about the value for iron, the corresponding fraction is 0.50.

The assumption of constant heating is not a good one for such long intervals of time, and Urey (1952, p. 53) has given the solution for this problem, allowing for exponential decay of the radioactive elements. For the partial heat flow from a single radioactive series, with decay constant λ, the flow of heat at the surface is

$$-K\left(\frac{\partial T}{\partial r}\right)_{r=a} = \frac{A_0 a e^{-\lambda t}}{3}\left[\frac{6kt}{a^2}\sum_{n=1}^{\infty}\frac{1-\exp\left(\lambda t - \dfrac{n^2\pi^2 kt}{a^2}\right)}{\dfrac{n^2\pi^2 kt}{a^2} - \lambda t}\right]$$

Here A_0 is the rate of heat generation by this series per unit volume, at the time $t = 0$; the rate at time t is $A_0 e^{-\lambda t}$. Thus the numerical factor in brackets is the ratio of heat flow at the surface, at time t, to the contemporary rate of generation of heat for the given series. As an example, let us consider the potassium decay with $\lambda = 0.55 \times 10^{-9}$ year. The ratio has been computed for two values of k, as before, and for $t = 4 \times 10^9$ years: for $k = 32$ km^2/10^6 years, the ratio is 0.53; for $k = 320$ km^2/10^6 years, the ratio is 1.27. These values should be compared with 0.18 and 0.50, respectively, as given above for constant heating. The differences will, of course, be smaller for the uranium^{238} and thorium series, greater for the uranium^{235} series.

These results may be used to obtain another estimate for the maximum allowable potassium content of the deep mantle, by assuming that all the surface heat flow is produced by this series, and that the concentration of potassium remains constant, or does not increase, with depth. Then we find that the rate of heat generation at present cannot exceed twice the surface heat flow, for $k = 32$ km^2/10^6 years; that is, the total heat production at present could be 4×10^{20} cal/year, or 10^{-7} cal/year-g for the mantle. Since the rate of heat production by potassium is at present 27×10^{-6} cal/year-g, we arrive at a maximum average potassium content of 1/270 or 0.37 percent. This is still considerably higher than is permitted by the melting criterion, since the integrated heat production over 4000 million years with this concentration is 1500 cal/g; the acceptable maximum for uniform distribution is not more than one-third of this value, or about 0.13 percent. This is still too high, since no allowance has been made for heating by uranium or thorium, nor for concentration toward the surface.

A lower limit for the average potassium content may be obtained on the assumption that there must be enough potassium to supply the $argon^{40}$ of the atmosphere. This lower limit, given as an average for the mantle, is 0.014 percent for $t = 4000$ million years (Birch, 1951).

In assessing the various limits found in these calculations, it is important to remember that our present information regarding the distribution of radioactivity in rocks and meteorites in nowise commits us to the belief that more heat is being generated than is being lost for the Earth as a whole; on the other hand, the surface heat flow does not give precise information about the existence of deep-seated radioactivity. Other kinds of data must be employed to decide these questions.

Chapter 6

RADIATION DAMAGE AND ENERGY STORAGE

6.1 RADIATION DAMAGE AND ITS USE IN AGE DETERMINATION *

HEINRICH D. HOLLAND †

It has been known for many years (Slater, 1951), that the majority of the energy dissipated by alpha, beta, and gamma rays on passing through crystals is expended in ionization processes. Only recently has it been shown (Seitz, 1949, 1952; Slater, 1951), that a small fraction of the energy of these particles, as well as much of the energy of neutrons (Siegel, 1949), and of recoil nuclei is expended in the dislocation of atoms from their normal lattice positions.

The effects of ionization within crystals are numerous. The coloration of many substances has been discussed at length (Mott and Gurney, 1948; Daniels et al., 1953), as has the luminescence (Pringsheim, 1949; Leverenz, 1950) and thermoluminescence (Daniels et al., 1953) of irradiated materials. The observed effects are to be ascribed to the return of excited electrons to their original position (luminescence), to the permanent or semipermanent trapping of such electrons within the structure (thermoluminescence), or to secondary processes induced by the dislocation of electrons, such as diffusion in alkali halide crystals.

The dislocation of atoms from their normal lattice positions normally affects all the physical properties of the irradiated crystals. In the alloy system Au-Cu complete disordering has been induced by the passage of neutrons, leading particularly to changes in the electrical properties of the irradiated crystals (Siegel, 1949). In crystals of zircon, $ZrSiO_4$, the optical properties, specific gravity, hardness, re-

* The research on which this section is based was supported in part by the Office of Naval Research.

† Department of Geology, Princeton University, Princeton, New Jersey.

sistance to solvents, infrared spectrum, and X-ray diffraction pattern all are changed considerably by such dislocations. Crystals of some compounds (sodium carbonate and sodium formate) may be completely destroyed and new compounds formed by irradiation with particles producing atomic dislocation.

Such changes in the properties of solids can be used to measure radiation dosage, i.e., the quantity of radiation received per unit weight of the irradiated material. Thus, if the rate of irradiation also can be determined, the time elapsed since the start of irradiation can be found. In the materials discussed below irradiation commenced at the time of crystallization.

In order to apply this method of time measurement to determine the age of geologic materials, two conditions must be met:

1. The relation between radiation dosage and radiation damage must be constant throughout the geologic history of the material. This implies that the rate of annealing of the structure damage has been zero or otherwise constant throughout the geologic history of the sample.

2. The rate of irradiation must be measurable and must have been either constant in the past or related by some predictable expression to the present rate of irradiation.

The usefulness of methods of age determination which depend on the effects of the displacement of electrons from their normal lattice positions is limited by the first condition. It has been found (Daniels et al., 1953; see Section 6.2) that electrons may return to their normal lattice positions at appreciable rates at temperatures normally maintained or reached by geologic specimens.

The second condition eliminates specimens in the irradiation of which the radioactivity of the environment is of importance but has not been constant, and materials for which the radiation dosage is affected by the size and shape of the irradiated crystals and where these have not remained constant. These restrictions are normally of importance where the effects of beta and gamma radiation are measured, for the range, particularly of the latter, may be greater than the size of the specimen being studied.

There remain then those methods of age determination which are based on the effect of the displacement of atoms. Since the displacement of atoms from normal lattice positions usually affects all the physical properties of crystals, the measurement of the change of any physical property of any crystal damaged in this manner offers a potential method of age determination. However, only easily measurable changes in properties of minerals which are of widespread geologic occurrence and which have reasonably constant chemical composition warrant investigation for age-determination purposes. The heat of recrystallization of the rare-earth oxides has been investigated (Kerr and Holland, 1951; Kulp et al., 1952*b*), and these data have been suggested for age determination purposes (Holland and Kulp, 1950). The results warrant further consideration of these minerals, although the complexity and variability of the chemical composition of the minerals in this group may limit their usefulness. A more fruitful field of investigation appears to be offered by the mineral zircon which satisfies both the criteria of abundance and constancy of chemical composition. The remainder of this paper is devoted to a discussion of the use of radiation damage in this mineral as a method of age determination.

Zircons have long been known to exhibit a variability of physical properties which could not be explained in terms of compositional variations. The work of German investigators in the 1930's demonstrated that the earlier classification of zircons into three distinct groups was not reasonable, for no discontinuity in the physical properties was found (Chudoba and von Stackelberg, 1936; von Stackelberg and Chudoba, 1937; Lietz, 1937–1938; Bauer, 1939; von Stackelberg and Rottenbach, 1939–1940*a*, *b*). It was noted that the decrease in specific gravity and changes in hardness (Chudoba, 1937), refractive indices (Anderson and Payne, 1937), and birefringence could be correlated with an increase in the unit cell dimensions and a decrease of order within the crystals as shown by blurring of X-ray diffraction lines. The stones of lowest density were found to yield an X-ray pattern in which the characteristic diffraction lines of zircon were completely absent, indicating that the observed changes in the physical properties are due to a progressive destruction of order within the crystal lattice.

In order to study the relationship between radiation dosage and disorder in zircons a suite of gem zircons from Ceylon was obtained by this writer. It was shown that the age of the stones is about 600 million years (see Table 9), and that almost all their radioactivity is due to the decay of uranium and its daughter elements (Gottfried, 1953). The total number of alpha particles δ received by each milligram of zircon is therefore:

$$\delta = A\left[\frac{8(e^{\lambda_{\mathrm{U}}\times 6\times 10^{8}\times 365\times 24}-1)+\frac{7}{139}(e^{\lambda_{\mathrm{AcU}}\times 6\times 10^{8}\times 365\times 24}-1)}{8\lambda_{\mathrm{U}}+\frac{7}{139}\lambda_{\mathrm{AcU}}}\right] \quad (1)$$

where λ_U = decay constant of U^{238} in hours^{-1}, λ_{AcU} = decay constant of U^{235} in hours^{-1}, and A = present alpha activity in α/mg-hour. The plot of Figure 6.1 shows the density, ρ, of various Ceylon zircons as a function of their alpha activity. The smooth relationship indicates that the changes in density are due to the irradiation of the

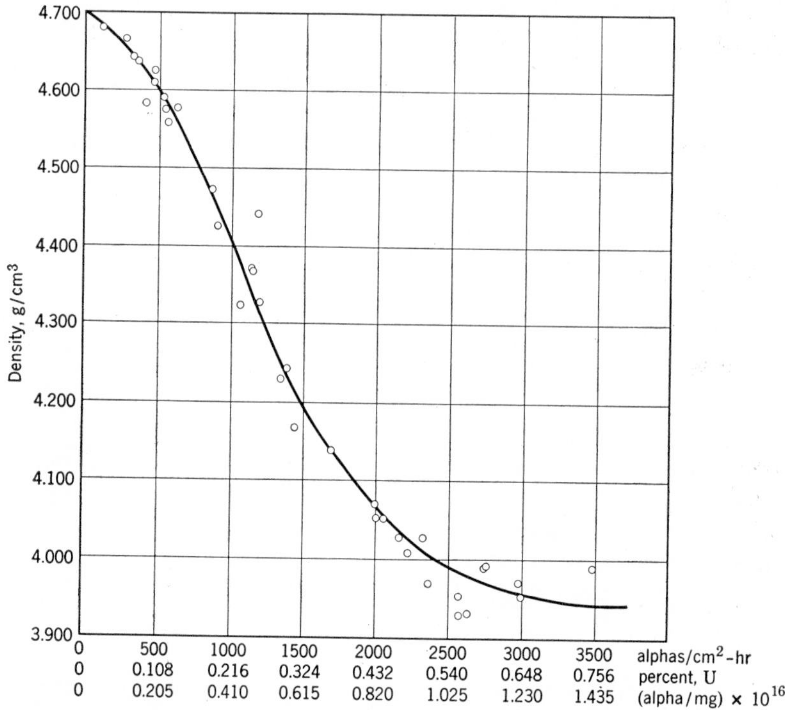

Figure 6.1 Density of gem zircons from Ceylon, plotted as a function of their radioactivity.

structure, and that a dosage of 2×10^{16} α/mg and the concomitant radiation are sufficient to disorder the structure completely. On the basis of the work of Seitz (1949), the number of atoms displaced within the zircon crystal by beta and gamma rays should be negligible; the number displaced by each alpha particle should be of the order of 50, and the number displaced by recoil nuclei after alpha emission of the order of 1000. Thus a dosage of 2×10^{16} α/mg would produce about 2×10^{19} displacements. The number of atoms per mg of zircon is 2×10^{19}, so that there is at present satisfactory agreement between the predicted and observed radiation dosage required for disordering the zircon structure completely.

The curve of Figure 6.1 can be used for purposes of age determination. The density of a given zircon uniquely determines the radiation dosage received; this is related to the present alpha activity and to the age of the zircon t by equation 2:

$$\delta = A \left[\frac{8(e^{\lambda_U t} - 1) + \frac{7}{139}(e^{\lambda_{AcU} t} - 1) + 6\phi(e^{\lambda_{Th} t} - 1)}{8\lambda_U + \frac{7}{139}\lambda_{AcU} + 6\phi} \right] \quad (2)$$

where λ_{Th} = decay constant of Th^{232} in hours^{-1}, ϕ = ratio of U^{238} to Th^{232} atoms in sample, t = age of sample in hours, and the other symbols have the same meaning as in equation 1. The use of the curve in Figure 6.1 for age-determination purposes is, however, limited by the difficulty of determining accurately the density of most naturally occurring zircons (Hurley and Fairbairn, 1953).

The optical properties of zircons also are affected by irradiation, and changes in these properties can be used for purposes of age determination in the same manner as the curve. However, it has been found that during the initial stages of irradiation the indices of refraction change very little; and, as this range is particularly important for dating geologic specimens, measurement of the optical properties is not a fruitful approach toward making age measurements.

The most accurate measurement of radiation damage, especially when the dosage is small, can be obtained by a determination of the interplanar spacings by means of X-ray diffraction techniques, as has been pointed out by Hurley and Fairbairn (1953). In Figure 6.2 the c dimension of the unit cell of a number of Ceylon zircons has been plotted as a function of the radiation dosage received. This curve can be used to determine the age of zircons in the same manner as the curve in Figure 6.1, discussed above. The preliminary results using this technique are very encouraging (Holland et al., 1953; Hurley and Fairbairn, 1953).

Whereas it should be possible to determine the age of most zircons by this method, difficulties will be encountered in zircons of abnormal composition and zircons that have been heated excessively since their formation. Among the first group are those that have become hydrated, and among the latter those that have passed through a period of intense metamorphism. The rate of annealing of radiation damage between room temperature and 1200° C is now being studied; it may be possible to date periods of metamorphism in this manner, and to obtain an approximate geologic thermometer at the same time from data on the residual damage in zircons of different radioactivity in highly metamorphosed igneous rocks.

In conclusion, radiation damage in crystals offers means of determining the age of geologic materials. Effects produced by atomic dislocations in abundant minerals of constant composition appear to

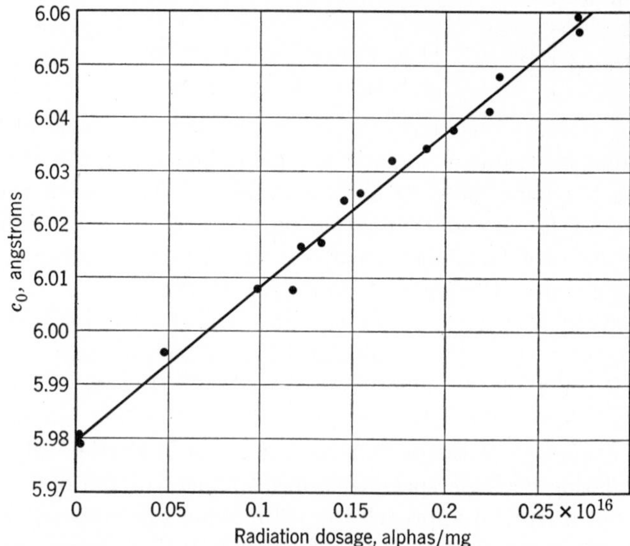

Figure 6.2 Relations of the c_0 dimension of the unit cell to the number of alpha disintegrations per milligram of Ceylon zircons.

be the most promising. Among these, changes of the unit cell dimensions in zircon crystals by irradiation promise to be the basis of a rapid method of age determination.

6.2 THERMOLUMINESCENCE OF CARBONATE SEDIMENTS *

EDWARD J. ZELLER †

When heated, many minerals emit visible light. This property is called thermoluminescence and is the result of the release of energy stored as electron displacements in the crystal lattice (Leverenz, 1950). Activation of thermoluminescence in a crystalline substance is believed to occur through the ability of radiations to free electrons from ions which make up the crystal lattice of the substance. These

* The author is indebted to the Atomic Energy Commission, Research Division, for its support of a research program of which this work is part.

† Department of Chemistry, University of Wisconsin, Madison, Wisconsin.

electrons then become trapped in imperfections in the lattice where they are held until the crystal is heated, giving them enough thermal energy to escape from their traps. The actual light emission occurs during the transition from the trap to normal lattice position. In a sense, the imperfections or "holes" are a statistical concept. Electrons which have been dislodged by some electromagnetic force remain as part of a dynamic system but are at an energy level higher than that of their normal state. Thermal effects allow the electrons to return to their former positions, and the energy is released as photons. The exact nature of the electron traps is not known, but impurity inclusions, ion vacancies, and ion dislocations are thought to be the causes of most of the traps.

Since the discovery that carbonate sediments show a general increase in natural thermoluminescence with increasing geologic age, attempts have been made in the laboratories of the University of Wisconsin to produce a usable thermoluminescence age-determination method. Experiments have shown a proportional relationship between the amount of light emitted by a thermoluminescent substance and the amount of radiation to which the substance has been subjected. In theory, the geologic age of a sample could be determined by measuring the alpha radioactivity of the sample and the amount of light released. It is possible to bombard samples with alpha particles and thereby determine the amount of thermoluminescence induced in the sample for each unit of artificial irradiation. We have attempted to determine the degree to which the relationship between thermoluminescence and total irradiation would hold under geologic conditions.

6.2.a Activation of thermoluminescence

In nature, the most likely radiations which could activate thermoluminescence are alpha particles and recoil nuclei which come from the decay of radioactive elements. Radioactive atoms are included as impurities in the crystal lattice of carbonate minerals. All the natural samples that have been studied show a measurable alpha activity, and it appears reasonable to relate thermoluminescence to this activity. Natural gamma radiation undoubtedly accounts for some of the activation but its relative effectiveness is much lower.

In comparing the effects of gamma rays with those of alpha particles, it is essential to consider the basic similarities and differences in processes by which these two types of radiation affect the lattice. Only very rarely is a gamma ray able to impart enough energy to an ion to actually move it from its lattice position. The ionizing effects of gamma rays are largely confined to the production of primary and secondary electrons through the photoelectric effect and Compton scattering. Alpha particles are able to produce more complex radiation damage effects than gamma rays. Though most of their energy is expended in ionization, they are also capable of dislocating lattice ions by collision.

The effects of gamma radiation are more or less evenly distributed throughout the crystal lattice. On the other hand, the ionic dislocations and the electron displacements produced by alpha-particle radiation are initially confined to the immediate area of the particle's short path through the crystal. Rieke (unpublished thesis, Univ. of Wis., 1954) has shown conclusively that electrons freed by alpha radiation from polonium are capable of slow diffusion throughout the crystal lattice of single large crystals of lithium fluoride. Diffusion effects also occur in single crystals of the carbonate minerals; however, long-range electron diffusion does not occur in carbonate sediments because of the inability of the electrons to cross the crystalline grain boundaries.

Under natural conditions the source of the alpha particles which produce radiation damage lies within the crystal which is affected. Therefore, the alpha particle itself is not the only source of damage because the nucleus from which it is ejected recoils with an equal momentum. The alpha particle, because of its high initial velocity, expends most of its energy in ionization, and it is not until the velocity has been greatly reduced, near the end of its path, that ion dislocations are produced.

The relationship between the initial velocity of the recoil nucleus and that of its alpha particle is the inverse of the proportion of their relative weights, or about 1/55. Thus the initial velocity of the recoil nucleus will be relatively low, and its ability to cause lattice dislocations will be proportionately large. Even under the most favorable circumstances only a very small proportion of the energy of the alpha particle and its recoil nucleus is expended in the production of lattice dislocations, and these effects become noticeable only after extremely heavy alpha bombardment. Lattice dislocations may influence the thermoluminescence of a substance either through their ability to act as electron trapping centers or more commonly through the destruction of existing electron traps. High degrees of lattice disorder always seem to result in decreased thermoluminescence. Metamict minerals are generally non-thermoluminescent, and calcites which have been subjected to very large dosages of alpha radiation show a reduction in thermoluminescence intensity.

6.2.b Technique of age determination

Thermoluminescence is measured by means of an apparatus consisting of an electric furnace for heating the sample, a multiplier

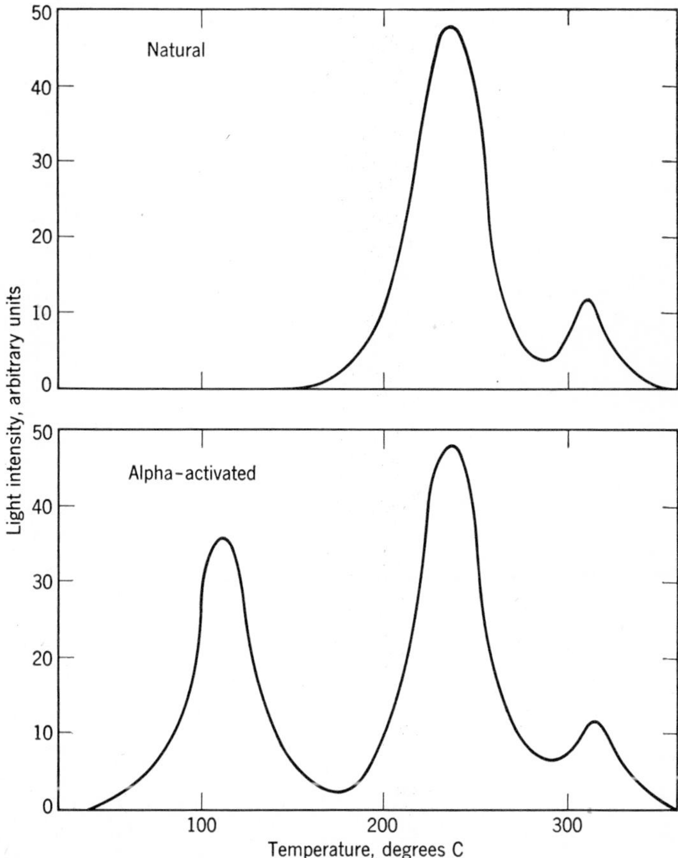

Figure 6.3 Thermoluminescence glow curves of a limestone sample in its natural condition and after alpha irradiation. The low-temperature peak is drained under ordinary rock temperatures.

phototube to convert the light emitted into electric current, a preamplifier, and a two-point recording potentiometer. The temperature of the electric furnace is recorded simultaneously with the light emitted by the sample. Figure 6.3 shows two glow curves from the same limestone sample. The curve of natural thermoluminescence is obtained by placing some of the powdered sample directly on the furnace. The alpha-activated glow curve was made by exposing some of the powdered sample to alpha radiation from polonium before placing it on the furnace. The natural glow curve shows two peaks, one at 235° C and the other at 312° C. The alpha-activated glow curve has a third peak at 110° C. This peak is not present in natural glow curves because ordinary rock temperatures are sufficiently

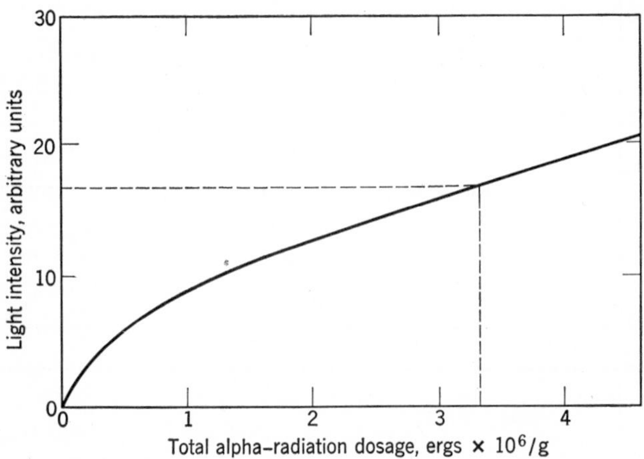

Figure 6.4 Typical calibration curve showing the relationship between thermoluminescence light intensity and the total alpha-radiation dosage received by a sample of limestone.

high to permit the escape of any electrons from the energy level corresponding to the 110° C peak.

To determine the geologic age of a sample it is first necessary to determine the shape of the calibration curve for that particular sample. This curve shows the intensity of thermoluminescence of the 312° C peak plotted against radiation dosage received by the sample. The 312° C peak is always used in these calculations because it is the only one that persists in samples subjected to ordinary rock temperatures. It is necessary to plot the calibration curve for each sample because the shape of the curve varies with the chemical composition.

When the relationship between intensity of thermoluminescence and artificial radiation dosage for a particular sample is known, the amount of radiation necessary to produce the natural thermoluminescence can be determined as illustrated in Figure 6.4. In this figure a natural thermoluminescence of 17 arbitrary light units intersects the calibration curve at an alpha-particle radiation exposure of 3.30×10^6 ergs. The amount of artificial radiation damage necessary to produce this amount of thermoluminescence is assumed to be equal to the amount required under natural conditions. The natural alpha radioactivity is measured by means of an alpha scintillation counter (See Section 1.12), and with this value it is possible to calculate the time required for the lattice to receive an equivalent radiation dosage under natural conditions.

In order to apply the results of laboratory studies to geologic specimens, several important assumptions must be made. It must be assumed first that the total quantity of radiation (and not the rate at which it is received) is the significant factor influencing thermoluminescence intensity. Repeated tests have indicated that this assumption is justified when artificial radiation sources of the intensities used in our laboratories (of the order of 1 curie) are dealt with.

In an attempt to compare artificial and natural radiation damage, it is necessary to assume that similar types of radiation produce similar results. Alpha particles from the polonium source used for irradiations in the laboratory do not have the same energy as alpha particles from thorium or uranium. It has been assumed that, when the proportional energies have been taken into account, the results can be expected to be comparable.

Obviously, calculations of this type are valid only if the natural thermoluminescence is truly the cumulative effect of all the natural radiation to which the sample has been subjected. Most of the problems involved in the measurement of the geologic age of carbonate sediments by the thermoluminescence method result from the instability of the crystal lattice of carbonate minerals. Since the number of traps, both filled and unfilled, existing at any time is dependent primarily upon the impurities included in the crystal lattice, each recrystallization is certain to affect the saturation percentage. The number of traps and the number of electrons in each trap may change. Each time a sediment is recrystallized, impurities may be added, removed, or simply redistributed, but each circumstance will have a distinct effect upon the total number of electron traps. If the sediment is heated through geologic processes to a temperature that permits drainage of the traps, refilling would begin again and the age obtained would be that of the return to lower temperature.

6.2.c Effects of impurities

Repeated experiments have shown that several of the commonly occurring impurities in carbonate sediments can influence the shape and magnitude of their glow curves. Manganese and strontium serve as activators, increasing thermoluminescence, whereas iron is an important inhibitor. From the geological point of view, the exact kind or magnitude of effects is less important than the fact that significant changes can be made by addition of small quantities of trace elements to the carbonate lattice. Changes in the chemical makeup of sediments occur during sedimentation and diagenesis and after lithification has taken place. Manganese may be selectively leached or deposited, and both strontium and iron are sufficiently mobile to change their concentrations as impurity ions in the carbonate lattice. The composition of a carbonate sediment undoubtedly reflects its crystal history as well as its source and environment of deposition. Experimental evidence indicates that the glow curve of a carbonate sediment is closely related to the impurities present in the sediment, and the glow-curve shape can be expected to change with chemical changes.

Effective as the common impurities may be in changing the character of the glow curve, the most important trace elements by far are the radioactive elements themselves. Little is known of the extent to which uranium and thorium can be leached or deposited selectively in the carbonate. It seems reasonable to expect these elements to be affected by the same processes that change the concentrations of other elements. Age calculations are based upon the assumption that the rate of irradiation remains essentially constant throughout the geologic history of the sample, with allowance being made for radioactive decay with time. If this is not true, serious inaccuracies will be introduced into the age calculations.

Besides variations in concentration of the trace impurities, the crystal phase conversions, which affect the lattice of calcium carbonate and the inclusion of magnesium to produce dolomite, likewise have marked influences upon the glow curves of the sediment. Each end member of a series may show its own characteristic glow curve which is influenced by any activator or inhibitor ions that have been included in its lattice. Impurities that fit readily into the lattice of one phase may not be accepted into the lattice of another. The relationship of aragonite and calcite and the conditions that bring about their phase conversion are not completely understood, and an equilibrium may exist between the crystal phases. If a sample that shows the crystal form of calcite retains some groups of cells of aragonite within its lattice (Evans, 1948, p. 256), these areas themselves might act as electron trapping centers.

6.2.d Pressure effects

It has been discovered that pressure has marked effect upon artificially obtained glow curves of both chemically precipitated calcium carbonate and natural carbonate. Figure 6.5 shows the pressure effect upon height of the 110° C and 312° C peaks. The pressure is ap-

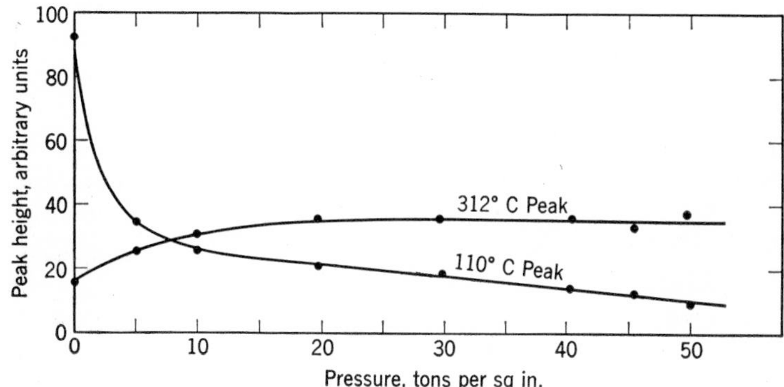

Figure 6.5 Effect of compression upon thermoluminescence of otherwise identical samples of alpha-activated calcium carbonate.

plied to dry samples of the precipitate in a pelleting mold in an hydraulic press. After the pellets have been formed, they are all subjected to equivalent radiation dosages and glow curves are run in the normal manner. The height of the 110° C peak decreases markedly with increasing pressure, and the 312° C peak increases. The mechanism by which energy storage is shifted from low- to high-temperature trapping levels is not understood, but its effect in introducing errors into age determinations is obvious since it is the 312° C peak which is always used in age determination.

6.2.e Summary

The thermoluminescence of a sample is definitely a function of the age and the rate of radiation, but it also can be shown to be greatly affected by impurity content, thermal history, and the pressure to which the sample has been subjected. The physical and chemical instability of the crystal lattice of the carbonate minerals is so great that it would appear to render the thermoluminescence method of age determination exceedingly unreliable. This is certainly true unless extreme care is used in selecting the samples to be used. It is felt that reliable age determinations can be made in some instances. Most of these will be limited to fairly recent sediments or to recent periods of faulting, intrusion, or metamorphism.

Future research in the use of thermoluminescence as an age-determination method might profitably be directed toward the more stable minerals. The carbonates originally appeared the most attractive because of their great abundance and their direct connection with stratigraphic events. Their thermoluminescence is especially sensitive to their physical and chemical history. This sensitivity may greatly restrict the usefulness of the method of age determination, but it may open new fields of investigation which will add to our knowledge of the geological processes that affect the carbonate sediments.

6.3 RADIOACTIVITY, ENERGY STORAGE, AND VOLCANISM *

FARRINGTON DANIELS †

Volcanoes provide us with spectacular evidence that localized areas of the Earth's crust can attain very high temperatures. Metamorphism and hot springs are additional examples, which show that certain areas become heated intermittently at certain times in geologic history.

It is the purpose of this section to inquire into the possibility that occasionally the smooth, continuous evolution of heat from the nuclear disintegration of uranium and thorium and other radioactive elements may be converted into intermittent heating. If part of this energy of radioactivity can be stored for a while and released suddenly at a later time, there may be an occasional heat evolution of unusual magnitude. Such an hypothesis is possible from qualitative considerations, but it becomes less plausible in the light of quantitative measurements.

Experiments thus far indicate that the storage of radioactive energy in displaced crystal lattices under ordinary conditions is too small to be significant; but metamict minerals with considerable amounts

* The author is indebted to the Atomic Energy Commission, Research Division, for its support of a research program of which this work is part.

† Department of Chemistry, University of Wisconsin.

of stored energy do exist. Moreover, it is reported in Section 6.2 that the application of high pressure causes electronically stored energy to become less susceptible to thermal release.

Theories for geologic heating are discussed in Chapter 5. Theoretical study of nuclear heating has been handicapped in trying to explain why a given volume of rock has become hot, then cold, and then hot again, as for example, in some granitization processes or volcanic eruptions. It is unlikely that a large mass of radioactive elements would be moved around to give the necessary local and temporary heating. Nuclear energy is produced continuously at very slowly decreasing rates. But the conversion of part of the energy of the radioactivity into dislocations of the surrounding crystal lattice and its storage as potential energy could, theoretically, lead to an increased evolution of heat for a while at a later time.

Most of the energy produced in the nuclear decomposition of uranium and thorium and their daughter elements comes from the alpha particles and the recoil atoms produced by the ejection of the alpha particles. Within a fraction of a second, however, most of this energy is converted into ordinary heat, i.e., kinetic motions of the atoms, and the temperatures rises very slightly. If some mechanism were available to convert part of the kinetic energy into potential energy, the temperature rise would be smaller. If this potential energy could be stored up and eventually released rapidly and adiabatically, we would have a mechanism for intermittent geologic heating.

Energy storage and later release at high temperatures in minerals containing uranium and thorium has been established in thermoluminescent rocks (Section 6.2) and in metamict minerals (Section 6.1). The first of these seems to be too small to be geologically significant, and the second appears to be limited to rather unusual and comparatively rare minerals. The fact that such phenomena do exist is sufficient justification for studying them intensively and exploring other possible relations between radioactivity and volcanism.

6.3.a Thermoluminescence

When certain fluorites, limestones, granites, and other rocks are heated, they emit light, a phenomenon which is called thermoluminescence (Section 6.2). A typical thermoluminescence glow curve for limestone is shown in Figure 6.3. In the glow curve illustrated, no trapped electrons are released, and no light is emitted until the temperature is high enough to supply the necessary kinetic energy, and then as the temperature is raised still higher more electrons are released and more light is emitted. Finally a maximum is reached (at 235° in the limestone shown in Figure 6.3) beyond which fewer electrons are released because most of the traps have already been emptied. At still higher temperatures, traps of higher energy levels are emptied and new peaks in the glow curves are evident, each one corresponding to a definite type of crystal-lattice defect.

This storage of energy is the type of storage that we are looking for. One can imagine that part of the alpha and recoil-atom energy is first converted into electron and lattice displacements and stored as potential energy but that after a long time the traps become filled with electrons or the lattice displacements are annealed out as rapidly as they are formed. Then there is less opportunity to convert kinetic energy into potential energy, the heat is supplied faster than it can be conducted away, and the temperature rises, eventually reaching such a temperature that the stored energy may be released. The more energy released, the higher is the temperature, and the higher the temperature, the more heat is evolved, thus providing a rapid evolution of heat which can approach adiabatic conditions.

In spite of the attractive features of this hypothesis, it cannot be of geological significance. Morehead and Daniels (1952) have measured the light evolved in thermoluminescence. The energy emitted as light in certain crystals was $1/_{20,000}$ of the energy of the gamma radiation which was absorbed in activating the crystal for thermoluminescence. Measurements of heat are far less sensitive than the measurements of light, but there seems to be no evidence yet that really large fractions of radiation energy can be stored in simple crystal lattices.

6.3.b Maximum possible heat storage

A gram of uranium in equilibrium with all its daughter elements evolves about 0.7 calorie per year. A gram of thorium in equilibrium with its daughters evolves about 0.2 calorie per year. Many rocks contain 1 part per million of uranium and 3 parts per million of thorium, and such a rock will evolve 1.3×10^{-6} calorie of heat per gram per year. If a rock contained 10 parts per million of uranium and 30 parts per million of thorium, it would evolve 260 calories per gram in 20 million years. If there were some mechanism for storing all this potential energy and releasing it suddenly and adiabatically, the temperature of the rock would rise to 1000° C and the rock would melt—assuming a heat capacity of 0.2 and a heat of fusion of 60 calories per gram. Obviously there is no mechanism for storing *all* the energy and releasing it suddenly. Only a small fraction of the energy can be stored, but there are rocks which contain much more than 10 parts per million of uranium and which have remained undisturbed for much more than 20 million years (see Section 2.1).

6.3.c Metamict minerals

Some metamict radioactive minerals (fergusonite, samarskite, zircon, and others) contain reasonably large amounts of stored energy. In some the radiation damage and the displacement of the atoms in the crystal lattice has been so great that a beam of X-rays shows an altered diffraction pattern or none at all, and the density is abnormally low. If these metamict crystals are heated to a sufficiently high temperature, they are annealed and the atoms in the crystal lattice are restored to their normal positions. Most important for the present discussion is the fact that the potential energy is released as heat. Morehead and Daniels (1952) found 20 calories per gram in a polycrase mineral and Kurath (unpublished thesis, Univ. of Wis., 1954) found 65 calories per gram in fergusonite. Many other metamict crystals showed varying amounts of stored energy released on heating. These measurements were made in a differential thermal analyzer. Faessler (1942) has carried out similar experiments which showed up to 89 calories of stored energy per gram in metamict minerals. For reference it may be stated that TNT evolves 1000 calories per gram on detonation. Pabst (1952) has discussed these experiments.

For several reasons differential thermal measurements of this type may not be able to detect all the stored energy of radiation-damaged crystals. The experimental measurements often cannot be carried above 700° C, whereas some energy of lattice deformation is not released until a considerably higher temperature is reached. Kerr and Holland (1951) found that some stored energy in zircons was not released until a temperature of 950° was reached. It is not possible to find evolution of heat by this method unless it occurs within narrow temperature limits. If the heat of crystal damage is released uniformly over a wide temperature range, the differential thermal analysis apparatus will not be sensitive enough to measure it.

6.3.d Measurement of radiant energy storage in crystals

A new method of measuring potential energy stored in a crystal lattice under bombardment by alpha particles has been developed by

Kurath (unpublished thesis, 1954). In these experiments an intense polonium source is placed above a very thin metal cup which is filled with the powder to be subjected to radiation. A similar cup filled with the same material is shielded from the alpha particles. As the alpha particles heat the material in the first cup a slight rise in temperature is produced. If some of the energy of the alpha particle is not converted directly into heat but is stored in the form of potential energy, as in a displaced crystal lattice, the heat evolution will be somewhat less than expected. Kurath was able to detect differences in the amount of energy that is not converted directly into heat. Crystals of alkali halides, metals, and minerals have been measured, and in some cases only 94 percent of the alpha-particle energy is converted into heat. In other words, it has been demonstrated that up to 6 percent of the alpha-particle energy can be stored in the crystal lattices under these conditions.

These measurements do not give information concerning the amount of heat that can be stored for long periods of time. It is likely that the energy from recoil nuclei which are produced in radioactive minerals will contribute considerably more to the atomic displacements than the alpha particles and may permit a greater transformation of energy into stored, potential energy.

Whereas metamict minerals retain considerable amounts of stored energy, uraninite, carnotite, and many other minerals of high uranium or thorium content do not store appreciable amounts of energy even though the bombardment by alpha particles and recoil nuclei is very intense. It is likely that atoms in the crystal lattice of all radioactive minerals are displaced frequently, but usually these displaced atoms return quickly to their normal positions.

Most metamict minerals contain rare-earth elements and all have a complex chemical composition and crystal structure. It may well be that the metamict minerals are unique in storing energy by lattice displacements simply because it is difficult for the displaced atoms to find their normal positions in the crystal lattice. The alpha particles may generate so much localized heat, particularly at the end of their paths, that a small region of the crystal is heated and melted. This localized molten area then cools quickly to a glassy material. If these glassy "thermal spikes" recrystallize only with great difficulty, it may be possible to store the energy. When the glassy material of the thermal spikes can recrystallize rapidly, it is not possible to store the energy and the crystals do not become metamict. Simple crystals and ionic lattices do not give metamict behavior.

It has been shown that the energy of radioactivity stored in the form of thermoluminescence is quite small. The energy stored by alpha particles, at least for very short periods of time, can be as much as 6 percent in simple crystals, and it is known that the storage of metamict crystals can be considerable. The question arises whether there are conditions in nature under which it may be possible to store considerable amounts of energy in disordered crystal lattices. It is extremely difficult to carry out calorimetric experiments in the laboratory under high pressures. In some thermoluminescence studies, as described in Section 6.2, the application of pressure increases the energy released as thermoluminescence at high temperatures.

6.3.e Uranium content of volcanic material

If the radioactivity of uranium and thorium supplies some of the heat in some volcanic actions, these elements should be found in volcanic lavas, ashes, and gases. During the course of the investigations in this laboratory many samples of such volcanic material have been collected and analyzed. The most significant are described by Adams in Section 2.2. Lava and ashes, both acidic and basic, from many different volcanoes contain from less than 1 ppm up to 11 ppm of uranium. In most cases the alpha counts are high enough to show that thorium is present also. The amount of radioactive material given off by volcanoes is small, and it varies greatly with the location of the volcano and with the stage of eruption.

The uranium content of lavas and ashes usually increases as the differentiation in the volcano proceeds. At first it was thought that some uranium might be lost in volcanic eruptions in the form of volatile uranium compounds. A search for uranium in the gases evolved from fumaroles at the Paricutin Volcano in Mexico failed to show significant amounts of uranium.

A thorough thermodynamic study of the volatility of uranium halides from rocks has been carried out by Mason (unpublished thesis, Univ. of Wis., 1954). Although the thermodynamic values of free energy, enthalpy, and entropies are not well known at high temperatures for many of the uranium compounds, it has been possible, nevertheless, to make estimates of the vapor pressure of uranium halides in mixtures of various inorganic compounds. These estimates indicate that the escape of uranium in the form of chlorides or fluorides from rocks heated to 1000° C is very unlikely. In the presence of a large excess of ferrous chloride or aluminum chloride, there may be a chance of some volatility of the uranium halides.

6.3.f Summary

Possibilities of storing some radioactive energy in rocks have been studied in the hope of understanding better the intermittent localized heating of rocks near the Earth's surface. Electron-stored energy as exhibited in thermoluminescence is too small to be significant geologically. Metamict minerals, though rather rare, give definite examples of the storage of energy. Simple lattices containing uranium and thorium do not store the energy produced by radioactive disintegration because the displacements of atoms in the crystal lattice are quickly restored by annealing at Earth temperatures. The metamict minerals have complex lattices in which the atom displacements are not readily annealed, and they point the way to further research designed to find conditions under which radiation damage is not annealed out. Researches should be carried out to determine if the annealing rate of some disordered lattices can be decreased by the application of high pressures such as exist at considerable depths in the Earth's crust.

Chapter 7

HYDROCARBONS FORMED BY THE EFFECTS OF RADIOACTIVITY AND THEIR ROLE IN THE ORIGIN OF PETROLEUM*

WALTER L. WHITEHEAD †

La transformation de l'oxygène en ozone nécessite une dépense d'énergie utilisable. La production d'ozone sous l'effet des rayons émis par le radium est donc une preuve que ce rayonnement représente un dégagement continu d'énergie.

—P. et M. Curie, *Compt. rend., Acad. Sci.,* 20 nov. 1899.

The chemical effects accompanying the disintegration of large amounts of strongly radioactive material were first observed by Pierre and Marie Curie (1899) during the research concerned with the discovery of radium. They were familiar with the coloration of glass and porcelain containing radioactive solutions and with the odor of ozone in the air near highly active substances. The decomposition of water in which radioactive salts were dissolved and the evolution of gas when radon came in contact with stopcock grease were also known to the early workers. Ramsay and Soddy (1903) and Bragg (1907) made some quantitative studies of the decomposition of water, and Lind (1911) proposed a relation of the number of molecules of ozone formed to the number of ion pairs produced in oxygen when exposed to alpha particles. More extended studies were later made by Lind (1919, 1928*a*, *b*), including those on the chemical effects of alpha particles on hydrocarbons. One outcome of these re-

* Grateful recognition is due to the American Petroleum Institute, sponsor of the ten-year research on the role of radioactivity in petroleum genesis, and the chairmen and members of its Advisory Committee. The author wishes to record his obligation to his co-director, Dr. Clark Goodman, of the Department of Physics, Massachusetts Institute of Technology, and to the research personnel concerned with the investigations to be described, Irving A. Breger, R. E. Honig, C. W. Sheppard, Virginia L. Burton, and Geraldine Sullivan Geary, and finally to Dr. W. J. Mead, director of the project in its early years.

† Department of Geology and Geophysics, Massachusetts Institute of Technology, Cambridge 39, Massachusetts.

searches in radiation chemistry was the proposal by Lind and Bardwell (1926) that, if geological conditions were met where alpha radiation affected gaseous hydrocarbons, a liquid mixture of hydrocarbons similar to petroleum should be produced.

Such a proposal is contrary to the generally accepted opinion of geologists that petroleum originates chiefly from liquid, solid, or semisolid organic complexes. After a number of measurements of the radioactivity of sedimentary rocks and associated petroleum, Bell, Goodman, and Whitehead (1940) and Tiratsoo (1941) suggested that the liquid and gaseous hydrocarbons in petroleum may be formed by the effects of radiation on complex organic substances in source sediments.

As a consequence of this suggestion, the American Petroleum Institute since 1942 has sponsored a research project to determine the possible relationship between terrestrial radioactivity and the origin of petroleum. During early phases of the investigation, studies were carried out to establish the effects of alpha particles on certain pure organic substances which had been isolated in earlier research by Trask (1932) and others from bottom sea muds of the type believed to be source beds for oil. A large variety of these substances and related compounds have been bombarded both by alpha particles and by deuterons. The results of the work have been published in various journals and reprinted in the Biennial Research Volumes of the American Petroleum Institute (1943–1952). In the light of evidence gathered thus far it seems likely that the amounts of petroleum actually found in sedimentary rocks are much too large to be explained by chemical effects of radioactivity.

A number of the workers concerned with the broader aspects of radiation chemistry met at the University of Notre Dame in 1947 (*Symposium,* 1948), where twenty papers were read. In late years these and other researches on the chemical effects of alpha particles, deuterons, neutrons, and X-rays have been concerned principally with safety, with biological studies, or with the changes in lubricants under radiation.

7.1 RADIATION CHEMISTRY OF HYDROCARBONS

The research of Lind on the effects of alpha particles on hydrocarbons has been reviewed in its bearing on the genesis of petroleum by Sheppard (1944). Lind found that aliphatic hydrocarbons are transformed under alpha radiation into gaseous and liquid hydrocarbons and hydrogen. From methane are formed ethane, propane, butane, pentane, other higher members, and hydrogen. From ethane not only hydrogen and methane are liberated but also liquid hydrocarbons are condensed at earlier stages of the reaction than with methane. Bombardment of further members of the series, propane and butane, and careful tests of the gaseous products established that no unsaturates remain in the gas phase. Lind concluded that from a single member of either high or low molecular weight, all other members, above and below in the hydrocarbon series, should be obtained.

In order to compare the effects of alpha particles and deuterons Honig and Sheppard (1946) repeated the experiments of Lind on methane and butane, both with alpha particles from radon and with deuterons in the cyclotron. They confirmed by mass-spectrometric analysis Lind's observations on the composition of the gaseous products. They concluded that the unsaturation observed in the product from butane must at least in part be olefinic and may be partly aromatic.

Few investigations have been made on the behavior of the higher aliphatic hydrocarbons when subjected to radiation. Richards (1926) found that hydrogen was produced from solid paraffin bombarded with alpha particles. The present author and his associates also have determined hydrogen to be the main gaseous product from alpha irradiation of octacosane (94.3 percent H_2) and hexadecane (95.5 percent H_2). The gas from the latter hydrocarbon contained about 1 percent each of methane, ethane, propane, and butane.

The formation of cuprene by polymerization of acetylene during irradiation by alpha particles has been studied by Lind (1928*a*), Heisig (1932) and Rosenblum (1937). Rosenblum found benzene in the gaseous product. Watson (1947) noted three types of cuprene, distinguished by electron micrographs, apparently related to the kind of radiation used in forming the substance.

The reactions of hydrocarbons when exposed to radiation are of interest in petroleum genesis principally in connection with the aging of crude oils in reservoirs or with condensation of petroleum from gaseous hydrocarbons. The origin of petroleum from the source materials contained in sediments is concerned largely with the decomposition of more complex organic substances.

7.2 INVESTIGATIONS OF ORGANIC ACIDS

7.2.a Fatty acids in marine sediments

It has long been known that the oily material obtained from certain marine microscopic organisms contains fatty acids. Diatoms were collected on the Pacific Coast, and the oily lipid was extracted by petroleum ether. The extract (4.5 percent of the dry weight) contained 35 percent fatty acids (Thayer, 1931).

In analyses made by Clarke and Mazur (1941) of the organic components in marine diatoms collected off Woods Hole or grown in pure culture, free fatty acids constituted 60 to 80 percent of the lipids extracted by ether, or 4 to 9 percent of the dry weight of these diatoms. The results indicate that these diatoms contained about 1.6 percent by dry weight of free saturated fatty acids, mostly palmitic and stearic. Fresh-water siliceous and marine calcareous sponges also gave oils with appreciable contents of fatty acids. Clarke and Mazur (1941) also analyzed the organic material extracted by ether from marine bottom mud and identified free fatty acids.

Apparently, saturated fatty acids over a considerable range in the series are to be found in organic marine sediments. Aliphatic acids from formic to valeric, with an average molecular weight equivalent to that of propionic acid, have also been identified (Menaul, 1944) in water produced with condensate from the Katy field, Texas, and from the South Jennings field, Louisiana.

7.2.b Bombardment of fatty acids

During the experimental work on irradiation of the straight-chain fatty acids, various reports on progress were published by Sheppard and Whitehead (1946), Honig (1946) and Sheppard and Burton (1946). Summaries of the final results are given by Breger and Whitehead (1951) and by Whitehead, Goodman, and Breger (1951).

The experimental technique used in this research has been previously published (Sheppard and Whitehead, 1946), but it will be rapidly reviewed here. The bulb used in the bombardments (Figure 7.1) has a volume of about 200 cc. The material to be irradiated is coated on its interior. The stem is provided with a hook seal, *A*, which may be broken by a magnetic plunger at the time of analysis. The radon needles, *R*, are dropped into a side chamber, *C*, through the evacuation tube, *B*. The system is then evacuated, and the constriction of *B* is sealed. By careful shaking, the glass radon needles are broken under impact of the glass pellet. The side chamber is then heated to assist the diffusion of the radon into the main bulb. A relatively small part of the radon remains in the side chamber, which is sealed off and removed. The quantity of radon in the main bulb is determined by gamma-ray measurement, and the bulb with attached manometer is set aside until the radioactivity has decayed

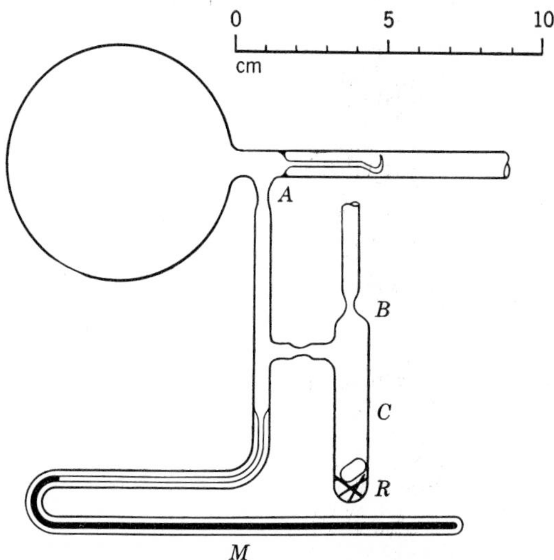

Figure 7.1 Apparatus for bombardment of fatty acids by radon alpha particles. The material to be irradiated is coated on the interior of the bulb.

to a negligible level. In most experiments the progress of the bombardment was followed by measuring the pressure of the gas evolved (Figure 7.2).

When early experiments were carried out with caprylic, lauric, and palmitic acids, the predominant reactions were found to be decarboxylation and dehydrogenation:

$$CH_3(CH_2)_xCH_2COOH \rightarrow CH_3(CH_2)_xCH_3 + CO_2$$

$$CH_3(CH_2)_xCH_2CH_2(CH_2)_yCOOH \rightarrow CH_3(CH_2)_xCH{=}CH(CH_2)_yCOOH + H_2$$

The decarboxylation reaction leads to the formation of carbon dioxide and the hydrocarbon corresponding to the chain of the acid. Dehydrogenation results in the formation of unsaturated acids. Hydrocarbons, therefore, could be produced by alpha-particle bombardment from the fatty acids known to exist in petroleum source sediments.

Further investigations were later undertaken with acetic, propionic, arachidic, behenic, and melissic acids.

After irradiation, the volume of gas produced was determined and the gas was analyzed mass-spectrometrically. The solid or liquid product was isolated quantitatively. Since the quantity of radon used for the bombardment was carefully measured, it is possible to express

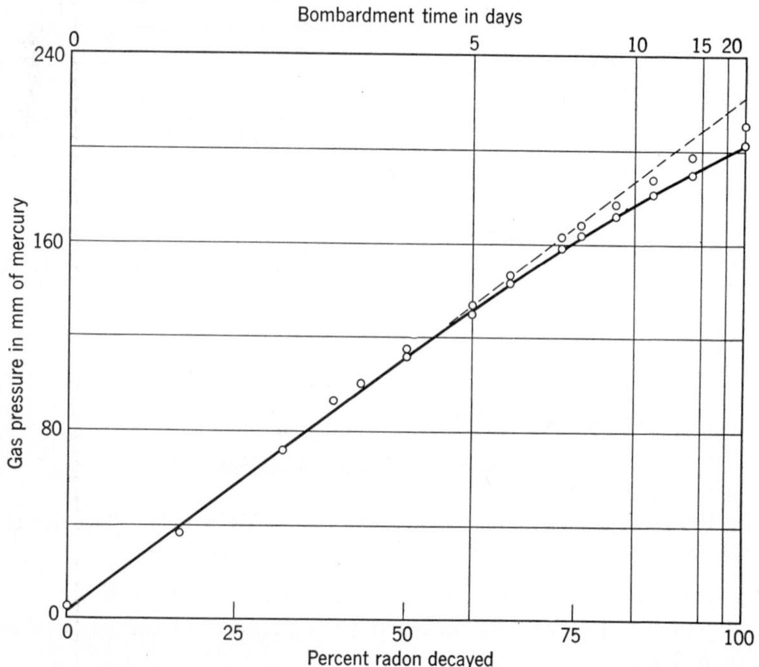

Figure 7.2 Pressure in the bulb, plotted as a function of bombardment time in the apparatus shown in Figure 7.1.

yields in terms of molecules of product formed per 100 ev of energy.

The yields of carbon dioxide, carbon monoxide, and water are plotted in Figure 7.3. Carbon dioxide formation is greatest for acetic acid and decreases as a straight-line function of the number of carbon atoms in the acid molecule. The yield of carbon monoxide is lower but follows the same trend. Water is not formed in identifiable quantities in the acetic or propionic acid bombardments. It is a minor product of longer-chain acids and increases as a straight-line function of the size of the acid molecule up to the C_{16} acid. Beyond C_{16} the water yield shows a tendency to decrease.

In Figure 7.4 plots are shown of the hydrogen yield and of the production of hydrocarbon from the decarboxylation of each fatty acid. As in the case of carbon dioxide and carbon monoxide, the hydrocarbon yield falls as a straight-line function of the size of the acid molecule. Hydrogen rises as a linear function of the acid size up to the C_{16} acid. Experiments with arachidic and behenic acids have proved that the hydrogen and water yields decrease beyond the

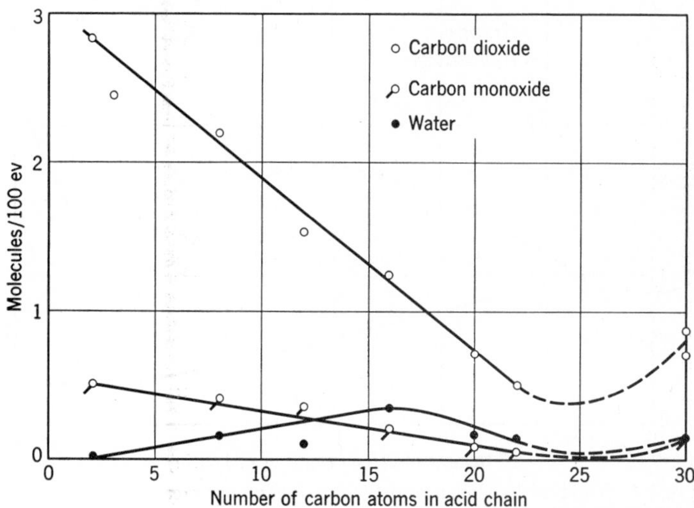

Figure 7.3 Yield of carbon dioxide, carbon monoxide, and water, plotted as a function of the number of carbon atoms in the chain of the irradiated fatty acid.

C_{16} acid. It appeared desirable to extend the study to the C_{30} range to determine if the curves would flatten out and become asymptotic to the axis of zero production. For this reason melissic acid was bombarded. Figures 7.3 and 7.4 indicate that, in this range, the yields do not continue to fall and become asymptotic, but tend to rise. This last experiment indicates the difficulty of attempting to interpret data based on incomplete experiments on a group of compounds.

No explanation of the physical mechanism involved in the reactions represented by these curves will be attempted. Nevertheless, several conclusions can be proposed on the basis of this work. It is apparent, for instance, that in the decomposition of fatty acids, the dehydrogenation reaction is far more important with the higher-molecular-weight compounds than the decarboxylation reaction. Moreover, there is no evidence of a variety of free-radical decompositions with the lower-molecular-weight acids, such as has been suggested (Burton, 1947).

Since CO_2, CO, and H_2O are the major oxygenated products from the radiochemical decomposition of fatty acids, these compounds must account for nearly all the oxygen of the decomposed carboxyl groups.

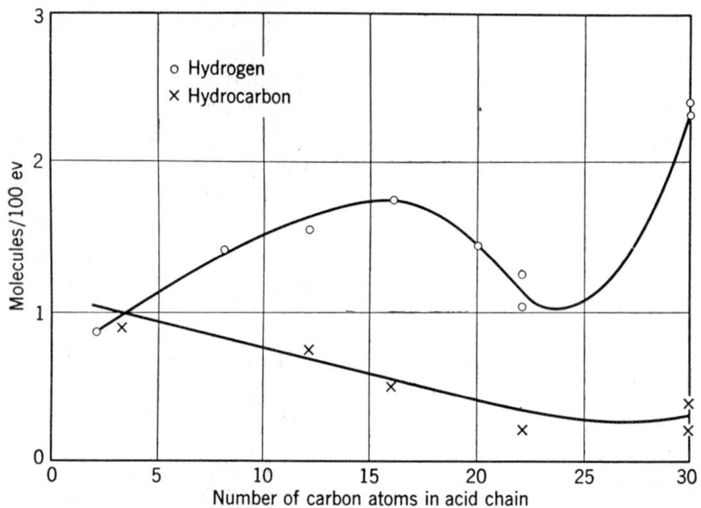

Figure 7.4 Yield of hydrogen and production of hydrocarbon by decarboxylation, plotted as a function of the number of carbon atoms in the chain of the irradiated fatty acid.

To establish the relationship between the yields of CO_2, CO, and H_2O, a plot (Figure 7.5) was made on the ratio

$$\frac{\text{Hydrocarbon}}{CO_2 + CO + H_2O}$$

The denominator of this ratio contains four oxygen atoms and only 2 arise from a decarboxylation, so that the theoretical value should be 0.5 if all these products arise from the same reaction. The experimental value falls at 0.37. This value remains constant over the entire range of acids studied, and one may infer that all four of these components are formed from the decarboxylation reaction. The difference of this experimental value from the theoretical value of 0.5 probably results from a small amount of reconversion of primary decomposition products.

When the ratio

$$\frac{H_2}{CO_2 + CO + H_2O}$$

is similarly plotted for each acid from acetic to palmitic, a line having a slightly rising slope is obtained. This line indicates that dehydrogenation becomes an increasingly important reaction with the longer-chain acids.

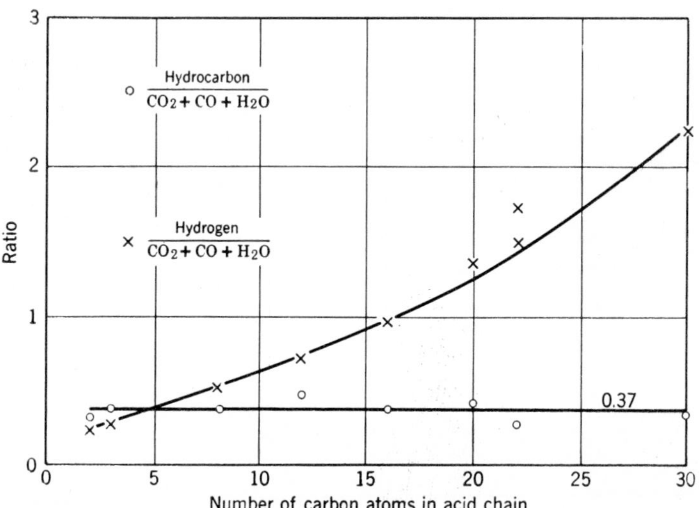

Figure 7.5 Ratio of the produced amounts of hydrogen and hydrocarbon to the amounts of carbon dioxide, carbon monoxide, and water, plotted as a function of the number of carbon atoms in the chain of the irradiated fatty acid.

As a final phase of these experimental studies, it was of particular interest to determine the effects of temperature on the yield of products from the irradiation of one or two particular acids. For this reason palmitic acid, C_{16}, was bombarded in the solid state at —69°, 1°, 18°, and 48° C. The results are shown in Figure 7.6. There is little change in yield below 0° C, but above this temperature the production of hydrogen, carbon dioxide, and carbon monoxide tends to rise. The production of water decreases as a straight-line function of temperature.

A similar series of experiments was undertaken with behenic acid, C_{22}. Since this compound has a higher melting point than palmitic acid, it was possible to extend the upper temperature of bombardment to 68° C. The yields of gaseous products increase between —75° and 0° C, and then fall sharply between 0° and room temperature. Beyond room temperature the yields tend to increase slightly.

In conclusion the following points can be made as a consequence of this work:

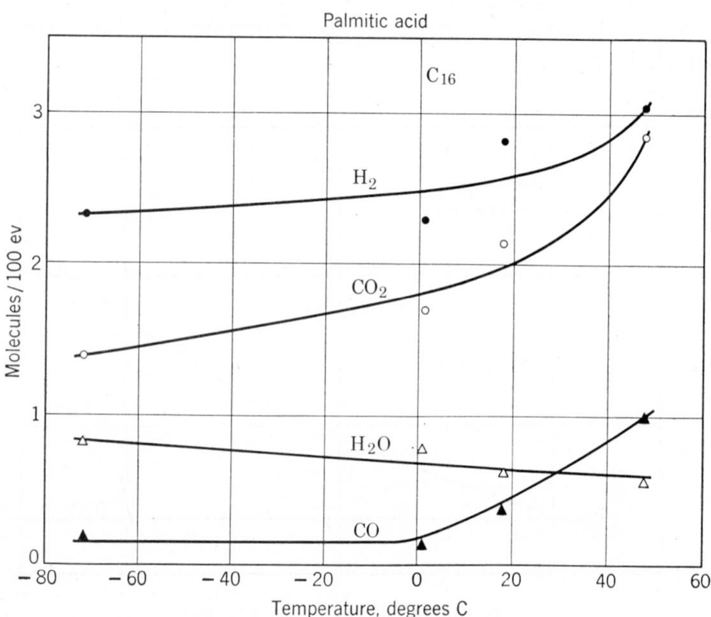

Figure 7.6 Yield of hydrogen, carbon dioxide, carbon monoxide, and water, plotted as a function of the temperature at which palmitic acid was irradiated.

1. The decarboyxlation of fatty acids is a straight-line function of the size of the acid molecule between C_2 and C_{22}.

2. The dehydrogenation of fatty acids by alpha particles is a complex function of the size of the acid molecule.

3. There is no evidence that the decarboxylation mechanism varies with the size of the acid molecule.

4. Hydrocarbons present in crude oil can be produced by the radioactive decomposition of fatty acids ranging from C_2 to C_{30}. Acids having from 2 to 10 carbon atoms are known to be present in oil-field brines, and a number of acids are known to be present in marine muds.

5. Temperature has little influence on the alpha-particle decomposition of palmitic acid below 0° C. Above this point decomposition in-

creases with temperature. The decomposition of behenic acid is strongly temperature-dependent, reaching a maximum at about 0° C.

7.2.c Bombardment of cyclic acids

The possibility of forming cycloparaffins is of especial interest to the theory of petroleum genesis by the effects of radiation, because the members of this group of hydrocarbons are present to a considerable extent in almost all crude oils.

Naphthenic acids are known to occur in many crude oils in the range from 0.03 to 1.6 percent. Although the majority of these acids contain cyclopentane rings, cyclohexane base acids have also been identified. In particular, cyclohexanecarboxylic acid was found in Baku crudes by Tschitschibabin et al. (1933), and Ney et al. (1943) reported the same acid in California petroleum. Homologs of this series have also been identified in other California and Texas crude oils. The origin of these acids has remained an undecided matter after considerable discussion.

The study of the effects of alpha particles and deuterons on cyclohexanecarboxylic acid was primarily undertaken to determine if the anticipated decarboxylation would lead to the formation of ring compounds, cyclohexane in particular, or if ring cleavage would produce straight-chain compounds.

Two bombardments of the acid were carried out by alpha particles from radon, and, in order to obtain sufficient liquid conversion product for complete analysis, two deuteron bombardments were run in the Massachusetts Institute of Technology cyclotron. All the gas evolved was collected and analyzed as shown in Table 7.1. A colorless, liquid conversion product was separated from the irradiated acid. This liquid appears to have the composition of cyclohexane.

Table 7.1 Gas evolved in the bombardment of cyclohexane-carboxylic acid by alpha particles and deuterons

(Composition in percent)

Bombardments	H_2O	CO	CO_2	CH_4	C_2H_6	C_3H_8	C_6H_{12} *	C_2 †
Alpha	1.7	10	66	0.3	0.3	0.2	0.5	21
Deuteron	3.1	2.6	67.5	1.5	0.3	0.5	2.4	22

* Cyclohexane.

† Obtained by difference.

The conclusions are that cyclohexane rings, and presumably the more stable cyclopentane rings, are not opened as a result of alpha-particle or of deuteron bombardment and that irradiation of a naphthenic acid has led to its transformation into a naphthenic constituent of crude oils.

7.3 EXPERIMENTS WITH OTHER SUBSTANCES

A great number of organic compounds have been subjected to the effects of electric discharge or of radiation. Breger (1946–1947) lists 252 such experiments and elsewhere discusses more specifically the transformation of organic substances by alpha particles and deuterons (1948).

7.4 HYDROGEN

An outstanding feature of the experiments with alpha particles and deuterons is that hydrogen is always contained in the gaseous product. With certain complex materials, such as asphaltenes and Athabaska tar, the hydrogen content of the gas formed during bombardment surpasses 90 percent. The gases formed during bombardment of the organic acids usually range in hydrogen between 20 and 50 percent.

Brooks (1931, 1948), in pertinent criticism of the origin of petroleum by radioactive processes, has listed the absence of hydrogen and usually of helium from natural gases as one of the principal objections to such origin. The presence of optically active substances in crude oils is also mentioned by Brooks as not to be expected with radioactive processes. The formation of unsaturates by dehydrogenation is believed by Brooks to be contrary to the observed facts with respect to the geologically old, light paraffinic crudes. Lind (1928*b*) also regarded the unsaturates formed in his experiments with hydrocarbons as constituting an obstacle to the theory he proposed.

In considering these objections, Bell and others (1940) stated that the amount of helium produced in alpha-particle reactions is small compared to the quantity of hydrogen or hydrocarbons formed, for each alpha particle affects about 100,000 molecules. If the source material were of solid or semisolid organic derivation and the first reactions were chiefly those resulting in condensed solids or colloids and liquids and gas, optically active substances might well be retained in the resulting liquid mixture. Hydrogen conceivably could be lost from the natural gas associated with the crude oil by hydrogenation of the hydrocarbon compounds.

Hydrogenation has occurred under alpha radiation of hydrocarbons, but less frequently than polymerization and condensation. The suggestion is made (Lind, 1928*a*) that hydrogenation of unsaturated hydrocarbons may be an important factor in the removal from earth gases of the hydrogen liberated by alpha radiation from hydrocarbons and water. Hydrogenation has also been proposed by Pratt (1934) to explain the increase of the hydrogen:carbon ratio in the evolution of crude oils.

Purified oleic acid has been bombarded with deuterons in the M.I.T. cyclotron. In discussing this experiment Burton (1949) concludes: "It has been shown that the hydrogen produced by decomposition of an organic molecule under the influence of radioactivity can enter the double bond of a neighboring molecule. It has thus been demonstrated that hydrogen which may be produced by the effects of radioactivity on the organic constituents of a petroleum source sediment could, in part, be removed from the gas phase by reaction with unsaturated components of the sediments."

Another process tending to reduce hydrogen content is the microbial transformation of molecular hydrogen in marine sediments, described by Zobell (1947). He states that the absence of free hydrogen from marsh gas and other natural gases is caused by the microbial utilization of hydrogen as fast as it is produced.

7.5 EVALUATION OF THE EFFECTS OF RADIOACTIVITY

The principal factors affecting a quantitative evaluation of the contribution to crude oil by hydrocarbons formed from the effects of radioactivity are: (1) The yield factor per unit of energy introduced into the organic system by the decay of radioactive elements, (2) the loss of radioactive energy by absorption in the inorganic constituents in sediments, and (3) the content and localization of radioactive elements in organic marine sediments and sedimentary rocks.

With data on these factors, the part of the organic material converted, in a given time, into hydrocarbons may be calculated, but, in order to calculate the contribution to petroleum from any given volume of sediment, the concentration of significant hydrocarbon-producing organic substances in the sediment must be known.

7.5.a Yield factor

The yield factors for the substances bombarded quantitatively were determined on the basis of extracted and isolated products of the radiation in terms of molecules of hydrocarbons produced per 100 ev of energy expended in the source material by the alpha particles. As noted in a previous section, the yield factor for the fatty-acid series, about 0.37 molecules per 100 ev, is constant throughout the series. A comparison with the theoretical yield, 0.5 molecules, indicates some loss in isolation of the hydrocarbon, or expenditure of a part of the introduced energy in secondary reactions.

7.5.b Loss of energy by absorption

The loss of radioactive energy between the source point of the radiation and the organic material is dependent on the localization of the

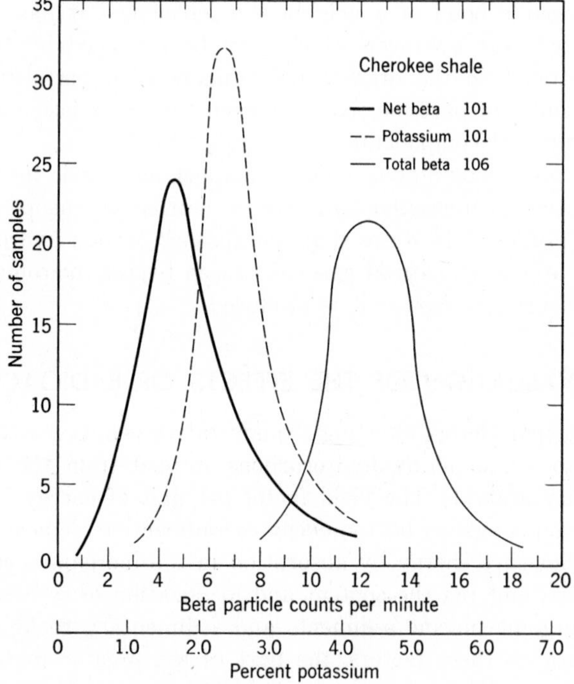

Figure 7.7 Frequency distribution of the potassium content and beta activity of 101 samples of Cherokee shale.

radioactive elements in the sediment. If these elements are contained in the inorganic components of the sediment, loss by absorption is higher than in a sediment with the radioactive elements concentrated in the organic constituents. The approach to this subject may be direct, either by observation of the tracks of alpha particles or by isolation of the inorganic constituents and measurement of their radioactivity. The latter method was attempted and proved impracticable because the admixture of organic and inorganic substances in the sediments investigated was so intimate. An indirect approach to the

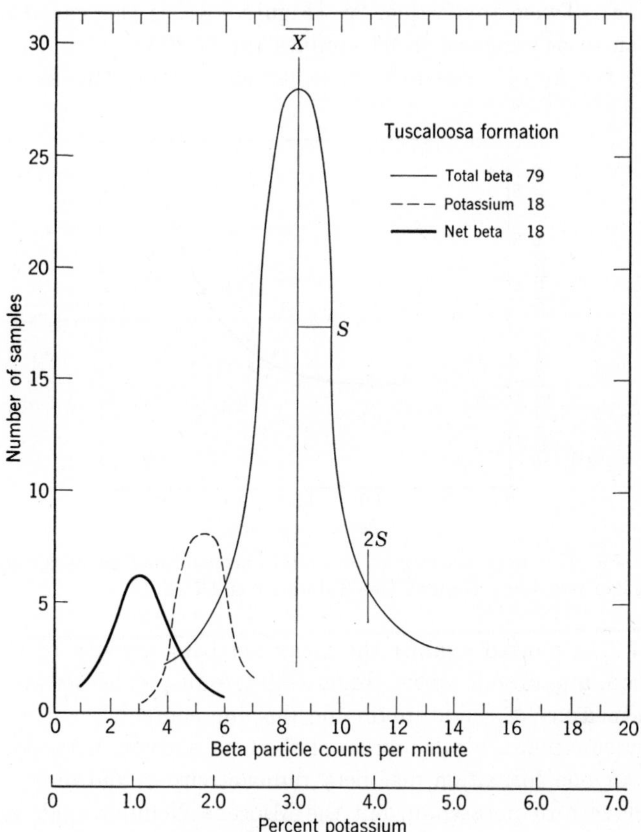

Figure 7.8 Frequency distribution of the potassium content and beta activity of samples of the Tuscaloosa formation.

distribution of the radioactive elements is the study of the relation of radioactivity to the quantity of some element contained in the material.

Analyses of a sufficient number of samples from each formation were made for potassium to plot frequency distribution curves. The curve for the Cherokee shale is shown in Figure 7.7 (numbers in upper right corner are number of samples analyzed). The maximum indicates the mean value for potassium in samples from the formation, and the symmetry of the curve is evidence of the reliability of this mean value. The width of the curve from the mean value to the point where the change in slope occurs is a measure of the variation in the samples from the formation and is designated the standard deviation. Twice this value, 2*S* (Figure 7.8), is the variation from the mean to be expected in 95 samples out of 100.

When the mean potassium value for each formation, as shown in

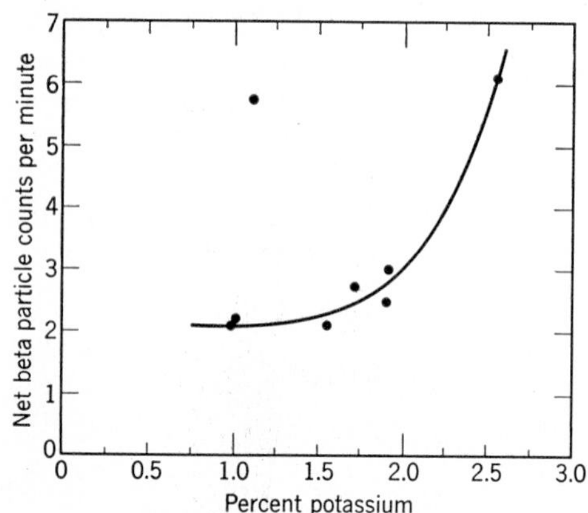

Figure 7.9 Net beta activity of several formations plotted as a function of their median potassium content (see Tables 7.2 and 7.3).

Table 7.2, is plotted against the mean net beta activity of the same formation, a parabolic curve (Figure 7.9) results. The net beta activity is a measure of the uranium and thorium content, for it represents the beta emission after deduction of the beta activity from potassium. In all but one formation, net beta radioactivity is shown to increase with increase of potassium, but the Miocene Nodular shale does not conform to this relation.

The organic carbon content was determined for 315 samples from 8 sedimentary formations (Burton and Sullivan, 1951). Over 100 analyses were made on the Miocene Nodular shale and on the Cherokee shale. Linear relations are shown by the values in Table 7.3 and in graphs, Figures 7.10 and 7.11 (Burton and Sullivan, 1951). Excellent correlation between organic carbon content and radioactivity implies some genetic relationship between the elements in the uranium-thorium series and the organic carbon in the sedimentary formations studied.

More positive deductions seem to be possible from the phosphorus content of samples from the same two formations. From 8 cores of the Miocene Nodular shale, a total of 85 samples was analyzed for phosphorus. The relation of net beta emission to the phosphorus content in each of these samples is illustrated in Figure 7.12. The figure

Table 7.2 Potassium determinations for various rocks

	No. of Samples	Mean % K	2*S* Variability ±% K
East Texas (Upper Cretaceous)			
Austin chalk	77 {41	0.43	0.36
	77 {36	1.61	0.39
Eagle Ford shale	32	1.55	0.89
Woodbine sandstone	83	0.99	0.90
Mississippi (Upper Cretaceous)			
Selma chalk	33	1.91	0.34
Lower Eutaw	24	1.72	0.31
Tuscaloosa	48	1.92	0.34
Oklahoma (Pennsylvanian)			
Cherokee shale	101	2.55	0.80
California			
Miocene Nodular shale	134	1.12	0.66
Michigan			
Antrim shale (Devonian)	6	2.77	0.1

Table 7.3 Carbon content and radioactivity of several rocks

Formation	Number of Determinations	Average Carbon Content	Average Net Beta Count per Minute	Uranium, ppm (composite sample)
Miocene Nodular shale	130	5.4	6.3	16
Cherokee shale	105	3.3	5.8	. . .
Lower Eutaw shale	12	1.1	2.8	12
Eagle Ford shale	13	0.93	2.4	3.9
Austin chalk	27	1.5	3.9	3.3
Selma chalk	15	1.4	2.8	7.9
Tuscaloosa sandstone	6	0.97	3.2	6.5
Woodbine sandstone	7	0.99	2.4	6.7
Antrim shale	. . .	. . .	. . .	20

indicates an increase in the uranium-thorium content with increase in phosphorus content. Since phosphorus is present as nodules of calcium phosphate, these data suggest a correlation between inorganic content and radioactivity. Although the Cherokee shale, where not

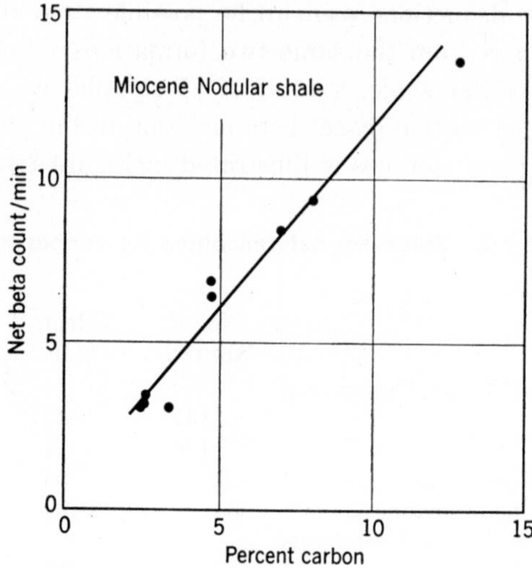

Figure 7.10 Net beta activity of samples of the Miocene Nodular shale plotted as a function of organic carbon content.

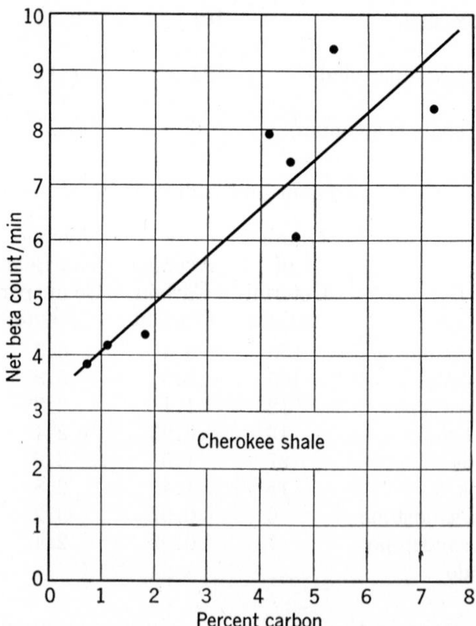

Figure 7.11 Net beta activity of samples of the Cherokee shale plotted as a function of organic carbon content.

nodular, contains normally less than 0.3 percent phosphorus, the determinations on 29 samples have a similar trend.

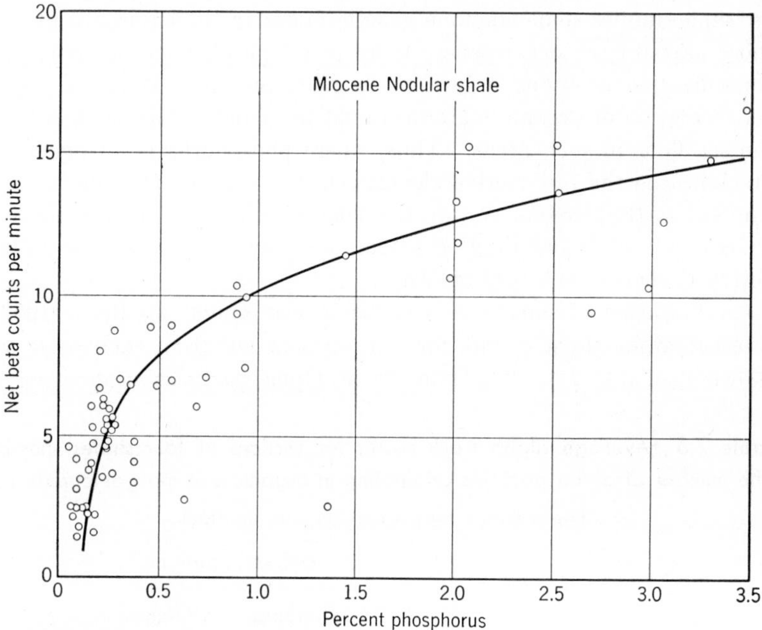

Figure 7.12 Net beta activity of samples of the Miocene Nodular shale plotted as a function of phosphorus content.

An interesting relation is shown between organic carbon content and phosphorus in the averages of samples of the Miocene Nodular shale from 8 homogeneous cores. The averages in Table 7.4, when plotted, fall near a straight line.

Table 7.4 Organic carbon and phosphorus in eight samples of the Miocene Nodular shale (core averages)

Net Beta Count/Min	Percent Carbon	Percent Phosphorus
3.0	2.6	0.16
3.0	3.4	0.14
3.1	2.6	0.13
3.4	2.7	0.09
6.4	4.8	0.23
6.8	4.8	0.46
9.4	8.1	0.93
13.5	12.8	2.20

Increase of activity with increase in both organic carbon and phosphorus is found in each of the two formations studied. The apparent linear relation of carbon to phosphorus content in the Miocene Nodular shale implies some common genetic factor in the environment. In those parts of the ocean where there is a high phosphorus content, a concentration of living organisms is often present. Hence a higher concentration of organic material might be found in the sediments on the sea floor in such areas. Thus, where phosphorus is an agent for precipitating the radioactive elements in the sea, the phosphorus also can be partly responsible for the concentration of organic matter, which itself when precipitated as colloids may carry down the radioactive elements (see Section 2.3).

Confirmation of some such conclusion was sought by Ross (1952). Average alpha-track counts for thin sections cut from each shale are shown in Table 7.5. The number of alpha particles originating in

Table 7.5 Average alpha track counts for sections of four shales showing the number of alpha particles originating in organic and inorganic material

(The sections were about 20 microns thick.)

	Alphas/minute-cm^2	
	Inorganic	Organic
Miocene Nodular shale	0.83	0.50
Cherokee shale	3.82	1.16
Woodford (Texas)	5.80	3.30
Woodford (Oklahoma)	6.50	2.00

inorganic material is about 2½ times greater than the number originating in organic material in the thin sections. The photographs show that many alpha particles which originate in phosphatic material pass into surrounding organic material. The expenditure of energy of the alpha particles is greater than 30 percent in the organic material, but probably somewhat less than 50 percent of their total energy is available for the transformation of the organic constituents in the shale.

7.5.c Radioactivity

Since about three-quarters of the energy released in the radioactive decay of the uranium and thorium series is given off by the alpha particles emitted, the radiation of these particles is much more effective in the formation of hydrocarbons than that from the beta particles or gamma rays. The alpha-particle emission of 7 formations is indicated by the data shown in Table 7.6.

Table 7.6 Alpha activity of composite samples of several formations

Formation	Emission (alphas/cm^2-hr)
Cherokee shale	4.44
Selma chalk	4.14
Austin chalk	3.10
Eagle Ford shale	3.97
Woodbine sandstone	3.88
Lower Eutaw	3.32
Tuscaloosa	4.35
Miocene Nodular shale (46 samples)	2.6–15
Woodford shale	50–60

From the rate of emission per unit area in thick samples, the alpha activity per unit mass may be calculated (Keevil and Grasham, 1943; Nogami and Hurley, 1948). In this way, the radiation energy produced per unit mass of each formation may be determined. By using these values of energy, the yield factors measured in typical reactions producing hydrocarbons, and the absorption factor for the energy lost in the inorganic constituents, the amount of hydrocarbon produced in the sediment may be calculated. The assumptions necessary are (1) the average molecular weight of the organic-source substance, and (2) the concentration of this substance.

7.6 CONCLUSIONS

Uranium was determined fluorimetrically in 8 composite samples (Table 7.3). Comparison of these data with radium determinations by the radon method indicates that radium is in equilibrium with the uranium. For these formations an average total radioactivity (both uranium and thorium), expressed in radium equivalent, may be about 4×10^{-12} g Ra/g sediment. The energy output of a sediment of this activity is 2×10^{20} ev/10^6 years-g of sediment.

Assuming an average molecular weight of 200 for the organic material affected by alpha particles, the hydrocarbon produced in the organic material with a yield factor of 0.5 molecule/100 ev and with 50 percent of the energy effective will be

$$\frac{2 \times 10^{20}\ \text{ev}/10^6\ \text{y-g}}{200\ \text{ev/molecule}} \times \frac{200\ (\text{mol. wt.})}{6 \times 10^{23}} \times 0.50$$

$$= 1.67 \times 10^{-4}\ \text{g hydrocarbon/g organic material in}\ 10^6\ \text{years}$$

The range in this quantity, as indicated by the measurements of radioactivity of the sedimentary formations studied, may be an increase by a factor of 2 for the Antrim shale, a tenfold increase for the Woodford shale, or a decrease by one-half to one-third for the Austin and Selma chalks (see Table 7.6). The increase from the effects of beta and gamma radiation is believed to be not more than 25 percent.

To calculate the amount of hydrocarbon produced in one million years for any given formation of known radioactivity, the concentration of significant organic material in the sediment must be known. Few data of this kind are available. Trask (1932) gives estimates of the content of some fatty acids in sediments, and Clarke and Mazur (1941) determined the content of such acids in diatoms. Burton found 3 percent of convertible material in an extract (5 percent) of a recent sediment. This figure, 1.5×10^{-3} g of convertible organic substance to the g of dry sediment would compare favorably with that of Clarke and Mazur, when the sediment contained about 10 percent diatoms. On the basis of such content, 3×10^{-7} g of hydrocarbon per million years-g of sediment might be produced by radiation from the uranium and thorium series and from potassium.

This figure may be compared with the content of free hydrocarbons in sediments on the Gulf Coast, given by P. V. Smith, Jr., at the meeting of the American Association of Petroleum Geologists (March 24, 1953), 9 to 283 ppm of dried sediments. It seems that the hydrocarbons produced by radioactive processes may attain only one-hundredth, or even a lesser part, of the maximum actually found to be present in marine sediments.

7.7 DISCUSSION

This conclusion is reached on the basis of experimental data. Nevertheless, laboratory experiments were made under conditions different from those to be found in a soft marine mud recently deposited. Muds at shallow depth may contain over 60 percent water by volume, and well-compacted shale may contain as much as 50 percent water. In the early stages of compaction, clay minerals, precipitates, and other inorganic components are suspended in a mixture of organic material and sea water containing dissolved organic compounds. Surface processes are in an optimum environment at this stage of sedimentation. Adsorption of potassium and radon, or of soluble radioactive elements, may cause an increase in the chemical efficacy of radiation. Radioactive elements dissolved in interstitial sea water containing soluble organic substances, known from experiments to be present in bottom muds (Whitehead and Breger, 1950), could be unusually effective. Research to date has included few experiments with such complex systems.

A suggested source of energy in the sediments is the recoil of the parent atom of the alpha radiation. On the basis of their studies of the disorder caused by alpha particles in crystals, Hurley and Fairbairn (1952) conclude that the effect of an alpha particle in solids is greatest at the end of its track (Ross, 1952), and that the changes in lattice structure are confined to a small region there and to another area in the close vicinity of the recoil of the parent radioactive atom. An alpha particle continues to ionize until kinetic energy drops to about 40,000 ev. Most of the remaining energy is lost by atomic collision. Therefore, for a 6 Mev alpha particle over 99 percent of its energy is dissipated through excitation, and less than 1 percent through atomic collisions near the end of its track. The parent atom will recoil with approximately a sixtieth of the energy of the alpha particle, about 10^5 ev. Almost all this energy is effective in atomic collisions. Thus the collision effects caused by the recoil parent atom are greater than those from the alpha particle near the end of its track.

In theoretical discussions of the chemical effects of alpha particles, Lind and Bardwell (1926) have concluded that the rate of chemical reaction is known experimentally to be proportional to the rate of production of ion pairs. Sheppard (1944, p. 942) infers from the analysis by Bethe (1930) that the energy which produces excitation and bond rupture is always proportional to the number of ion pairs produced in a gas. Slater (1951, p. 256) also states that the changes in a molecular compound produced by radiation are likely to be a result of electronic ionization or excitation, rather than of the nuclear recoils. Calculations indicate that 10^5 molecules of hydrocarbon are formed by each alpha particle. This number is considerably greater than the number of atoms displaced in the zircon lattice by an alpha disintegration, 4.5×10^3 (Hurley and Fairbairn, 1952).

The conclusion appears to be tenable that excitation and ionization play a dominant role in the chemical conversion of organic substances by alpha radiation. Hydrocarbons are formed by the effect of radioactivity, but the amounts generated are small, even under the most favorable conditions.

Chapter 8

GEOPHYSICAL EXPLORATION BY NUCLEAR METHODS

8.1 RADIOMETRIC PROSPECTING AND ASSAYING *

DONALD HASKALL JOHNSON †

Nuclear radiations have been used in geophysical studies since shortly after the discovery of radioactivity in 1896. Early techniques, using photographic materials, spinthariscopes, and electrometers, were generally slow and insensitive. With the development of the Geiger-Müller counter,‡ a sensitive, accurate instrument was available, but, because of the delicacy and weight of early counters, they were limited to laboratory use.

Not until rugged, portable counters were developed, just before World War II (Rajewsky, 1943; Ridland, 1945), did nuclear radiation instruments emerge as practical tools for geophysical field work. After the improved portable Geiger-Müller counters, portable scintillation counters were developed. Both types of counter were applied in airborne and carborne surveys as well as foot surveys, and nowadays the nuclear radiation counter is the most common of all geophysical instruments.

The following paragraphs are concerned with various techniques and problems in the application of Geiger-Müller and scintillation counters to geophysical prospecting. For prospecting, counters are used to detect gamma and sometimes beta radiation. The short range of alpha radiation makes its detection impractical in the field.

* The work reported here was supported in part by the Division of Raw Materials of the Atomic Energy Commission.

† U. S. Geological Survey, Denver, Colorado.

‡ As used here, *counter* refers to a complete apparatus for registering radioactivity; *detector,* to the sensitive element in the apparatus that actually detects radiation. A Geiger-Müller tube is a detector; when its output is fed into earphones, a ratemeter, or a scaler, the assemblage is a counter. This is contrary to older usage, wherein *counter* referred to the Geiger-Müller tube, but in accordance with the present terminology of many scientists and essentially all laymen.

8.1.a General considerations

Background. A counter will indicate radioactivity everywhere. This omnipresent radioactivity or background is contributed by three distinct sources: (1) cosmic rays, (2) radioactive impurities in the counter itself, and (3) the usual trace amounts of radioactive material in the vicinity of the counter. A brief consideration of each of these sources is desirable.

1. COSMIC RAYS. The earth's atmosphere is constantly bombarded from without by charged particles, mostly protons and light nuclei (about 75 percent protons, 25 percent alphas, and a fraction of the rest), moving at high velocities. Interaction of these primary particles with nuclei of the atmosphere results in secondary radiation consisting of mesons, fast electrons, photons, etc., all of which constitute cosmic rays.

These cosmic radiations have great energies, and the probability of their detection by a counter is very high. Although some of the radiation can be absorbed by a few inches of lead, many cosmic rays penetrate several feet of lead. Lead, iron, or mercury shields, commonly ½ to 2 inches thick, and various anticoincidence circuits (Elmore and Sands, 1949) are used to reduce cosmic ray intensity in some applications (Slack, 1952; Kulp et al. 1952*c*), but it is impossible to shield against cosmic radiation completely. The intensity of cosmic radiation increases with barometric altitude (Figure 8.1). The increase becomes significant in airborne work and in mountainous regions. Intensity of cosmic radiation also varies slightly with geomagnetic latitude, as a result of the interaction of the earth's magnetic field and the primary cosmic radiation. The total intensity of cosmic radiation is least at the geomagnetic equator, and increases to about latitude 40 north and south, whence it is almost constant to the magnetic poles (Figure 8.2). The change in cosmic ray intensity with change of geomagnetic latitude is more pronounced at higher altitudes because the secondaries created in the atmosphere "smear out" the latitude effect. The effect may be ignored in the United States and Canada, as they are north of the fortieth geomagnetic parallel.

2. COUNTER MATERIALS. Although the materials used in making counters are carefully chosen for low radioactivity, it is impossible to obtain completely non-radioactive substances. All ores and other raw materials, normally considered non-radioactive, contain trace amounts of potassium, thorium, radium, uranium, etc., and these

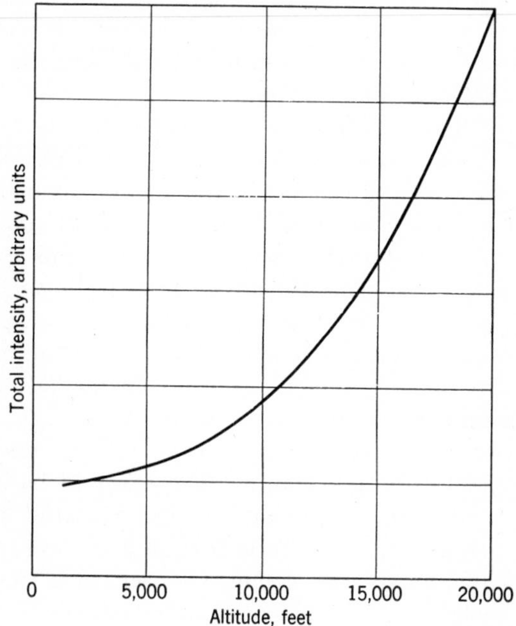

Figure 8.1 Total cosmic ray intensity measured by a brass Geiger-Müller counter, plotted as a function of barometric altitude above sea level.

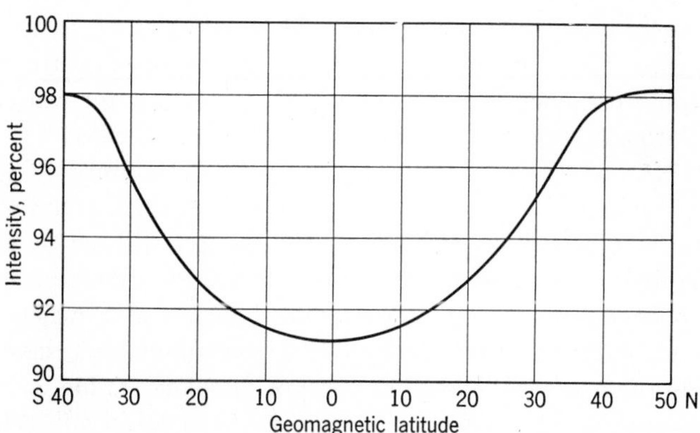

Figure 8.2 Total cosmic ray intensity at sea level, plotted as a function of geomagnetic latitude. The vertical scale is exaggerated. Modified after Compton and Turner.

radioactive impurities cannot be completely eliminated in manufacture. Thus any counter will record nuclear radiation arising within the counter itself. This internal radioactivity, normally very slight, is constant for a particular counter.

Counters are light-sensitive. Fairly high counting rates are observed if light is allowed to leak into the Geiger-Müller tube; a scintillation counter will block completely if a very small amount of stray light penetrates to the cathode of the photomultiplier tube.

3. ENVIRONMENTAL RADIOACTIVITY. As all materials contain trace amounts of radioactive elements, it is manifestly impossible to place a counter in an environment of no radioactivity. Even the least radioactive rocks contain traces of potassium, thorium, uranium, etc. The atmosphere contains radon, the concentration of which varies with meteorological conditions (see Section 4.1.c). The human body contains potassium and minute quantities of radium, uranium, etc.

4. DETERMINATION OF BACKGROUND. The effect of background can usually be ignored where only qualitative indications of high and low radioactivity are desired, as in reconnaissance surveys or where the counting rate from an outcrop or mineral specimen is very high compared to the background. Where counting rates near the background value must be determined or for quantitative work, such as precise surveys and radio-assaying, a determination of the background count is necessary (Peirson, 1951*b;* Russell and Scherbatskoy, 1951).

The background counting rate should be determined as accurately as the other field measurements. Field measurements are best recorded as gross counting rates, without correction for background; the background correction is best made later in the office.

A *working* or *"field" background* may be determined in the area where a counter is to be used. A place of low radioactivity should be chosen so that the environment of the counter will not be changed, as by paving, construction, excavation, or contamination.

A *zero background* may be determined over water which usually exhibits virtually no radioactivity. It is best to choose a lake or reservoir, as these are not likely to contain dissolved radon, and measurements can be made far enough from shore to avoid any significant contribution from the shores. The measurement should be made in an uncontaminated boat over water several feet deep so as to absorb radiations from the bottom. Measurements under various weather conditions may be repeated to allow for variations in atmospheric radon, although these variations are generally small.

If a careful radiometric survey is to be made in an area of high relief, it is desirable to compensate for the variation in cosmic ray intensity with altitude (Figure 8.1). If the zero background of the counter to be used is determined at several different altitudes, a curve of zero background *versus* altitude for that counter can be plotted. Net counting rates are determined by subtracting the zero background for each altitude, as read from the curve, from the gross counting rates measured in the field at that altitude.

Units. Radioactivity measurements may be expressed in various units; those that have been used most commonly in geophysical prospecting are: counts per minute, multiples of background, and milliröntgens/hour.

Geiger-Müller and scintillation counters of various types and makes differ markedly in their response to nuclear radiations, and even two counters of the same make and model may not agree. Scintillation counters normally detect only gamma rays, but most Geiger-Müller counters have windows that may be opened to admit beta radiation in addition to gamma rays. Therefore, measurements expressed in counts per minute are meaningless unless the type, model, and window position of the particular counter are specified and its absolute sensitivity is known. Reporting measurements in counts per minute should be scrupulously avoided.

Multiples of background may be meaningful to those who know what background was used, but, as background varies from place to place, such measurements cannot be compared with others unless the background is given in some absolute unit. Even if the results are to be used by others in the same place, the use of multiples of background as a unit is to be discouraged. The relative efficiency of detection for terrestrial gamma rays *versus* cosmic rays is much greater for scintillation counters than for Geiger-Müller counters. An outcrop that reads 10 times background on a scintillation counter may show only twice the background count on a Geiger-Müller counter.

Reporting in terms of milliröntgens per hour requires that the counter be calibrated in this unit. Calibration is relatively easy, however, and, provided the same type of gamma radiation (usually radium) is used in calibrating two instruments, measurements made by them can be compared easily and directly. All instruments used by the U. S. Geological Survey are calibrated with radium needles. It is strongly recommended that geophysical radioactivity measurements be reported in milliröntgens per hour whenever feasible. The source of radiation used in calibration also should be reported.

Calibration. A counter is calibrated by placing it in known fluxes of nuclear radiation and adjusting the counter circuitry so that the counter reads the correct value over its various scale ranges. The flux may be produced conveniently by a radium needle of known strength, hung at a known distance, and in a fixed position with respect to the counter. One millicurie of radium in a platinum capsule 0.5 mm thick produces a flux of 0.84 milliröntgen per hour at a distance of 1 meter. The actual flux intensity can be computed by the inverse square law. Circuit adjustments should be made while the radiation source is in place. A counter should be recalibrated each time major repairs are made.

Standardization. The response or sensitivity of a counter is not constant with time, but varies with various factors such as temperature, battery voltage, and counter age. It is therefore necessary to check the counter frequently to see that its response has not changed unduly. A counter should be repaired or recalibrated when its response varies from its standard by more than a stated amount, commonly 20 percent.

Standardization is achieved by observing the response of the counter to a fixed radiation flux to which the counter's normal response is known. The flux should be considerably larger, say 20 times larger, than background, and the environment should remain essentially unchanged.

One method is to place a small but intense source, such as a radium-dial watch or a radioactive button such as are commonly furnished with radiation instruments, at a known distance and in a carefully fixed position relative to the detector. The position and orientation of the source on or near the counter must be accurately reproduced each time. Another method is to seal some low-grade radioactive ore in a double-walled cylinder which may be slipped over the detector so as to completely cover the tube or crystal. The space containing the ore should be sealed to prevent spilling of ore or leakage of radon. This type of standard is the easiest to use accurately. It has the advantage of partially shielding the counter from its environment, but the disadvantage of being limited to one size and type of counter. A method that is especially applicable to carborne counters is to choose a place of moderate radioactivity in the survey area and use the normal counter reading at that place as a reference standard.

It is advisable to standardize a counter each time that it is used, allowing it to warm up before reading. If the counter is to be used all day, it should be standardized in the morning and again in the evening. Standardization readings should be long enough to reduce statistical errors to low values. If successive standardization readings are plotted on a graph, the long-term performance of the counter is revealed. A slowly falling plot may indicate failing B batteries; a rising plot with a Geiger-Müller counter may foretell the end of

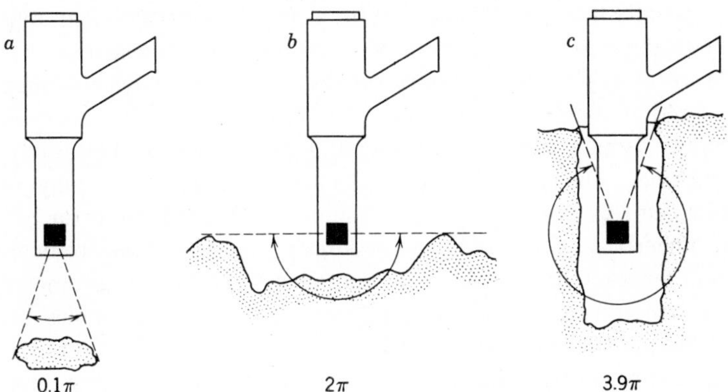

Figure 8.3 The solid angle subtended by various radioactive sources with respect to the sensitive element of a portable scintillation counter. If the radioactive mineral content were equal and uniformly distributed, the three net meter readings, *a*, *b*, and *c*, would be in the proportion 1:20:39.

the useful life of the Geiger-Müller tube. Some instruments will show a sharply rising plot when the A batteries reach the end of their useful life.

Geometrical considerations. Gamma radiation is absorbed as it passes through air, rock, metals, and other materials. Absorption in air is generally negligible for distances up to about 100 feet. Rock, metals, and similar materials absorb much more gamma radiation. Thus gamma radiation arising in granite is largely absorbed in the first few inches, and only a negligible amount of gamma radiation emerges from a depth in the rock greater than 1 foot. Consequently, an outcrop of radioactive rock generally may be considered a radioactive surface.

The response of a counter to an extended source of radioactivity is proportional to the solid angle subtended by the source from the center of the counter's detecting element (Figure 8.3). The solid angle is usually expressed in relation to the surface of a unit sphere (surface area: 4π).

Although gamma counters respond to radiation from all directions, their sensitivity to incident radiation may vary considerably with direction. This is particularly true of certain types of Geiger-Müller counters and of all counters in which the detecting element is housed within the counter so as to be partly shielded by the case and other components. The directional sensitivity of a counter can be determined by rotating the counter in a constant beam of parallel gamma rays (usually from a radium needle a few feet away) and reading the counting rate as a function of angle in three dimensions.

The *solid-angle effect* (sometimes called the *mass effect*) must be considered in field measurements of radioactivity. The solid angle is roughly 4π in a mine or borehole, and 2π on an extended, relatively flat surface. On rough outcrops the effect of geometry may overshadow the real variation in rock radioactivity, and the error caused by an uncertain solid angle can be greater than the actual radioactivity differences. In an effort to minimize variation of geometry in very rough terrain it may be necessary to drill shallow holes in the rock (Szalay, 1948*a*; Szalay and Csongor, 1949) or dig pits in the soil. A reasonable approximation to constant geometry can be achieved in average terrain by holding the counter some distance away from the rock (Figure 8.3). This procedure increases the area effectively "seen" by the counter and thus equalizes the effect of minor irregularities. It is extremely important that the geometry be kept constant if a survey is to have any meaning.

Under certain conditions, in surveying from aircraft for instance, the solid angle subtended by the source may be unknown. The resulting measurements could be very misleading, unless examined in the light of known geology. A large outcrop of weakly radioactive granite, for example, may give a pronounced radioactivity peak, but an exposed narrow vein of pitchblende may go undetected in spite of its high radioactivity, because the solid angle that it subtends is virtually zero.

Absorption by rock. The absorption of radiation by rock is important also in geophysical prospecting with gamma-ray counters. In foot and car traversing, a small hill may hide a radioactive deposit that crops out and would be detected by a traverse on the other side of the hill. Burial prevents the detection of many radioactive deposits; 2 feet of barren, unfractured rock will conceal a deposit of high-grade ore. Commonly, however, there is a gradation of radioactivity outward from a deposit, and fracturing permits outward migration of radon and/or soluble radioactive materials from the deposit (see Section 4.1). Residual rock debris and soil overlying a radioactive deposit may contain fragments of radioactive material for some distance away from the deposit itself. Under such conditions, buried radioactive deposits may be detected at distances and depths greater than would be indicated by absorption considerations. Nevertheless, burial greatly reduces the radiation reaching the surface, and reported discoveries by nuclear radiation methods of radioactive ore at distances of more than a few feet in rock or soil are suspect.

*Absorption by air.** When measurements of surface radioactivity are made from aircraft, the layer of air interposed between the source and the detector is sufficiently thick to necessitate consideration of gamma-ray absorption in it. Even though Compton scattering (see Section 1.8) is the only process that need be considered in this connection, and the geometry is relatively simple, the analytical calculation of the intensity of the gamma radiation from a known source is prohibitively complex. The gamma-ray absorption in an air layer about 1000 feet thick is great enough to make detection of all but the largest natural sources impractical from greater altitudes. Therefore, the absorption behavior is discussed only within this limit.

Figure 8.4 shows the relative gamma-ray intensity measured by a scintillation counter (with a sodium iodide crystal 4 inches in diameter and 2 inches thick) in flight above a layer of carnotite ore, 6 inches thick and laid out in a square 40 by 40 feet. The uranium content of the ore was 0.35 percent, and the ore was covered by a thin rubberized fabric to minimize the escape of radon. At a flight altitude of 500 feet, directly overhead, the geometry of this source was about 0.00016π. The plane was not always exactly overhead. Points more than 25 feet offside are shown as open circles and are corrected for the decreased solid angle of the projected source area.

Integrating the results for the small source to infinity, we obtain a curve with the approximate slope of the lines in Figure 8.5. The points shown are actual measurements made at various altitudes over an effectively infinite flat outcrop of shale and residual soil derived from it. The source contained 0.00017 percent uranium and 1.6 percent potassium, which thus accounted for most of the radioactivity. The measurements were made simultaneously with four identical scintillation counters with 4-inch crystals. The minimum pulse-height

* Abstracted from an unpublished report by A. Y. Sakakura; experimental data by F. J. Davis and coworkers.

acceptance levels of the counters were set at 0.05, 0.1, 0.2, and 0.4 Mev, respectively. The slopes of the lines drawn through the experimental points do not vary with the minimum pulse-height setting. It is concluded that the energy distribution of the gamma rays is effectively constant from the ground up to about 1000 feet.

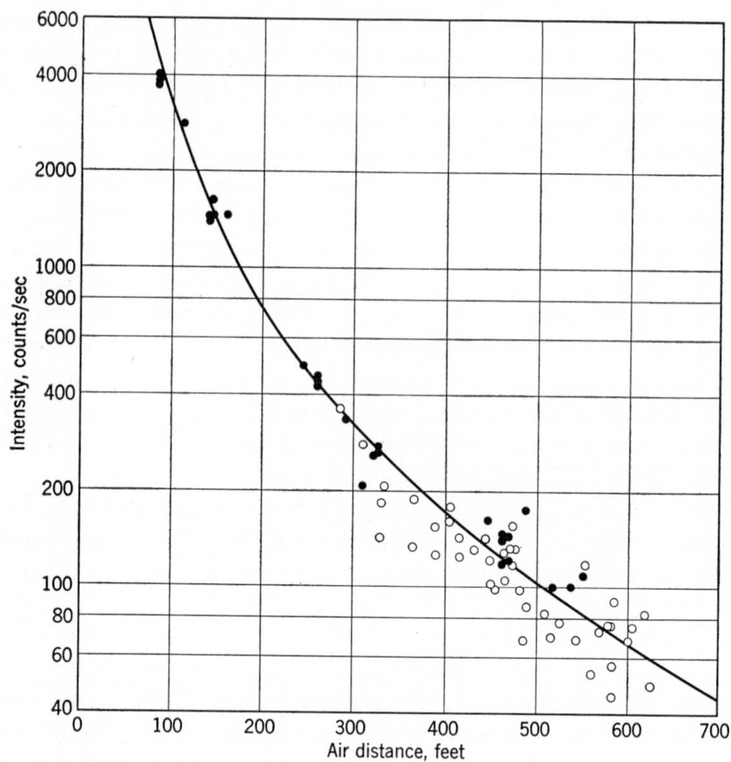

Figure 8.4 Intensity of gamma radiation from a "point" source, plotted as a function of the altitude of the observing aircraft above the source. F. J. Davis et al. (personal communication).

Radioactive elements. Of the naturally occurring radioactive elements only the thorium and uranium series (Figure 1.2) and potassium are abundant enough to affect the counters used in geophysical prospecting. The specific radioactivity of potassium is much lower than that of uranium or thorium, but potassium is relatively common and many rocks (some granites, syenites, other igneous rocks, and argillaceous sedimentary rocks) derive their radioactivity primarily from potassium (Senftle, 1948). Counters used in geophysical field work are generally incapable of distinguishing between radiations from different elements. If a particular mineral is determined to be radioactive, a simple bead test can be used to check for uranium (Papish and Hoag, 1927; Erlenmeyer et al., 1950), but ordinarily laboratory methods must be used to determine the radioactive elements in a rock.

Because the radioactive element is rarely determined in geophysical

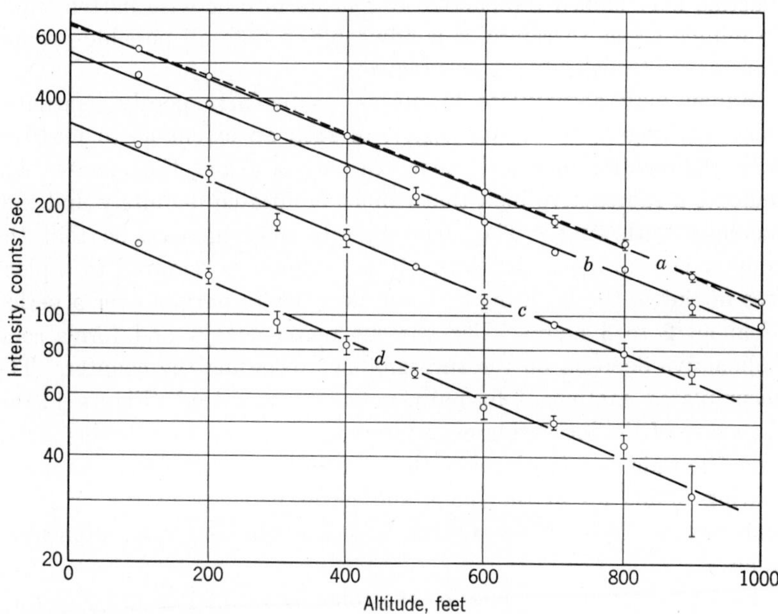

Figure 8.5 Intensity of gamma radiation from an effectively infinite plane source, plotted as a function of the altitude of the observing aircraft above the source. The intensity was observed simultaneously with four scintillation counters set at different minimum-energy acceptance levels: $a = 0.4$ Mev, $b = 0.2$ Mev, $c = 0.1$ Mev, $d = 0.05$ Mev. F. J. Davis et al. (personal communication).

field work or in simple radiometric assaying, it is customary to report the radioactive content of rocks and minerals in terms of the amount of uranium in equilibrium with its daughter elements that would produce the same radioactivity. For example, a sample may be said to contain 0.01 percent *equivalent uranium* (eU) even though all the radioactivity is actually due to potassium.

Contamination. Some areas may become so contaminated with radioactive materials as to make radiometric field work difficult or impossible. The principal causes of such contamination are mining operations, radon accumulations, and fission products from nuclear weapons tests.

In a district where uranium or thorium ores are mined, radioactive minerals are frequently scattered by drilling and blasting, and by falling from ore trucks. Considerable quantities of radioactive material thus may be distributed in patterns different from their original distribution; an airborne radiometric survey of a uranium mining area gives an excellent map of the ore haulage roads. In mines, blasting may embed radioactive fragments in otherwise barren walls. In mining areas, therefore, it is advisable to take all possible precautions against misleading measurements.

Radon may accumulate in places, particularly poorly ventilated mine workings (see Section 4.1.c), to such an extent as to interfere with radiometric measurements. In such a place, the counter will indicate a radioactive high that cannot be located definitely and that increases with time. The counting rate may increase so that the counter can no longer be used. If the counter is removed to a place free of radon, the counting rate will decrease to normal over a period of about 2 to 3 hours. The gaseous radon decays and forms solid radioactive deposits on the surroundings, including the counter. The accumulated coating of bismuth, polonium, and lead (Figure 1.2) is the cause of the increasing counting rate; as the coating decays, away from the radon contamination, the counting rate decreases. A similar coating builds up in the lungs and nasal passages of the operator, and may be detected for a short time after he leaves a radon-filled mine.

Radon contamination may be overcome by ventilation or by making readings quickly before the contaminating coating builds up to a troublesome degree. In deep mines, the counter can be carried to the measurement station in a gastight plastic bag and removed for use.

A new source of contamination has arisen with the testing of nuclear weapons. At each bomb burst, a cloud of fission products and neutron-activated material is released into the air, and this contamination is distributed by air currents. Contamination appears shortly after the blast near the bomb site and may reach areas hundreds or thousands of miles distant within a few days (Holter and Glasscock, 1952, and others). Within hundreds of miles of the blast, contamination of the earth's surface may be so great as to prohibit radiometric geophysical work. Even at distances over a thousand miles, the background of a Geiger-Müller counter frequently increases 3 to 5 times, and that of a scintillation counter 20 to 50 times. The distribution and "fall out" pattern of the fission products are governed by meteorological conditions. Precipitation carries down large quantities of the fission products. Contamination produced by nuclear explosives is relatively short-lived. It generally disappears within a few weeks after its first appearance. The rate of decay is shown in Figure 8.6.

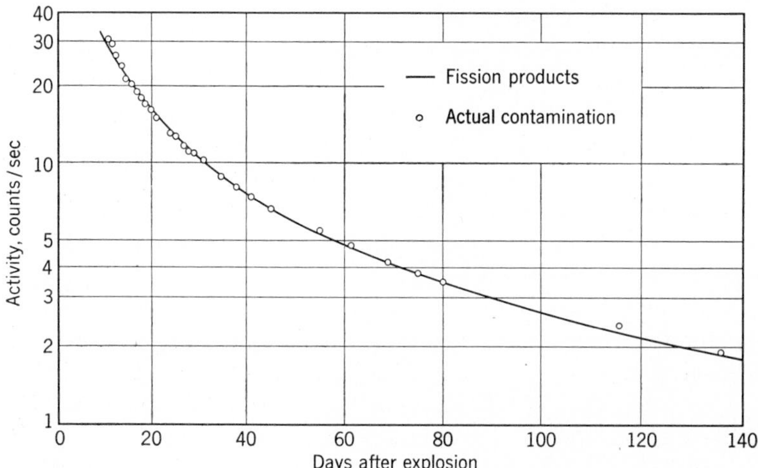

Figure 8.6 Decay rate of fission product contamination from nuclear explosions. The solid line is the theoretical decay curve of mixed fission products. After Holter and Glasscock (1952).

8.1.b Instrumentation

Although the subject of instruments has been treated in Sections 1.11, 1.12, and 1.13, some of the considerations that affect the choice of instruments for geophysical field work will be discussed here.

Because the scintillation counter is much more efficient in detecting gamma radiation than the Geiger-Müller counter, it may be preferred for most radioactivity surveys (Kirchheimer, 1953), particularly where the gamma radiation of the rocks is of the same order of magnitude as cosmic radiation. The scintillation counter is generally more affected by heat; some scintillation assemblies are damaged by temperatures above about 110° F. In cold weather, on the other hand, the scintillation counter operates well down to the temperature where batteries freeze. Geiger-Müller tubes filled with organic quenching agents lose sensitivity at temperatures below 30° to 40° F; tubes with halogen quenchers are usable to much lower temperatures. Scintillation counters tend to be less stable than Geiger-Müller counters, and they must be treated more gently in the field. The scintillation counter is still several times more expensive than a Geiger-Müller counter of comparable quality.

Three general types of counting-rate indication are used in nuclear radiation detectors: (1) direct aural or visual indication, (2) scalers, and (3) rate meters. Direct indication, in which each count is presented as a click in earphones or as a flash of a neon bulb, is limited to low counting rates; few prospectors use such indicators any more.

Scalers (see Section 1.13.a) electronically divide the input pulses from the radiation detector into fewer output pulses, according to the scaling factor of the circuit. Scalers have the advantage of showing accurately the number of counts recorded, but the disadvantage of not indicating change in counting rate during a counting interval. They are admirably suited to radiometric assaying and to grid surveys and point readings where the instrument remains stationary.

Rate meters electronically integrate the pulses received from the detector and indicate the counting rate on a meter. Radiations are received statistically so that the meter reading fluctuates statistically (see Section 1.9). The fluctuation of the meter can be controlled by choosing the proper *time constant* of the resistor-capacitor combination used for integration. A short time constant gives a rate meter that responds quickly to changing counting rates, but with considerable fluctuation in the meter. A long time constant gives a steady meter reading, but requires that more time elapse before the circuit reaches equilibrium and the meter indicates the correct value. Meter fluctuation can be reduced without increasing the time constant by increasing the counting-rate input, i.e., by using a detector that has a higher counting rate; herein lies the major advantage of the scintillation counter. Recording rate meters give a continuous permanent record and are used in logging and in some carborne and airborne installations.

Auxiliary instruments are desirable in many radiation studies. Automatic timers to deliver equal periods of counting time and automatic count selectors to regulate for equal numbers of pulses are often used with scalers, particularly in assaying. Alarm circuits, set to operate at preselected counting rates, are invaluable in traversing, particularly with carborne instruments (Nelson, 1953; Peirson, 1951*a*).

8.1.c Radiometric surveying and prospecting

Radiometric surveys can be grouped roughly into areal reconnaissance, detailed local surveys, and spot examinations. Areal surveys are generally carborne or airborne, but occasionally such surveys are made on foot or horseback. Local surveys and spot examinations are almost invariably made on foot. Techniques and equipment used in radiometric surveying are governed by many factors, such as type of terrain, information required, and men and time available. Accordingly, only general methods and equipment will be discussed below.

Carborne methods. Carborne equipment makes possible the rapid reconnaissance of large areas, provided the areas have sufficiently extensive road networks or are passable off the road by jeeps or similar vehicles. Carborne radiometric traversing is applicable to rapid search for surface deposits of radioactive ores, for finding radioactive anomalies for more detailed surveys, and for determining roughly the relative distribution of radioactivity in large areas (D. H. Johnson, McKeown, Narten, and Nelson, unpublished reports).

The essential parts of the carborne equipment are a scintillation detector,* an indicator, and a power supply, as in any counter. The detector should be mounted as high on the car as practicable so as to increase its area of search to the side (Condit and Graves, 1952). The direction of greatest sensitivity should be normal to the axis of the car. A detector is often mounted on each side of a car to increase the counting rate and to permit directional searching. For normal traversing, the outputs of both detectors are fed in parallel to the indicator; for directional search, either the right or the left detector may be used alone. The detectors may be shielded by lead to decrease radiation from unwanted directions.

For car traversing, the only satisfactory indicator is a rate meter. The rate meter circuit must have a relatively short (fast) time constant to detect rapidly changing counting rates along the roads traveled. The meter itself may be of either the visual or the recording type. If the visual meter is used, it must be watched constantly unless an alarm is used. With a recording meter a continuous, permanent record of a traverse is obtained, and anomalies can be detected on such a record after the traverse is completed, as well as during traversing. A car's odometer may be connected to drive the chart of a recording rate meter so that the length of the record is proportional to distance driven. Index marks may be made on the chart to indicate check points, and the observer's notes may be transcribed onto the chart, giving a single complete permanent record. In most operations, however, a recorder is not strictly required. When

* Geiger-Müller tubes were used before the development of the carborne scintillation detector.

a high is encountered, most geologists prefer to make an examination on the spot.

Automatic alarms are frequently used with car counters. Basically, an alarm is an electronic device that can be set to ring a bell or flash a light when a designated counting rate is exceeded. The alarm point is adjustable to adapt to varying field conditions. A circuit that can be connected to most rate meters with little change in the rate meter is given by Nelson (1953). Circuits requiring greater alterations of the rate meter are shown in various publications dealing with counters (for instance, Peirson, 1951*a*; 1953).

Carborne radiometric surveys are usually made in areas where road maps exist. If the roads provide insufficient access to the area, geologic and topographic maps help in planning cross-country traverses to supplement the road surveys. Carborne surveying of uncharted areas is difficult, and the advantage of speed is largely lost under such conditions. Airborne exploration with air-photo or *shoran* navigation is more efficient in regions where no maps are available.

Many factors must be considered in evaluating increases in counting rate observed during a traverse. A large outcrop of slightly radioactive rock may give as great an increase in counting rate as a small outcrop of highly radioactive rock; the peak may be sharper for the small, highly radioactive outcrop. A change in the geometry of the rock surrounding the car, as in a road cut or on a fill, causes an appreciable change in counting rate without change in radioactivity of the rocks. Sometimes radioactive materials used in construction of a road will give an increased counting rate independent of the roadside rocks. Any suspected anomaly should be further examined by a spot check on foot.

There is no substitute for experience in interpreting carborne rate meter readings. This is particularly true with regard to the evaluation of geometry, outcrop size, distance, etc. By correlating carborne instrument readings on outcrops of fairly uniform rocks with radiometric assays of samples from the same outcrops, an experienced operator soon learns to estimate the grade of new outcrops with fair accuracy.

Airborne methods. The methods and equipment of carborne exploration are applicable to operations from light aircraft with only minor changes. The light airplane usually operates at a speed of 80 to 100 miles per hour and flies as low as the pilot is willing to go (about 50 to 100 feet). The airborne instrument scans a fairly wide area, but at relatively high speed, so that the sensitivity and time-constant requirements are about the same as for carborne instruments. An ordinary portable scintillation counter, adjusted for maximum sensitivity and short time constant (and possibly equipped with an auxiliary amplifier driving a clock-driven strip-chart recording milliammeter) is adequate for use in small aircraft.

The airborne geologist cannot stop to examine his outcrop, and good plan position control is necessary. When an anomaly is observed, the pilot usually returns to the area immediately, to verify the measurement. The spot may be marked for ground observation by dropping a weighted streamer or a paper bag of flour or some pigment.

Large aircraft of the DC-3 type are used for radiometric surveying by the U. S. Geological Survey (Stead, 1950), by the Canadian authorities (Cowper, 1954), and by a few commercial surveying companies. Instruments used in these planes are scintillation counters of the highest possible sensitivity with very large crystals (usually 4 or 5 inches in diameter and 2 inches thick). Several scintillation assemblies are used in parallel, feeding into special rate meters. A radio altimeter continuously measures altitude above ground and automatically corrects the radiation measurement for absorption in the air. A gyro-controlled continuous-strip camera photographs the ground vertically below the plane, and the flight observer makes numbered index marks on the film and automatically on all the charts when the plane crosses a landmark that can be located on maps or air photos. A *shoran* system is substituted for the camera when the area surveyed lacks sufficient landmarks. The plane flies at an altitude of 500 feet in straight lines spaced about a quarter of a mile apart or wider at a speed of 140 to 145 miles per hour. The operating crew includes a pilot, a copilot-navigator, a flight observer, and two or three instrument men. It is obvious that such an operation is costly. The discovery rate has been favorable, however, and the planes continue to be used. In addition to the search for ore deposits, the large planes and their interlocking control equipment make it possible to compile maps of radiation intensity that can be used in various other geological studies (see Section 8.1.f).

Local surveys. Detailed local surveys are made to determine accurately the distribution of radioactivity in an area for such purposes as locating radioactive ore deposits, contacts, fissures, veins, or other features. The area involved may range from a single mining claim to a district of many square miles. Concealed faults and geologic contacts separating rocks of different radioactivities may be mapped with counters (Lester, 1950; Kirchheimer, 1953). Some concealed faults may be found by detecting radon leaking along the fault. Radioactivity anomalies have been proposed as guides to non-radioactive mineral deposits (Damon, 1950; Gross, 1952).

Surveys are made by continuous traversing along relatively closely spaced lines, or by readings at closely spaced fixed points, which may be scattered at random or laid out according to geologic conditions. The traverses or fixed points should be plotted accurately on a map, preferably along with geology and topography. Radioactivity can be shown either by recording individual readings on the map, or by plotting *isorads* or contours of equal radioactivity. Gross radiation intensity can be used directly for many purposes, but for some work it is desirable to correct for background. Detailed local surveys are almost always conducted on foot, and the counters must be light and easy to carry. Most surveys are made with rate meters, but, since the development of a reliable portable scaler, some surveys have been made with that instrument. Rate meters used for continuous traverses should have a time constant short enough so that small anomalies are not missed at normal walking speed; rate meters used for fixed-station measurements should have a longer time constant so as to give more accurate average readings. Some instruments are provided with a switch for long and short time constants. Portable scalers are suitable only for fixed-station measurements.

As in carborne traversing, experience is very important in interpreting results. Geometric effects are frequently pronounced, particularly in rugged terrain or in mine surveying. It is desirable to make readings with the detector held so as to keep the solid angle subtended by the rock exposed to the counter uniformly near 2π. Comparison of radiometric or chemical assays of samples with counter readings on the same rocks may permit an experienced man to calibrate his instrument roughly in terms of equivalent radioactive element content of the rocks.

Detailed radiometric surveys are made as a matter of course on most claims and mines that produce radioactive ores, but results are usually kept confidential. Brownell (1950) gives the results of a few such surveys. In some areas geologic features are associated with slight radioactive contamination, and a detailed radiation survey may be very useful in untangling the structural relationships. As an example, one may cite the Wet Mountains region of south-central Colorado, where fissures can be traced for miles by the radioactivity of their thorium mineralization. Dikes and sills in this region are also more radioactive than the country rock and can be traced even when covered by loose rubble or a few inches of soil. In the Red Desert area of Wyoming, a U. S. Geological Survey field party using Geiger-Müller counters (Beroni, private communication) prepared an isorad map on which concealed faults were delineated by the isorads. A radiometric survey is an essential part of a thorough geologic study of such areas.

Spot examinations. A spot examination is concerned with a restricted area, such as a single outcrop, a prospect pit, or a small mine. Generally the purpose is to locate rapidly the places of highest and lowest radioactivity, and the extent of radioactive zones. Sometimes a detailed study is made of an outcrop or mine face to distinguish radioactive minerals for sampling and identification.

Rate meters are best adapted to spot examinations. The detector, preferably beta-sensitive, is moved slowly over the area to be examined until the places of maximum and minimum radioactivity are located. For accurate locations, highly directional detectors may be necessary. Small end-window Geiger-Müller tubes, shielded by lead except over the window, have been used, but their counting rates are low. Perhaps the best device is a scintillation detector, shielded by lead except for a small opening.

Spot examinations are frequently made with relatively small detectors that may be inserted in crevices or holes; geometrical effects are usually ignored. The beta-radiation shield of a thin-walled Geiger-Müller tube is usually opened to increase the sensitivity; this nullifies the calibration of the counter, and readings obtained thus cannot be used quantitatively. An experienced operator can often estimate closely the grade of rock examined and keep low the number of samples necessary for an appraisal.

Most spot examinations are conducted for the purpose of evaluating prospects of radioactive mineral deposits. Such examinations must be very carefully interpreted according to geology, as geologic factors often greatly modify the indications given by the counter alone. The U. S. Geological Survey, the Atomic Energy Commission, many mining companies, and other agencies and individuals are constantly making spot examinations; some of their reports are available for study. Some reports by members of the U. S. Geological Survey are available for inspection at various Geological Survey field offices. Some are reprinted and distributed by the Technical Information Service, U. S. Atomic Energy Commission, Oak Ridge, Tennessee. The Technical Information Service also publishes *Nuclear Science Abstracts* in which brief abstracts of many of these reports may be found.

8.1.d Radiometric assaying

Nuclear radiation counters are used extensively in assaying ores, rocks, and other materials for radioactive elements. Such assays are very rapid, require a minimum of sample preparation, and are nondestructive so that the sample can be used later for other purposes.

A Geiger-Müller tube or a scintillation crystal, without the use of special absorbers, etc., cannot distinguish between radiation from radium, potassium, or other elements. Thus an ordinary radiometric assay does not indicate the actual composition of the sample. It is customary to assume a standard composition for samples and report all results in terms of that composition. Assays in the United States are often given in terms of *equivalent uranium* (eU), the amount of uranium in equilibrium with its daughter elements required to give the same counting rate as the sample in that particular type of instrument. Equivalent thorium (Szalay, 1948*a*, *b*; Szalay and Csongor, 1949), equivalent potassium (Peirson, 1951*c*), equivalent radium, and other units also have been used by some workers. These methods are not satisfactory in some districts where the ore may not be in radioactive equilibrium. When disequilibrium is pronounced and variable from sample to sample, the simple radiation methods must be replaced with more complex radiochemical separation techniques.

The general assay procedure is to select the sample by standard methods, place a known volume of it in a standard geometrical relationship with the detector, determine the counting rate, and compare with the counting rate produced by a standard sample of known composition. Standard geometry is assured by using sample containers of fixed size and shape that can be placed in a fixed position with respect to the detector. Shallow dishes filled level with the powdered sample are frequently used with lead- or iron-shielded end-window Geiger-Müller tubes for routine beta-ray assaying of samples containing more than 0.001 percent equivalent uranium. Sometimes a cylindrical jacket is placed coaxially around a detector, and the sample is poured into the space between the detector and the jacket. If samples of fairly constant density are used in a rigid sample holder that is always filled to the same depth, the weight of the sample is automatically regulated. If the density varies, however, the samples should be weighed, and corrections made for sample weight and density (see Walton, 1952, and Section 1.8). Scintillation alpha counters and ionization chambers are used for radiometric assaying of samples of very low radioactivity (see Sections 1.11.a and 1.12). An instrument is shown schematically in Figure 1.16. Inhomogeneous distribution of radioactive material in rocks of low radioactivity may give wide dispersion on samples from the same locality (Keevil et al., 1943). Serious difficulties are encountered in sampling these rocks (see Section 2.1.a).

Comparison standards are usually prepared by mixing powdered analyzed minerals. The standard should be held together by sintering or with a binder to minimize radon emanation, prevent loss of fines by winnowing, or prevent separation of materials of different densities by jigging. It is important that the standard be in radioactive equilibrium. Eldorado (Great Bear Lake, Canada) pitchblende is an excellent mineral for this purpose.

Laboratory assay equipment frequently includes semi-automatic scalers that can be preset for fixed times or numbers of counts, automatic sample changers, large numbers of comparison standards, etc. Alpha and/or beta rays are measured. Field assays require only a hand-operated crusher, a portable scaler or good rate meter, a comparison standard, a watch, and a sample holder. The most convenient sample holder for the field is probably the cylindrical jacket coaxially surrounding a beta-gamma detector.

An assay is made by making separate counts on the sample, the comparison standard, and the background, and determining the counting rates. The assay is given by the equation:

$$\frac{\text{Sample assay}}{\text{Standard assay}} = \frac{\text{Gross sample counting rate} - \text{background}}{\text{Gross standard counting rate} - \text{background}}$$

A great variety of radiometric assaying techniques is described in the literature (Curtiss, 1949). Russell (1944) was the first to apply modern equipment to the study of the radioactivity of oil-well cuttings. Methods for radiometric analysis of uranium ores were described by Hushley and Dixon (1947), Faul (1948), Rodden (1949), Szalay (1948*a*), Thommeret (1949), Lapointe (1950*a*, *b*), Horwood and McMahon (1950), and Eichholz et al. (1953). The scintillation technique was applied to radiometric analysis of rocks by Whitham (1952). Special immersion beta-gamma counters are available for the analysis of solutions. The efficiency of the process for various beta and gamma emitters was studied by Walton (1952). Radiometric methods of potassium analysis in liquids and solids were discussed by Barnes and Salley (1943), Spicer (1946), Gaudin and Pannell (1948), Friedmann (1951), and Wack (1952). Automatic sample changers were described by Peacock and Good (1946), Taylor (1950), and Lerner and Uecker (1951), and are available commercially. The effect of sample thickness and other technical details of the beta-ray assaying method were discussed by Hée et al. (1952). Theoretical aspects of alpha counting were discussed by Keevil and Grasham (1943) and Nogami and Hurley (1948).

Much effort has been spent on the development of a radiation method of analysis for thorium in the presence of uranium. Peirson (1951*c*) has proposed two methods, one based on alpha-ray energy discrimination, the other a beta-alpha coincidence method based on the difference between the halflives of polonium^{214}, a decay product of uranium, and polonium^{212}, a decay product of thorium. Eichholz et al. (1953) reviewed the problems of radiation assaying and described a method of uranium and thorium analysis by simultaneous measurement of beta and gamma activity of the sample. A method based on gamma-ray scintillation spectrometry is under study (Hurley, private communication) and appears to be promising.

8.1.e Geologic mapping

The rapidly increasing availability of radiometric instruments has brought applications to geologic problems not directly associated with radioactive ore deposits. We have previously mentioned (Section 8.1.c) a few such applications, illustrating the utility of various methods.

A study of the Round Lake batholith (Slack, 1952) has shown distinct and characteristic anomalies across the boundary between the batholith and surrounding basic lava flows. Similar phenomena are found in other regions, and radiation highs (Gross, 1952) or lows occasionally may be associated with ore deposits of non-radioactive elements. Isorad maps compiled from measurements made with the large aircraft, previously described, can be useful in geologic mapping (Stead, private communication). In some instances, large lithologic units can be traced, even though they are covered by residual soil. Application of radiation measurements to subsurface geologic problems is discussed by Faul and by Tittle in other sections of this chapter. Section 4.1 treats of the migration and occurrence of radon.

It must be emphasized, however, that in some geologic provinces all rocks are of such uniform radioactivity that no useful differences can be observed. Similarly, there are many faults, fissures, and contacts that exhibit no associated radiation anomalies.

8.1.f Exploration for petroleum

Various claims have been made in the trade literature that surface radioactivity anomalies are associated with deeply buried petroleum deposits. Exploration methods based on this phenomenon were discussed by Stothart (1950), Lundberg (1952), Lundberg et al. (1952), and Lundberg and Isford (1953). Several theories have been advanced to explain the reported radioactivity, most of them based on the assumption of hydrocarbon leakage from the deposit. The method is being applied by several operators, but results have not been released. No impartial study of the method has been published.

8.2 GAMMA-RAY AND NEUTRON LOGGING IN THE PETROLEUM INDUSTRY *

C. W. TITTLE †

Gamma-ray and neutron logs have several features which have caused a substantial increase in their use by the petroleum industry. The gamma-ray log is useful because:

(1) Shales are usually more gamma-radioactive than other sedimentary formations, and the gamma-ray log is frequently able to delineate the shale beds in a sequence.

(2) Gamma rays are penetrating and give usable logs in cased holes, though with reduced accuracy. Correlations thus can be made in old wells.

(3) The gamma-ray log usually correlates well with the electrical self-potential log and may be used to tie the electrical log depth scale to the casing collar log.

(4) Occasionally a radioactive bed is adjacent to a productive zone over a wide area. Such beds can serve as markers.

* Assistance of Messrs. M. J. Hill, G. Ireton, S. J. Poythress, Jr., R. B. Wilkins, and M. R. J. Wyllie, all of the Gulf companies, in collecting examples and crystallizing opinions is gratefully acknowledged. Examples furnished by Mr. L. Wilson of Mene Grande Oil Company, C. A., and Messrs. R. E. Bush of the Lane-Wells Company, and E. S. Mardock of Wells Surveys, Inc., are appreciated. Permission to reproduce Figure 8.8*a* was kindly granted by the Petroleum Branch of the American Institute of Mining and Metallurgical Engineers. Logs used as examples were made by the Lane-Wells Company. Appreciation is due Dr. Paul D. Foote, Director of Gulf Research and Development Company, for permission to publish this account.

† Gulf Research and Development Company, Pittsburgh 30, Pennsylvania.

The neutron log is of value because:

(1) It measures indirectly the hydrogen content of the formation, and therefore locates zones containing water or hydrocarbons, though it usually cannot distinguish oil from water.

(2) It can measure average porosity when properly calibrated, provided that the formation contains little clay, shale, or hydrogen in chemical combination with the solids. It will not measure porosity in some gas zones.

(3) It may be used at reduced accuracy in cased holes.

(4) There is sometimes a sufficient contrast in the hydrogen content of gas zones and oil or water zones to give an indication of the gas-oil or gas-water contact, in cased or uncased holes.

(5) Used with the gamma-ray log, the neutron log can be used frequently for geological correlations between rather widely spaced wells within an area.

8.2.a The gamma-ray logging tool

Gamma rays are emitted by certain radioactive elements present in varying degree in natural materials. The radiations are due principally to potassium and the decay products of uranium and thorium. Gamma rays can penetrate several inches of rock. The depth of penetration depends on the distribution of activity, but is of the order of 6 inches to 1 foot.

The gamma-ray device consists essentially of a suitable gamma-ray detector in a metal housing. The length of the sensitive element varies with the design. The detectors in use include ionization chambers (Swift, 1952), Geiger counters (Guelke et al., 1948, 1949; Feldman and Wright, 1949; Berbezier et al., 1952) and scintillation counters (DiGiovanni et al., 1953). The sensitive element of the ionization chambers or Geiger counters is generally 1 to 3 feet long; that of the scintillation counter is about 2 inches in length. The scintillation logs appear to have more meaningful detail than those made with ionization chambers or Geiger counters. Whether this additional detail is useful depends on the particular problem. Beds as thin as 1 or 2 feet can be defined by the ionization chamber and Geiger counter; the depth resolution of the scintillation counter is said to be about equal to the bore-hole diameter.

The signal from the detector is transmitted up the cable to the logging truck, where a permanent record is made in which gamma ray intensity is plotted against depth. Older gamma ray logs gave only relative indications of gamma ray intensity. No calibrated scale was provided, nor was zero intensity defined. This situation has gradually improved, with all service companies now offering some form of calibration and with some showing an accurately known zero. Calibration and a known zero allow quantitative comparisons and evaluation of statistical errors.

An example of a gamma ray log is shown in Figure 8.7.*a*. Shales

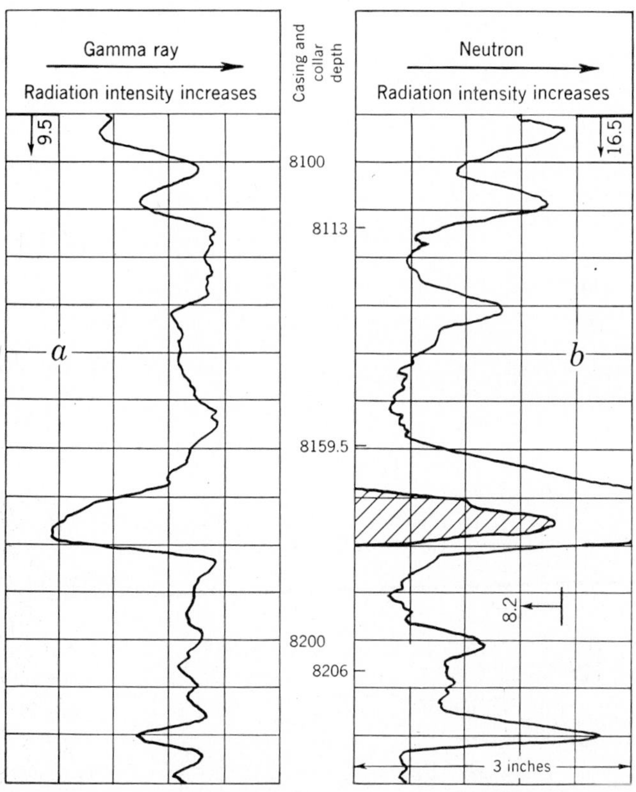

Figure 8.7(*a*) Representative gamma-ray log. The symbol in the upper left-hand corner means that the sensitivity is such that from this point downward a certain standard source gave a deflection of 9.5 inches. Zero was not known for this log. The minimum at 8220 feet probably represents a sand so thin that it was not fully developed on the log owing to the length of the detector (3 feet). (*b*) Representative neutron log. Sensitivity is shown in the same manner as for the gamma-ray log. The arrow and number near the bottom indicate that zero radiation intensity on the scale is 8.2 inches to the left of the vertical line. The crosshatched curve represents a deflection that went off scale to the right. Note general correspondence of minima on gamma-ray curve to maxima on neutron curve. These logs were made in a cased well. Positions of casing collars are shown in feet, having been recorded by a separate device run with the neutron log.

are usually high in gamma radioactivity, sands intermediate, and dense carbonate rocks and anhydrites low. These are only general rules to be used as a guide and not for absolute interpretations. Potash beds and radioactive ores are, of course, very high in gamma radioactivity (see Section 8.3).

The activity of sand or of a carbonate rock depends among other things on its shale content. The shale content can be so high as to make the reservoir rock indistinguishable from shale on the gamma-ray log, but often a distinction can be made in spite of the activity. High gamma-ray intensity in a sand may indicate an impermeable formation [see Figure 8.9.*b*].

Incidental uses of the gamma-ray log include a method of evaluating the effectiveness of well cementing by mixing a radioactive tracer into the cement. Radioactive tracers also have been applied to such production problems as water flow. Radioactive marker bullets are sometimes used as an aid in relative depth determinations; the gamma-ray log is used to locate the bullet after the casing is set.

8.2.b The neutron logging tool

When fast neutrons bombard a rock, they slow down by elastic and inelastic collisions with atomic nuclei, and diffuse into the rock. After a short time interval they are captured by atomic nuclei, which promptly emit gamma rays by the (n, γ) or radiative capture reaction. This process is not to be confused with induced radioactivity, a delayed effect which is unimportant in conventional neutron logging.

The penetration of the neutrons into the rock depends primarily on the amount of hydrogen in the material; penetration is small when hydrogen content is large. This property of neutrons is due to the outstanding ability of hydrogen to slow neutrons down, and to the fact that slow neutrons are much more readily absorbed than fast neutrons. Thus a large hydrogen concentration results in a bunching of the neutrons around the source and reduces their density at greater distances. The geometrical arrangement of the neutron source and the detector in the logging tool is such that an increase in hydrogen concentration causes a decrease in measured intensity.

The neutron device contains a neutron source and either a gamma-ray detector or a neutron detector. The two logs are called the neutron-gamma (Faul and Tittle, 1951) and neutron-neutron (Tittle et al., 1951) log, respectively. The source is usually a mixture of radium and beryllium or polonium and beryllium. The gamma-ray detector may be similar to that used in the gamma-ray device, but it is commonly smaller. The neutron detector is sensitive to neutrons, but not to gamma rays in the intensities encountered. One instrument is said to detect mainly epithermal neutrons, i.e., neutrons above thermal equilibrium energy (about 0.03 ev). There is reason to believe that such a system gives results superior to detection of thermal neutrons, but exact comparisons with neutron-gamma records have not been published. At the present time it is thought that neutron-neutron and neutron-gamma logs give essentially the same result.

The method of recording a neutron log is the same as that of the gamma-ray log. A typical neutron record is shown in Figure 8.7.*b*. Increasing hydrogen content causes a shift to the left, in the direction of decreasing radiation intensity. Porous zones give low readings; dense zones, such as anhydrite or dense limestone, give high ones. Shale is shown as a very low reading, usually even lower than that of the most porous zones. This is due partly to the hydrogen content of the shale and partly to the fact that many shales wash out in drilling and the neutron device then logs the well fluid in the enlarged diameter of the bore hole. Gypsum also gives a low reading due to its water of crystallization.

Porosity measurements with the neutron log are most useful in carbonate rocks, where the porosity is of the fracture or vugular type or is so low that other methods of measuring porosity fail. The logs are calibrated (Bush and Mardock, 1950, 1951; Fearon and Mardock, 1951) by comparison with porosities measured in the core. The calibration constants vary with the hole diameter (Scotty and Egan, 1952, 1953) and rock type. These factors limit the value of the log, and it is hoped that further development will allow a more general calibration. The usual scheme is to core one well in a field in order to get a neutron-log porosity calibration, and to drill other wells to the same size so that porosity may be determined by the neutron log. The log samples a sizable portion of the formation, something like a foot in radius and 1 or 2 feet long. It is probable that, where applicable, porosity measurements by neutron log are more meaningful than core porosities. Figure 8.8.*a* presents a good neutron deflection *versus* core-porosity correlation obtained in clean limestone, Figure 8.8.*b* a fair correlation in sandstone, and Figure 8.8.*c* a poor correlation due to clay in a dirty sand. Some success has been achieved in correcting for shale by use of the gamma-ray log.

Quantitative interpretation is facilitated by use of "standard units" of deflection, obtained by dividing the deflection in inches by log

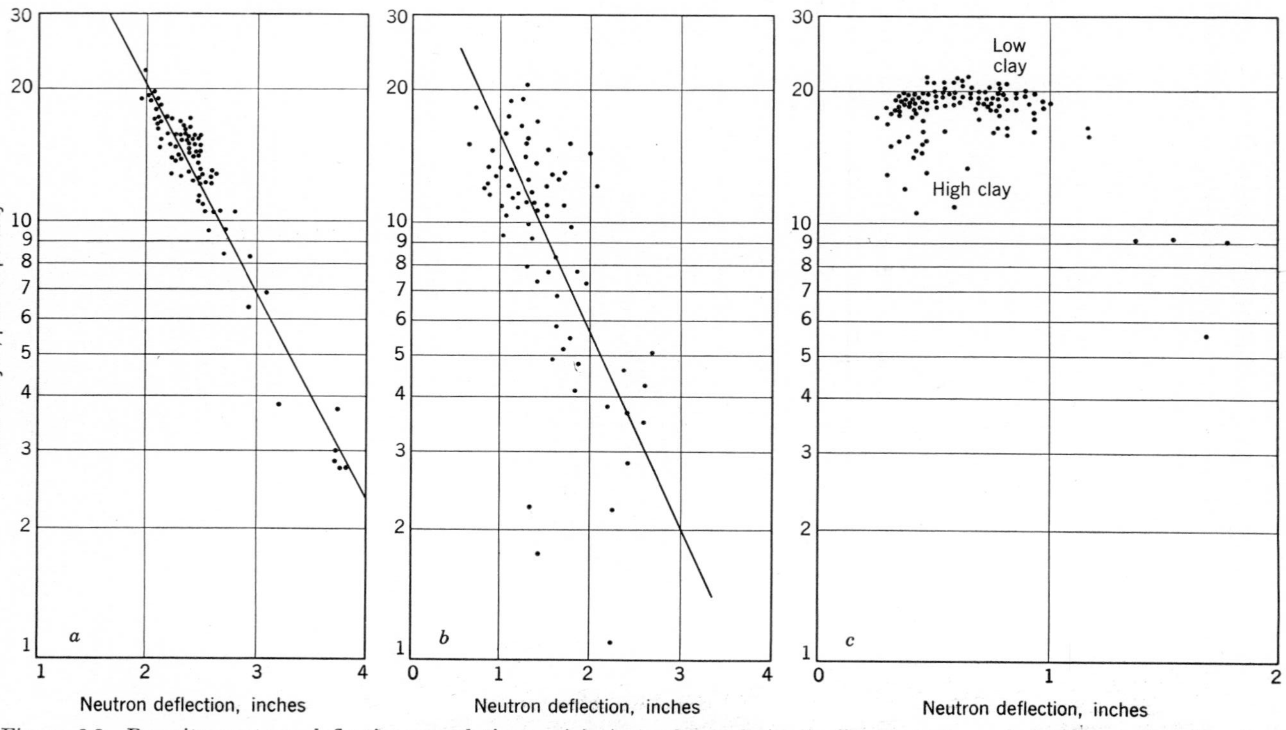

Figure 8.8 Porosity-neutron deflection correlations. (*a*) A good correlation in limestone (open hole); example taken from Bush and Mardock (1951). (*b*) A fair correlation in sandstone (open hole); scatter is due to admixed shale and possibly to hole diameter variations. (*c*) A poor correlation in a sand with high and variable clay content (open hole).

sensitivity in inches. Some companies indicate the counting rate in counts per second or minute on the scale of the log.

A reversal of the neutron deflection shown by older logs in caved portions of the bore hole was due to scattered gamma rays from the radium source. The difficulty was corrected by appropriately shielding the gamma-ray detector against the soft scattered radiation to yield the normal low reading adjacent to caved portions of the hole.

Ability of the neutron log to detect gas depends on the gas composition, its density under formation conditions, the presence of clay or shale, the gas saturation, the degree of invasion of the formation by the mud filtrate, and other factors. The chance of detecting a light gas in a clean sand is good. An outstanding example, not to be regarded as typical, is shown in Figure 8.9.*a*. This record was made in a cased hole. Figure 8.9.*b* is a less clear-cut case. Used with other information, such indications are of some value. An instance in which the neutron log did not detect the gas is shown in Figure 8.9.*c*. Most probable causes for the failure are fluid invasion and high gas density due to relatively large molecular weight and/or high pressures.

8.2.c General considerations

Gamma-ray and neutron logs are normally run with the instrument moving up the hole, so that the cable is under tension to give reliable relative depth indication. Logging speed varies with conditions, but 30 feet per minute may be taken as typical. Simultaneous recording of gamma-ray and neutron curves is now offered by some service companies.

A factor of importance is the time constant of the recording apparatus. A large time constant reduces statistical variation, but makes the response sluggish. A compromise is made, but the same value may not be most desirable for all applications. Most instruments have provisions for varying the time constant to suit conditions.

A check of the statistical fluctuation of the log (see Section 1.9) may be made by holding the tool in a fixed position in the well while running the recording chart at a convenient speed. An example is given in Figure 1.12. It is important that the same time constant be used for this check as in the logging run. Such a check is highly recommended in order to gauge significance of variations and test log performance. It is also useful to have the operator repeat a section of the log to indicate reproducibility and drift. Figure 8.10 is an example of a repeat run.

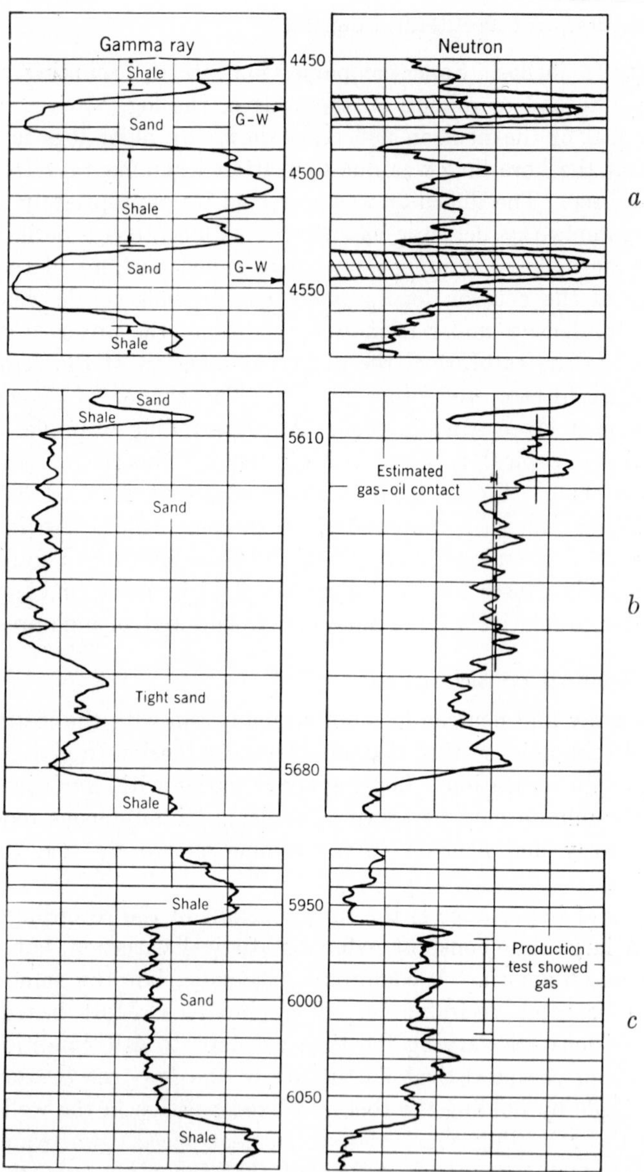

Figure 8.9 Detection of gas by neutron log. (*a*) Excellent example of dry gas in clean sands. High deflection is obtained opposite gas. Gas-water contacts as determined from electrical log are indicated by arrows labeled G-W. Gas-oil contacts under similar conditions show up as well on neutron log.

(*b*) Gas-oil contact, conditions not as favorable as in first example. Homogeneity of sand in region of gas-oil contact is indicated by gamma-ray log.

(*c*) Gas zone not defined by neutron log. Nearby known water sand gave same order of deflection.

Gamma-ray and neutron logs show some promise of supplementing electrical log interpretation (Wyllie, 1952). The gamma-ray curve may be applied to resistivity measurements to correct for interstitial shale or thinly interbedded shale and sand if the zero for the gamma-ray log is known. Where it is unknown, as with all older logs, this application cannot be made. It should be emphasized, however, that more experience is necessary to evaluate the method. The neutron

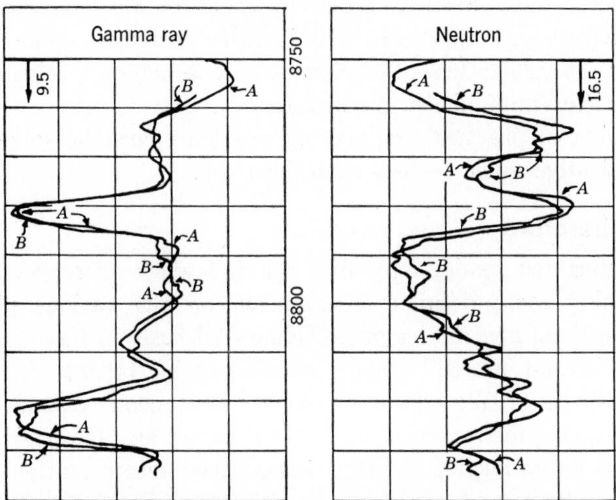

Figure 8.10 Repeat run of gamma-ray and neutron logs. *A* is original run; *B* is repeat run. At first glance it may seem that reproduction was poor, but the differences can be explained by statistics (compare Figure 1.12).

log has been used to derive resistivity formation factors by virtue of the empirical relation between porosity and formation factor and the ability of the neutron log to measure porosity under favorable circumstances.

8.2.d New developments

The potentialities of nuclear logging methods are great. Only two possibilities will be discussed here because they probably will be the first to be realized.

The gamma-gamma log (Faul and Tittle, 1951) is capable of measuring formation density. A strong gamma-ray source irradiates the formation, and scattered gamma rays are measured by a detector. The intensity of scattered gamma rays is a good function of sample density, or, more accurately, of the electron density, which is itself dependent on mass density to a high degree. It appears also that a useful correlation exists between formation density and porosity, the higher porosities corresponding to lower densities. Thus the gamma-gamma log may become a useful means of measuring porosity in the higher ranges. It is not expected to replace the neutron log as a porosity indicator in low-porosity rocks.

A form of the neutron-gamma log, using a scintillation gamma-ray spectrometer (see Section 1.12) to measure the neutron-capture gamma-ray energy spectrum, will identify formation type in many instances, by indicating the presence of characteristic chemical elements (Tittle, unpublished research).

A number of practical engineering problems must be solved before these and other such devices come into use.

8.2.e Literature

The interested reader may find the following references of value in obtaining more detailed information on the various phases of gamma-ray and neutron logging. General discussions have been given by Charrin and Russell (1953), Clewell et al. (1953), and Russell (1952). Swift (1952) has described a simultaneous gamma-ray and neutron logging instrument, and DiGiovanni et al. (1953) give details on a scintillation logging device. Quantitative interpretation has been treated by Bush and Mardock (1950, 1951), Fearon and Mardock (1951), Scotty and Egan (1952), Blanchard and Dewan (1953), and Dewan and Allaud (1953).

Use of gamma-ray and neutron logs for geological correlation has been considered by Morgan (1952). Results of research on basic processes involved in nuclear logging have been presented by Faul and Tittle (1951) and Tittle et al. (1951).

8.3 NUCLEAR LOGGING OF DRILL HOLES FOR MINERAL EXPLORATION AND SOIL STUDIES *

Although neutron and gamma-ray logging has long been used widely in the petroleum industry, the method did not find application in mining until it received the impetus of the postwar interest in uranium. Probably the earliest suggestion for gamma-ray logging of

* By Henry Faul, U. S. Geological Survey, Denver. The work reported here was supported in part by the Division of Raw Materials of the Atomic Energy Commission.

diamond drill holes was made by Rajewsky (1943). A slim-hole gamma-ray logging unit was built at the University of Chicago in 1945 (Faul, 1948), and a program of logging 1½-inch (EX) drill holes in the Colorado uranium region was begun. Other applications were made in South Africa (Guelke et al., 1948, 1949; Simpson, 1953), in Canada, both on the surface and underground (Feldman and Wright,

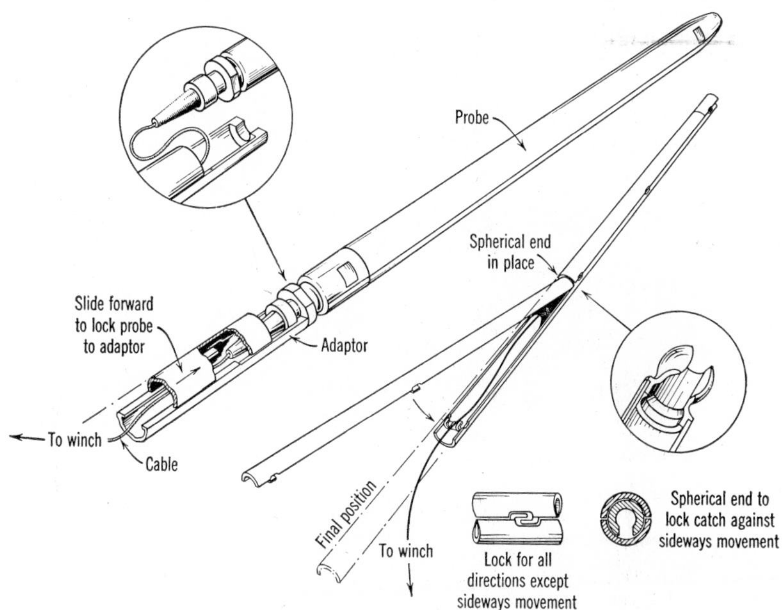

Figure 8.11 System of interlocking push rods for gamma-ray logging of horizontal and inclined drill holes in mines. Courtesy of the Atomic Energy Research Establishment, Harwell; British Crown copyright.

1949; Roberts, 1949), in France (Berbezier et al., 1952), and in Great Britain (Taylor, 1953). A scintillation counter for uranium exploration was described by DiGiovanni et al. (1953).

Holes drilled for mineral exploration are almost always much smaller than oil wells and it is not practical to adapt the highly sensitive ionization chamber apparatus (Scherbatskoy et al., 1947; Swift, 1952) to the small-diameter holes. Therefore, the Geiger-Müller counter is almost universally used. The sensitivity of a simple gamma counter is sufficient for uranium exploration, and its inherent stability makes it possible to develop a calibration for direct assaying of the ore in place. Reserve estimates can be made by using a gamma-ray log calibrated by comparison with artificial drill holes of known ore concentration and geometry. The technique has been applied successfully in the quantitative exploration for uranium, and for uraniferous phosphate and potash. Because of their greater sensitivity, scintilla-

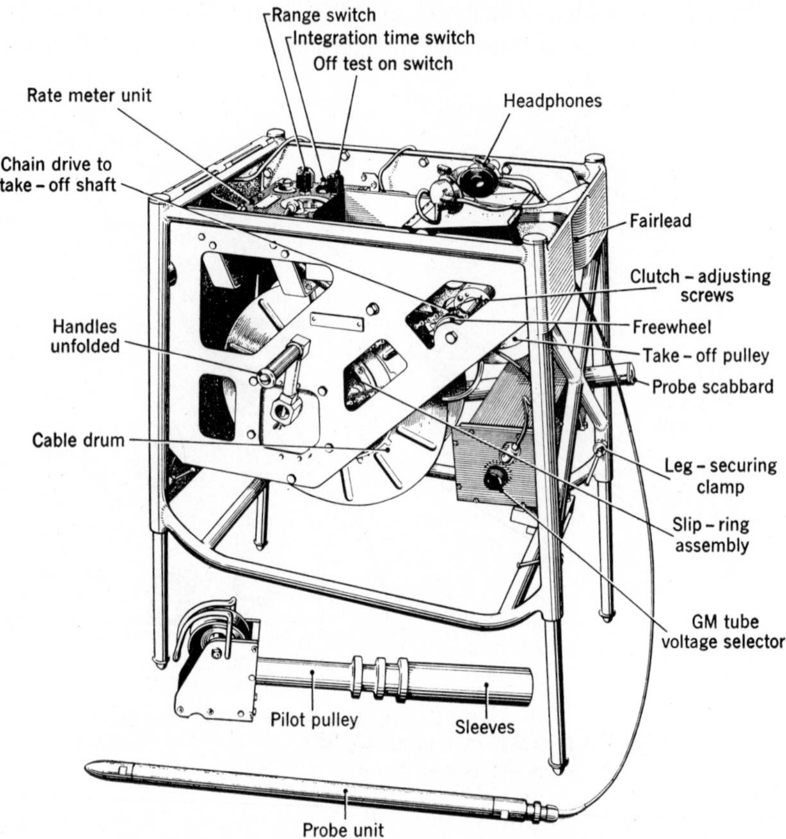

Figure 8.12 Compact portable apparatus for gamma-ray logging of exploratory holes on the surface and underground. Courtesy of the Atomic Energy Research Establishment, Harwell; British Crown copyright.

tion counters are used in applications where holes are large enough, the activity is generally low, and ore-grade material is not expected. Under favorable conditions it is possible to distinguish uranium, thorium, and potassium by scintillation spectrometry in the hole.

Most holes are relatively shallow so that the equipment used for gamma-ray logging in the mineral industry is smaller, lighter, and consequently more readily portable than the oil-well logging apparatus. It is frequenty desirable to log exploratory holes drilled underground, some of which may be horizontal or may even run up hill. In such holes one may use a fairly stiff cable or a series of interlocking push rods (Figure 8.11) to push the probe into the hole.

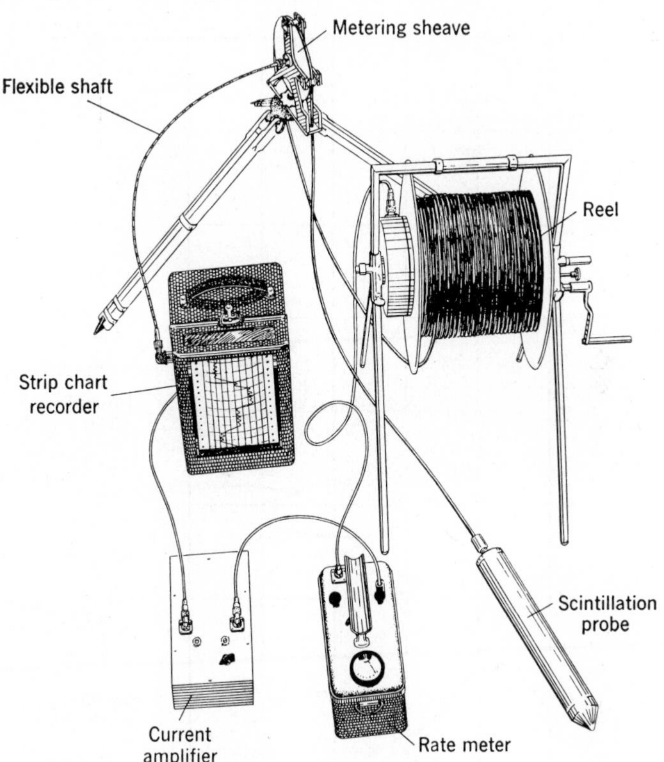

Figure 8.13 Portable scintillation gamma-ray logging equipment of the U. S. Geological Survey. The current amplifier, recorder, and tripod may be left off when the instrument is used in remote locations where transport is a problem. The reel holds 800 feet of type RG 59/U cable.

Some of the holes may be drilled with percussion drills so that the gamma-ray log in conjunction with the drilling-speed log and the color of the cuttings offers the only available information on the rock types traversed. Highly portable equipment may be needed for logging shallow holes in remote locations. Geiger and scintillation instruments of compact design are shown in Figures 8.12 and 8.13. Similar equipment was designed in France (Berbezier and Lallemant, 1952; Lallemant, 1953).

During the course of routine logging of holes drilled in the exploration for carnotite ore bodies on the Colorado Plateau, it was observed (Rogers, 1950, unpublished) that radioactivity anomalies can be found some distance from ore deposits. These anomalies are

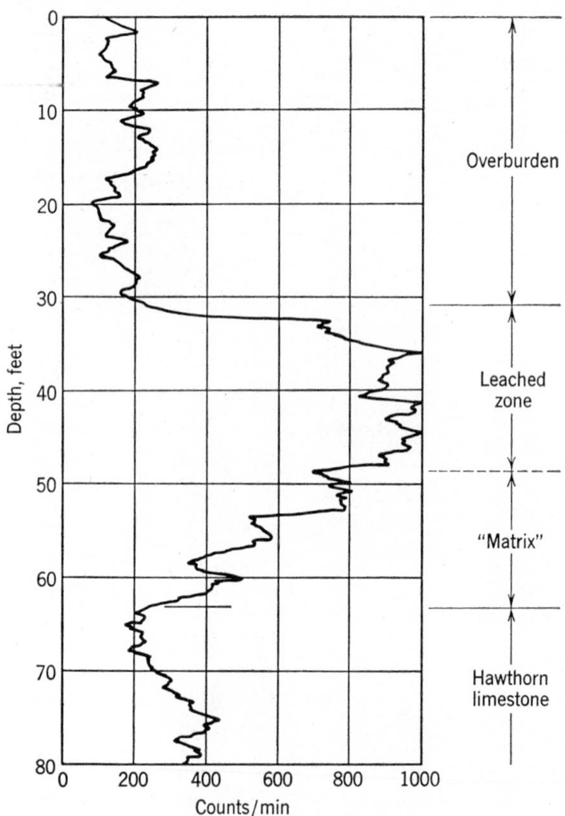

Figure 8.14 Gamma-ray log of an exploratory hole in the Florida land pebble phosphate deposit. The "matrix" is the layer mined. Log made by the U. S. Geological Survey.

apparently caused by radon and radium transported by ground water from the ore deposit and distributed in a pattern determined by the permeability of the rock. A statistical study of such anomalies found in the gamma-ray logs of widely spaced drill holes can be used to outline areas that are favorable for closely spaced drilling (Hinckley, 1952, unpublished).

The scintillation logging apparatus, with its increased sensitivity, offers particular promise for geologic logging of exploratory drill holes where radioactive ore is not expected. Contacts, fissures, and general rock types can be identified from the gamma-ray log, in a manner analogous to the procedure in petroleum exploration. In some operations it is more convenient to identify and assay the rock from a gamma-ray log, rather than by study of drill cuttings or core. As an example, one may cite the Florida phosphate deposits. The phosphatic sediment contains small amounts of uranium (see Section 2.3), and its vertical extent and uranium content are easily determined from a gamma-ray log (Figure 8.14). It is usually very difficult to place the contacts by visual inspection of drill cuttings.

Neutron and gamma-ray logging has been applied in the exploration for potash to distinguish the anhydrous sylvite (KCl) from the hydrated carnallite ($KMgCl_3 \cdot 6H_2O$) which is less desirable as an ore of potash. A neutron and gamma-ray method for estimating the moisture content and density of soils in place was described by Belcher et al. (1953), by Spinks et al. (1951), and by Lane et al. (1953). The limitations encountered in neutron logging and discussed in Section 8.2 apply here as well, except that the measurements can be carried out with greater accuracy, owing to the absence of interfering factors such as well fluid and casing. The nuclear methods of soil-density and moisture-content determination are more accurate and much simpler than previously used standard sampling techniques.

Chapter 9

DETERMINATION OF ABSOLUTE AGE

The fascinating impressiveness of rigorous mathematical analysis, with its atmosphere of precision and elegance, should not blind us to the defects of the premises that condition the whole process.

—T. C. Chamberlin, *Science,* June 30, 1899

The use of radioactive decay as a basis of time determination rests on the premise that a parent element decays at a known constant rate into a daughter element, either directly or in a radioactive chain, and that nothing is added or removed during the process. Furthermore, the rock or mineral, at the time it is formed, must either be free of the ultimate daughter isotope or contain this isotope in a known ratio with other isotopes so that the original content of the decay product can be determined. The physical and mathematical aspects of radioactive decay are discussed briefly in Sections 1.6 and 1.7.

Each of the principal methods that have been found useful for absolute age determination is discussed in a separate section of this chapter, and all the principal methods are briefly summarized below.

The lead methods are based on the series decay of uranium and thorium into lead. The complexity of the process (see Figure 1.2) makes possible a variety of approaches. The oldest of the lead methods, usually called the *lead:uranium method,* has suffered many ups and downs, but has lately regained some of its lost prestige, largely through the work of Larsen and his associates. It is a relatively simple method. In its present form (here called the *lead:alpha method*) it involves only a radiometric analysis for the parent uranium and a spectrochemical analysis of the accumulated lead. The method gives good results with carefully selected minerals (zircon and a few others) that contained very little lead when they were formed. A more refined procedure, usually called the *isotopic lead:uranium* method, involves mass-spectrometric analysis of the lead and can be applied to a wide range of uranium minerals. The isotopic lead: thorium method is analogous, but less useful. A variation of the lead:

uranium technique utilizes lead^{210}, a radioactive lead isotope in the decay series of uranium^{238}, for determination of the age of the mineral, and is called the *lead^{210} method.* Still another technique is based on the difference between the decay rates of the two uranium isotopes, uranium^{235} and uranium^{238} into their ultimate respective daughters, lead^{207} and lead^{206}, and is called the lead^{207}:lead^{206} method or simply the *lead:lead method.*

The *helium method* is based on determination of the content of radiogenic helium in uranium and thorium minerals. Hundreds of age determinations have been made by this procedure, but only few have survived the test of time. The principal difficulty lies in the inhomogeneous distribution of uranium and thorium in most rocks and minerals. The manifold aspects of the method are discussed by Hurley in Section 9.2.

The *strontium:rubidium method* and the *argon:potassium method* are relatively new procedures, both involving direct decay of parent to daughter. Both suffer from analytical complexities, but appear to hold great promise for the future.

Carbon^{14} is produced in the atmosphere by cosmic rays and is radioactive. The *carbon^{14} method* is based on the continued absorption of carbon^{14} by living plants. The radioactivity of the carbon in the plant or in the material derived from it is then a measure of its age, or, more specifically, a measure of the time when the original plant died. The method now is useful up to about 30,000 years.

The *ionium method,* based on the decay of precipitated thorium^{230} (ionium) in Pleistocene and Recent marine sediments, is discussed here briefly. The potential *radiation damage methods,* based on dislocations of atoms or electrons produced by bombardment of crystals with alpha rays, are discussed in Chapter 6. Several other methods have been proposed but not fully tested and are not discussed here. One of the most interesting is a technique based on the known fractionation of sulfur^{32} and sulfur^{34} in marine sulfates and sulfides as a result of the biological sulfur cycle during the past 700 to 800 million years (Thode, Macnamara, and Fleming, 1953).

In the instances where it has been possible to date a rock by more than one method, serious discrepancies between the various results are observed in some cases. For instance, the lead:thorium ages are usually different from the lead:uranium and lead:lead ages of the same rock. The cause of this difference is not fully known.

On the other hand, the fairly consistent agreement among recent results of the lead:alpha method, the isotopic lead:uranium method, and the lead:lead method has tended to strengthen the confidence in these methods. At the present state of the art, the geologic time scale relies heavily on these methods for most of the crucial dates.

The strontium:rubidium method has yielded some very high ages which, in many cases, cannot be confirmed by other methods because suitable mineral associations usually are not found. Where comparison has been possible, the strontium:rubidium age is usually much greater than the isotopic lead:uranium age or the lead:lead age. The new analytical method is sound and appears to be accurate. If the discrepancy were due to the assumption of an erroneous decay scheme for rubidium, one would expect that the difference factor would be constant, but such a tendency is not clear (see Table 9). The problem is being studied intensively in several laboratories, but at the time of writing the strontium:rubidium method is still uncertain.

Most age determinations are made by physicists and chemists who work in the laboratory. They may determine the present state of their sample with great accuracy, but it is clearly up to the geologist to supply the past history of the sample as well as he can piece it together from the study of the rock and its environment. It is essential to examine critically the premises on which age calculations are based. The cooperation between petrologists in the field and chemists and physicists in the laboratory has not been as good as one could wish, and there are many age determinations in the literature which are of doubtful value because adequate geologic control of the samples was lacking. We have attempted to compile the available age determinations in Table 9. The data presented here are selected for their geologic significance, and for their presumed analytical accuracy. The results are arranged roughly in the order of increasing age, but geologically related samples are grouped together even where the results of age determinations by various methods may differ widely.

No attempt has been made here to erect a new geologic time scale. The old argument still holds that stratigraphic time boundaries stem from the study of sediments, but nuclear determinations of absolute time can be made only on igneous rocks, with very few exceptions. The geologic time relationship between sediments and igneous rocks is rough and frequently obscure, even in areas that have been studied geologically in great detail. Most of the geologic time scales that have been published are based on uncritical compilation of a wide variety of data, so that the overall figures are necessarily very rough. From Table 9 the reader will be able to select the best available age for many geological provinces, together with a general impression of the uncertainties involved. The editor believes that any closer interpolation of the data would be premature at the time of writing (April, 1954).

Table 9. Age determinations on various materials, selected for geologic importance, and arranged roughly by locality in order of increasing age

The substance analyzed is shown in parentheses. Actual analyses for the heavy radioactive elements and lead and the isotopic composition of the lead (expressed in percent abundance of leads$^{204, 206, 207, 208}$, respectively), follow the locality and mineral identification of samples dated by the lead methods.

Carbon^{14} Age Determinations *

Stratigraphic Horizon	Locality and Substance	Lab. No. †	Author	Most Probable Age ‡ (years before 1950)
Boreal pine zone (Pollen zone B)	Cranberry Glades, W. Va. (peat)	C336	Li	9,434 ± 840
Like most ecologic zones in glaciated territory, this zone decreases in age in the direction of deglaciation.	Upper Linsley Pond, New Haven Co., Conn. (lake mud)	C39	Li	8,323 ± 400
	Cedar Creek Bog, Anoka Co., Minn. (peat)	C332	Li	7,988 ± 420
	Johnson Camp Bog, St. Louis Co., Minn. (peat)	C334	Li	7,128 ± 300
	Plissey Pond, Aroostook Co., Me. (peat)	C335	Li	5,962 ± 320
Transition from Lake Arkona to Lake Whittlesey	Cleveland, Ohio (wood)	W33	U	13,600 ± 500
Transition from Lake Warren to Lake Lundy	Castalia, Ohio (wood)	C526	U	8,513 ± 500
Alleröd layer (Pollen zone II)	Hawks Tor, Cornwall, England (peat)	C341	Li	9,861 ± 500
	Neasham, Northumberland, England (lake mud)	C444	Li	10,851 ± 630
	Knocknacran, County Monaghan, Eire (lake mud)	C355	Li	11,310 ± 720
	Wallensen im Hils, Hannover, Germany (lake mud)	C337	Li	11,044 ± 500
	—	K107	ALT	11,160 ± 320

* For footnotes and abbreviations see end of table (pages 280 and 281).

Table 9. Age determinations on various materials, selected for geologic importance, and arranged roughly by locality in order of increasing age (*Cont.*)

Stratigraphic Horizon	Locality and Substance	Lab. No. †	Author	Most Probable Age ‡ (years before 1950)
Position in layer				
(At top)	Ruds-Vedby, Denmark (wood)	K101	ALT	10,890 ± 240
(At top)	—(peaty mud)	K102	ALT	10,500 ± 400
(At top)	—(calcar. mud)	K103	ALT	11,060 ± 480
(Near top)	—(lake marl)	K113	ALT	10,930 ± 380
(Above middle)	—(calcar. mud)	K105	ALT	11,800 ± 410
(Below middle)	—(lake marl)	K106	ALT	11,880 ± 340
(At top)	Lake Bölling, Denmark (lake mud)	K110	ALT	10,770 ± 300
(Undetermined)	—(lake mud)	K112	ALT	11,700 ± 360
Two Creeks peat layer	Two Creeks, Wis. (wood)	C308	Li	10,877 ± 740
	—(wood)	C365	Li	11,437 ± 770
	—(peat)	C366	Li	11,097 ± 600
	—(wood)	C536	Li	12,168 ± 1500
	—(peat)	C537	Li	11,442 ± 640
	—(wood)	Y141	BDG	9,929 ± 406
	—(wood)	W42	U	11,250 ± 200
Lake Agassiz sediments	Moorhead, Minn. (wood)	C497	Li	11,283 ± 700
Lake Oshkosh sediments (10 ft below stratig. top)	Kimberly, Wis. (wood)	C630	U	10,676 ± 750
Lake Oshkosh sediments (14 ft below stratig. top)	Appleton, Wis. (wood)	C800	U	10,856 ± 410
Lagoon bay in ancestral lake in L. Michigan basin	Dyer, Ind. (wood)	C801	U	10,972 ± 350
Mankato outwash sediments	Bonfils, Mo. (wood)	C385	Li	12,148 ± 700
Peat horizon separating surface till from underlying till	St. Pierre les Becquets, Nicolet Co., Que. (wood)	L190A	U	11,050 ± 400

Table 9. Age determinations on various materials, selected for geologic importance, and arranged roughly by locality in order of increasing age (*Cont.*)

Age Determinations by Methods Other Than Carbon[14]

Locality and Mineral §, ‖	Author ‖ and No.	Method	Age (years × 10^6)
Potash deposits, Buggingen, Baden, Germany, and Alsace, France (lower Oligocene) (sylvite)	GGP	A^{40}/K^{40}	25^{+5}_{-3}
Potosi volcanic series, San Juan Mts., Colo. (zir) (730α, 8 ppm Pb)	LKH	Pb/α	26
Wasatch Mts., Utah (zir)			
Little Cottonwood (490α, 9 ppm Pb)	LG, Z23		47
Clayton cone (9125α, 180 ppm Pb)	LG, Z24		45
Alta stock (502α, 11 ppm Pb)	LG, Z25		52
Philipsburg batholith, Montana, qtz. monzonite (zir) (858α, 18 ppm Pb)	CGW, 53C198	Pb/α	50
Boulder batholith, Jefferson County, Montana		Pb/α	
alaskite, Elkhorn Peak (zir) (4990α, 127 ppm Pb)	CGW, 52C8		61
—(monazite) (6545α, 231 ppm Pb)			72
qtz. monzonite, 7 mi. SE of Helena (zir) (160α, 4.6 ppm Pb)	CGW, 52C10a		69
qtz. monzonite, Boulder (zir) (227α, 8 ppm Pb)	CGW, 52C45		69
qtz. monzonite, 3 mi. NE of Elk Park (zir) (203α, 6 ppm Pb)	CGW, 52C60		71

Table 9. Age determinations on various materials, selected for geologic importance, and arranged roughly by locality in order of increasing age (Cont.)

Locality and Mineral §, ‖	Author ‖ and No.	Method	Age (years × 10^6)
Mines in the Colorado Front Range (ur)		Pb^{206}/U^{238}	
Wood, Gilpin County (72.3% U, 0.11% Th, 1.063% Pb; 0.64, 63.13, 12.2, 24.0)	Nier, 24		57
—(62.13% U, 0.78% Pb; 0.426, 73.58, 9.30, 15.17)	SS-Ph		60 ± 6
Iron, Gilpin County (66.08% U, 0.89% Pb; 0.458, 72.37, 10.26, 16.91)	SS-Ph		70 ± 7
Copper King, Larimer County (18.24% U, 0.187% Pb; 0.053, 92.19, 5.59, 2.17)	Ph, 324		68 ± 7
—(29.71% U, 0.23% Pb; 0.022, 94.34, 4.98, 0.66)	Ph, 445-1		55 ± 6
Gilpin County (38.28% U, 0.053% Th, 0.643% Pb; 0.698, 59.64, 13.12, 26.54)	Nier, 25		59
German	KBE, K-8	Pb^{210}	58 ± 3
Rickards	KBE, K-6	Pb^{210}	61 ± 3
Uranium mines in the Morrison formation (Late Jurassic), Colorado Plateau		Pb^{206}/U^{238}	
Grey Dawn (ur) (64.15% U, 0.77% Pb; 0.332, 79.11, 8.57, 11.99)	SS, 73		65 ± 6
Corvusite (ur + nm) (31.05% U, 0.37% Pb; 0.251, 81.38, 8.51, 9.86)	SS, 189		70 ± 7
Matchless (nm) (28.28% U, 0.377% Pb; 0.195, 84.11, 7.81, 7.89)	SS, 187		80 ± 8
LaSal No. 2 (nm) (7.27% U, 0.0965% Pb; 0.385, 74.68, 10.13, 14.80)	SS, 178		70 ± 7
—(24.95% U, 0.544% Pb; 0.665, 61.11, 13.01, 25.21)	SS, 108		80 ± 8
—(10.2% U, 0.14% Pb; 0.086, 90.79, 6.28, 2.84)	SS, 65		90 ± 9
Black Mama (nm) (16.9% U, 0.214% Pb; 0.024, 93.44, 5.87, 0.66)	SS, 120		90 ± 9

Table 9. Age determinations on various materials, selected for geologic importance, and arranged roughly by locality in order of increasing age (*Cont.*)

Locality and Mineral §·‖	Author ‖ and No.	Method	Age (years × 10^6)
Uranium mines in the Shinarump conglomerate (Late Triassic), Colorado Plateau (ur)		Pb^{206}/U^{238}	
Happy Jack (29.16% U, 0.33% Pb; 0.102, 90.16, 6.03, 3.71)	SS, 143		42 ± 4
—(73.46% U, 0.74% Pb; 0.154, 88.14, 6.43, 5.27)	SS, 64		65 ± 6
Cato Sells (60.14% U, 0.55% Pb; 0.093, 90.88, 5.82, 3.21)	SS, 72		60 ± 6
Shinarump No. 1 (55.9% U, 1.43% Pb; 0.839, 53.54, 14.74, 30.88)	SS, 63		75 ± 7
Camp Bird (9.39% U, 0.114% Pb; 0.200, 84.71, 7.68, 7.41)	SS, 182		80 ± 8
Monument No. 2 (57.26% U, 0.75% Pb; 0.368, 76.85, 9.28, 13.51)	SS, 71		70 ± 7
—(65.30% U, 0.925% Pb; 0.241, 83.02, 7.70, 9.04)	SS, 190		85 ± 8
—(70.05% U, 1.17% Pb; 0.255, 82.78, 7.82, 9.14)	SS, 79		100 ± 10
Southern California batholith (zir except where stated otherwise)		Pb/α	
(752α, 30 ppm Pb)	LKH		100
Mt. Wilson, qtz diorite (143α, 7 ppm Pb)	LG, G33		112
Mountain Center, qtz diorite (194α, 9 ppm Pb)	LG, G3		111
Palm Springs, qtz diorite (317α, 14 ppm Pb)	LG, G30		108
La Posta, qtz diorite (594α, 28 ppm Pb)	LG, G13		113
Aguanga, qtz diorite (280α, 10 ppm Pb)	LG, G10		86
Lakeview, qtz diorite (183α, 10 ppm Pb)	LG, S1		130
Green Valley, qtz diorite (160α, 5 ppm Pb)	LG, G11		75
Stonewall, qtz diorite (545α, 21 ppm Pb)	LG, G48		91

Table 9. Age determinations on various materials, selected for geologic importance, and arranged roughly by locality in order of increasing age (*Cont.*)

Locality and Mineral §, ‖	Author ‖ and No.	Method	Age (years × 10^6)
S. Calif. batholith (*Cont.*)			
Lakeview, qtz diorite (646α, 30 ppm Pb)	LG, Z7	Pb/α	115
Woodson, granodiorite (1235α, 50 ppm Pb)	LG, Z16		97
—(786α, 29 ppm Pb)	LG, Z20		89
—(1180α, 46 ppm Pb)	LG, S10		92
—(457α, 22 ppm Pb)	LG, G32A		116
—(433α, 22 ppm Pb)	LG, S2		122
—(xenotime) (6400α, 260 ppm Pb)	LG, X16		105
—(monazite) (5146α, 350 ppm Pb)	LG, Q16		136
—(5339, 360 ppm Pb)	LG, S6		132
Mt. Hole, granodiorite (1204α, 46 ppm Pb)	LG, Z17		92
N. Providence Mts., qtz monzonite (610α, 23 ppm Pb)	LG, G21		91
Soda Lake Mts., qtz monzonite (4660α, 160 ppm Pb)	LG, G24M		82
Roubidoux, granite (2700α, 103 ppm Pb)	LG, Z15		90
Cottonwood Springs, granite (190α, 10 ppm Pb)	LG, G15		126
Berdoo Canyon, granite (385α, 20 ppm Pb)	LG, G28		124
Rattlesnake, granite (1743α, 80 ppm Pb)	LG, X101		119
Sierra Nevada, Bishop, Calif.			
albite granite (zir) (618α, 26 ppm Pb)	LG, PB1		101
Pine Creek, qtz monzonite (zir) (796α, 37 ppm Pb)	LG, PB2		111
Lamark, qtz monzonite (zir) (400α, 15 ppm Pb)	LG, PB3A		90
—(zir and thorite) (5070α, 220 ppm Pb)	LG, PB3B		104
Basin Mtn., qtz monzonite (zir) (792α, 35 ppm Pb)	LG, PB4		106
Palisade, granodiorite (zir) (221α, 10 ppm Pb)	LG, PB7		109

Table 9. Age determinations on various materials, selected for geologic importance, and arranged roughly by locality in order of increasing age (*Cont.*)

Locality and Mineral §·‖	Author ‖ and No.	Method	Age (years × 10^6)
Idaho batholith		Pb/α	
qtz monzonite, Lost Horse Creek, Bitterroot Mts., Montana (zir) (275α, 6.2 ppm Pb)	CGW, 53C210		54
—(monazite) (3123α, 79 ppm Pb)			51
porphyritic qtz diorite, above Yankee Fork, Custer County, Idaho (zir) (825α, 30 ppm Pb)	LG, L113A		88
—(zir and thorite) (2200α, 100 ppm Pb)	LG, L113B		100
qtz diorite, Lowman, Boise County, Idaho (zir) (370α, 16 ppm Pb)	LG, L81		104
granodiorite, mouth of Vaughn Creek, Atlanta, Elmore County, Idaho (zir) (700α, 38 ppm Pb)	LG, L288		130
monzonite, Gem stocks, Wallace, Idaho (zir) (292α, 11 ppm Pb)	LG, ZHCD63		90
—(zir and thorite) (1739α, 100 ppm Pb)	LG, ZHCD62		115
Sunshine mine, Kellogg, Idaho (ur) (22.81% U, 3.7% Pb, 0.540, 69.20, 12.42, 17.84, and using a lead similar to N10, Table 9.1, for original lead correction)	KK	Pb^{206}/U^{238} Pb^{207}/U^{235} Pb^{207}/Pb^{206}	710 ± 10 750 ± 10 850 ± 50
Pala, Calif. (lep)	DA A	Sr/Rb(id) Sr/Rb	147 75–160
Crouzille vein, St. Sylvestre, Limoges, France (pit) (56.5% U, 0.06% Th, 1.20% Pb; 0.0553, 92.90, 5.26, 1.78)	De	Pb^{206}/U^{238} Pb^{207}/U^{235} Pb^{207}/Pb^{206}	146 147 157
Schmiedeberg, Erzgebirge, Germany (sooty pit) (0.475, 71.04, 10.5, 18.0)	E	Pb^{207}/Pb^{206}	210 ± 50

Table 9. Age determinations on various materials, selected for geologic importance, and arranged roughly by locality in order of increasing age (*Cont.*)

Locality and Mineral §, ‖	Author ‖ and No.	Method	Age (years × 10^6)
Jáchymov (St. Joachimsthal), Czechoslovakia (pit)			
(60.24% U, 3.22% Pb; 0.585, 66.17, 11.74, 21.5, using N24, Table 9.1, for the original lead correction)	Nier, 1	Pb^{206}/U^{238}	220
		Pb^{207}/Pb^{206}	145
—	KBE, K-15	Pb^{210}	206 ± 10
—	Ho	Pb^{210}	375
Maine pegmatites (lep)	A	Sr/Rb	
Topsham			210
Mt. Mica			250
Norway			290
Newry			310
Buckfield			310
White Mountain Magma Series, Conway granite, N. H. (zir)			
Redstone, four splits	LG, 16BNH8	Pb/α	
—(1010α, 85 ppm Pb)			201
—(1417α, 150 ppm Pb)			255
—(1050α, 105 ppm Pb)			240
—(836α, 86 ppm Pb)			247
Mt. Chocorua, three splits	LG, 33BNH17		
—(843α, 80 ppm Pb)			227
—(723α, 68 ppm Pb)			225
—(470α, 50 ppm Pb)			255
Devil Slide, Stark, amphib. syenite (465α, 44 ppm Pb)	LG, BNH20		227
Connecticut pegmatites			
Strickland quarry, Collins Hill, Portland	WH		
(microcline) (A^{40}/K^{40} = 0.0128 ± 0.0006)		A^{40}/K^{40}	{196 274
—(ur) (79.12% U, 2.98% Th, 3.07% Pb; 0.013, 93.54, 4.95, 1.50)		Pb^{206}/U^{238}	268
		Pb^{207}/U^{235}	266
		Pb^{208}/Th^{232}	239
		Pb^{207}/Pb^{206}	328
Spinelli quarry, Glastonbury (samarskite) (6.91% U, 3.05% Th, 0.311% Pb; 0.129, 77.48, 5.89, 16.5)	R-Nier, 23	Pb^{206}/U^{238}	253
		Pb^{207}/U^{235}	255
		Pb^{208}/Th^{232}	266
		Pb^{207}/Pb^{206}	280
Haddam quarry (lep)	A	Sr/Rb	280

Table 9. Age determinations on various materials, selected for geologic importance, and arranged roughly by locality in order of increasing age (*Cont.*)

Locality and Mineral §, ‖	Author ‖ and No.	Method	Age (years × 10^6)
Bedford pegmatite, Westchester County, N. Y. (cyrtolite) (7.29% U, 0.374% Pb; 0.085, 89.87, 6.19, 3.86)	R-Nier, 12	Pb^{206}/U^{238} Pb^{207}/U^{235} Pb^{207}/Pb^{206}	334 347 420
—(6.73% U, 0.351% Pb; 0.0409, 92.31, 5.60, 2.05)	R-Nier, 11	Pb^{206}/U^{238} Pb^{207}/U^{235} Pb^{207}/Pb^{206}	352 358 385
New Hampshire Magma Series		Pb/α	
Bethlehem gneiss (zir) (242α, 30 ppm Pb)	Ly, S4521		298
—(246α, 28 ppm Pb)	Ly, R8521		312
—(monazite) (2840α, 470 ppm Pb)	Ly, S4529		331
—(xenotime) (4053α, 530 ppm Pb)	Ly, S4528		327
Concord granite (monazite) (2706α, 45 ppm Pb)	Ly, C4521		333
pegmatite in Concord granite (zir) (5173α, 700 ppm Pb)	Ly, C552E1		327
Oliverian Magma Series, N. H. (zir)		Pb/α	
Oliverian granite, Mt. Wash. quad. (498α, 61 ppm Pb)	Ly, MW4521		318
Lebanon granite, Hanover quad. (217α, 27 ppm Pb)	Ly, H6521		321
aplite cutting Lebanon granite, Hanover quad. (980α, 130 ppm Pb)	Ly, H2521		328
Highlandcroft Magma Series, Hanover quad., N. H. (zir)			
sodaclase tonalite gneiss (882α, 156 ppm Pb)	Ly, H5521	Pb/α	424
Ruggles mine, N. H. (ur) (0.09, 89.63, 6.37, 3.99)	CFR, 81	Pb^{207}/Pb^{206}	455 ± 160
Mt. Monadnock, N. H., Littleton schist (biotite)	TD	Sr/Rb(id)	570
Mitchell County, N. C. (ur) (0.007, 94.48, 5.14, 0.40)	CFR, 82	Pb^{207}/Pb^{206}	355 ± 40

Table 9. Age determinations on various materials, selected for geologic importance, and arranged roughly by locality in order of increasing age (*Cont.*)

Locality and Mineral §‚ ‖	Author ‖ and No.	Method	Age (years × 10^6)
Wiseman mine, Spruce Pine, N. C. (samarskite)	KBE, K-4	Pb^{210}	325 ± 15
Statesville, N. C. (zir) (400α, 49 ppm Pb)	LKH, Z5	Pb/α	306
—(239α, 33 ppm Pb)	LKH, Z12		345
Sierra Albarrana, Cordova, Spain (pit) (0.13, 87.99, 6.51, 5.37)	CFR, 97	Pb^{207}/Pb^{206}	360 ± 150
Mansfeld, Germany (pit) (0.483, 70.2, 10.84, 18.48)	E	Pb^{207}/Pb^{206}	395 ± 35
Southern Appalachian Mts., Toluca, Shelby Co., Ala.		Pb/α	
qtz monzonite (zir) (450α, 83 ppm Pb)	LG, 490T11		442
pegmatite (zir) (456α, 81 ppm Pb)	LG, 490T16		426
pegmatite (monazite) (5526α, 1050 ppm Pb)	LG, 490T16		399
—(5311α, 1000 ppm Pb)	LG, 490T14		395
Güllhögen, Sweden (kolm) (0.462% U, 0.026% Pb; 0.048, 91.40, 6.72, 1.83)	Nier, 21	Pb^{206}/U^{238} Pb^{207}/Pb^{206}	388 770
—(same data, assuming Rn loss)	W	Pb/U	442
Madagascar pegmatites			
Soafia (thorianite) (13.83% U, 69.44% Th, 2.53% Pb; 0.0026, 37.79, 2.113, 60.09)	HB, 2	Pb^{206}/U^{238} Pb^{208}/Th^{232} Pb^{207}/Pb^{206}	380 480 450
Betroka (thorianite) (5.56% U, 77.44% Th, 2.11% Pb; 0.0092, 18.46, 1.05, 80.49)	HB, 3	Pb^{206}/U^{238} Pb^{208}/Th^{232} Pb^{207}/Pb^{206}	510 480 480
Bemasoandro, Malakialina (ur) (71.0% U, 1.93% Th, 4.09% Pb; 0.0009, 93.72, 5.31, 0.965)	HB, 5	Pb^{206}/U^{238} Pb^{208}/Th^{232} Pb^{207}/Pb^{206}	400 450 480
Sahatany (lep)	NAD	Sr/Rb(id)	690
Ceylon, India (thorianite) (11.8% U, 68.9% Th, 2.34% Pb; 0.004, 36.3, 2.11, 61.56)	Nier, 16	Pb^{206}/U^{238} Pb^{208}/Th^{232} Pb^{207}/Pb^{206}	531 461 485
—(21 crystals of gem zir, av.)	LG	Pb/α	574 ± 32

Table 9. Age determinations on various materials, selected for geologic importance, and arranged roughly by locality in order of increasing age (*Cont.*)

Locality and Mineral §, ‖	Author ‖ and No.	Method	Age (years × 10^6)
Isabella, Hottah Lake, Canada (pit) (0.01, 93.85, 5.63, 0.53)	CFR, 8	Pb^{207}/Pb^{206}	580 ± 60
Alto Lingonha, Mozambique (lep)	NAD	Sr/Rb(id)	570
Nyasaland (zir)		Pb/α	
pegmatite (185α, 47 ppm Pb)	LG, T1		609
—(375α, 85 ppm Pb)	LG, T2		545
nepheline syenite, four splits			
—(489α, 105 ppm Pb)	LG, 62117A		515
—(358α, 85 ppm Pb)	B		569
—(380α, 86 ppm Pb)	C		543
—(344α, 75 ppm Pb)	D		523
Capetown granite, S. Africa (zir) (0.106% U, 177 ppm Th, 59 ppm Pb^{206}; 0.28, 77.4, 8.62, 13.7)	Car	Pb^{206}/U^{238}	347
		Pb^{208}/Th^{232}	278
		Pb^{207}/Pb^{206}	550
Karibib-Usakos II, S.W. Africa (lep)	NAD	Sr/Rb(id)	600
	A	Sr/Rb	750
Albrecht's Höhe, Karibib, S.W. Africa (lep)	A	Sr/Rb	900
Uluguru Range, E. Africa (pit) (<0.003, 94.15, 5.70, 0.14)	E	Pb^{207}/Pb^{206}	620 ± 7
Dogon Daji, Nigeria (lep)	NAD	Sr/Rb(id)	625
Shinkolobwe, Katanga, Belgian Congo			
(pit) (74.9% U, 6.7% Pb; —, 94.25, 5.70, 0.042)	Nier, 2	Pb^{206}/U^{238}	616
		Pb^{207}/Pb^{206}	610
—(—, 94.22, 5.69, 0.087)	Nier, 4	Pb^{207}/Pb^{206}	610
—(—, 94.20, 5.73, 0.073)	Nier, 6	Pb^{206}/U^{238}	582
		Pb^{207}/Pb^{206}	625
("yellow component") (58.5% U, 8.4% Pb; <0.02, 93.65, 5.87, 0.48)	Nier, 3	Pb^{206}/U^{238}	973
		Pb^{207}/Pb^{206}	635
—(—, 91.70, 6.38, 1.92)	Nier, 5	Pb^{207}/Pb^{206}	655
—(68.5% U, 6.74% Pb; 0.006, 93.9, 5.85, 0.232)	Nier, 7	Pb^{206}/U^{238}	676
		Pb^{207}/Pb^{206}	655
(curite) (65.3% U, 9.7% Pb; —, 94.07, 5.76, 0.172)	Nier, 8	Pb^{206}/U^{238}	995
		Pb^{207}/Pb^{206}	625
(pit) (0.024, 94.09, 5.79, 0.11)	CFR, 86		655 ± 20

Table 9. Age determinations on various materials, selected for geologic importance, and arranged roughly by locality in order of increasing age (*Cont.*)

Locality and Mineral §, ‖	Author ‖ and No.	Method	Age (years × 10^6)
Shinkolobwe (pit) (*Cont.*)			
—(0.054, 92.96, 6.02, 0.97)	CFR, 87	Pb^{207}/Pb^{206}	637 ± 20
—(0.015, 93.94, 5.79, 0.25)	CFR, 88		637 ± 20
—(—, 94.21, 5.66, 0.13)	CFR, 83		612 ± 15
—(0.02, 93.68, 5.82, 0.51)	CFR, 85		615 ± 20
—(—, 94.08, 5.78, 0.14)	E		640 ± 30
—(—, 94.11, 5.75, 0.14)			630 ± 10
—(—, 94.07, 5.77, 0.16)			633 ± 15
—	KBE, K-9	Pb^{210}	650 ± 15
—	BHIP	Pb^{210}	614 ± 18
Kalongwe, Katanga, Belgian Congo (pit) (0.035, 93.90, 5.76, 0.32)	CFR, 84	Pb^{207}/Pb^{206}	615 ± 20
Telemark, Norway			
Brevik (thorite) (0.45% U, 30.10% Th, 0.35% Pb; 0.58, 5.23, 1.12, 94.51)	Nier, 20	Pb^{206}/U^{238} Pb^{207}/Pb^{206}	243 355
Tvedestrand (thorite) (0.008, 55.48, 3.45, 41.05)	E	Pb^{207}/Pb^{206}	610 ± 50
Auselmyren, Holt, Aust-Agder (cleveite) (67.18% U, 2.76% Th, 11.19% Pb; 0.0005, 92.08, 6.95, 0.97)	Nier, 18	Pb^{206}/U^{238} Pb^{208}/Th^{232} Pb^{207}/Pb^{206}	1085 840 1090
Quanah Mtn., Wichita Mts., Okla. (zir)	LWB		
(average of 13 samples)		Pb/α	635 ± 30
(average of 6 samples)		Pb/U + Th	644 ± 74
Post-Delhi pegmatite, Bisundani, Ajmer-Merwara, Rajputana, India (ur) (72.9% U, 1.4% Th, 7.95% Pb; <0.001, 93.29, 5.96, 0.752)	HLN	Pb^{206}/U^{238} Pb^{207}/U^{235} Pb^{208}/Th^{232} Pb^{207}/Pb^{206}	733 733 935 740
Llano Uplift, Texas, granites (zir)		Pb/α	
Town Mtn. (340α, 116 ppm Pb)	HJG, TM1		818
—(494α, 180 ppm Pb)	HJG, TM1		874
—(404α, 150 ppm Pb)	HJG, TM2		891
Oatman (552α, 205 ppm Pb)	HJG, 0T		891
—(535α, 210 ppm Pb)			942
Sixmile (629α, 230 ppm Pb)	HJG, SM		877

Table 9. Age determinations on various materials, selected for geologic importance, and arranged roughly by locality in order of increasing age (*Cont.*)

Locality and Mineral § ‖	Author ‖ and No.	Method	Age (years × 10^6)
Bagdad, Arizona, pegmatite	Car		
—(zir) (0.297% U, 272 ppm Pb^{206}; 0.19, 79.15, 8.83, 11.83)		Pb^{206}/U^{238}	630 ± 50
		Pb^{207}/U^{235}	750 ± 50
		Pb^{207}/Pb^{206}	1120 ± 70
—(muscovite)		Sr/Rb(id)	1650 ± 200
—(lep)		Sr/Rb(id)	1900 ± 200
Uncompahgre granite, Mesa County, Colo.	Car		
(apatite) (12.4 ppm U, 130 ppm Th, 3.14 ppm Pb^{206}; 0.893, 36.67, 15.87, 46.57)		Pb^{206}/U^{238}	1050
		Pb^{207}/Pb^{206}	1810 ± 160
		Pb^{208}/Th^{232}	200
—(biotite) (0.356, 39.77, 8.79, 51.09)		Pb^{207}/Pb^{206}	1700
		Sr/Rb(id)	1650 ± 200
Brown Derby mine, Ohio City, Gunnison County, Colo. (zir) (0.104% U, 151 ppm Pb^{206}; 0.422, 69.86, 12.14, 17.58)	Car	Pb^{206}/U^{238}	935 ± 150
		Pb^{207}/U^{235}	1100 ± 50
		Pb^{207}/Pb^{206}	1425 ± 110
—(lep)	Car	Sr/Rb(id)	1800 ± 200
	A	Sr/Rb	950
San Gabriel anorthosite, Calif. (zir) (18α, 7 ppm Pb)	LG	Pb/α	930
—(50α, 17 ppm Pb)			810
Bihar (Satpura) pegmatite, Singar, Gaya district, India (ur) (64.3% U, 8.12% Th, 8.92% Pb; <0.005, 89.38, 6.44, 4.18)	HLN	Pb^{206}/U^{238}	883
		Pb^{207}/U^{235}	912
		Pb^{208}/Th^{232}	1003
		Pb^{207}/Pb^{206}	995
Morogoro, Tanganyika (ur) (70.45% U, 0.2% Th, 8.30% Pb; 0.001, 94.20, 5.63, 0.17)	Nier, 17	Pb^{206}/U^{238}	803
		Pb^{207}/Pb^{206}	595
Okongava Ost 72, S.W. Africa (lep)	A	Sr/Rb	800
Warmbad, S.W. Africa (lep)	A	Sr/Rb	1000
Jakkalswater, Namaqualand (lep)	NAD	Sr/Rb(id)	1100
Post-Kheis pegmatite, Gordonia, Cape Prov., S. Africa (ur) (58.2% U, 8.06% Th, 9.40% Pb; —, 88.68, 6.52, 4.81)	HLN	Pb^{206}/U^{238}	1010
		Pb^{207}/U^{235}	1015
		Pb^{208}/Th^{232}	1215
		Pb^{207}/Pb^{206}	1037

Table 9. Age determinations on various materials, selected for geologic importance, and arranged roughly by locality in order of increasing age (*Cont.*)

Locality and Mineral §, ‖	Author ‖ and No.	Method	Age (years × 10^6)
Mt. Isa mine, Queensland, Australia (monazite) (0.0% U, 5.73% Th, 0.285% Pb; 0.038, 5.45, 0.96, 93.59)	Nier, 27	Pb^{208}/Th^{232} Pb^{207}/Pb^{206}	1000 1190 ± 400
Omaruru, S.W. Africa (lep)	A	Sr/Rb	1200
Kinderzitt, Namaqualand (lep)	NAD	Sr/Rb(id)	1210
Muika, Belgian Congo (lep)	NAD	Sr/Rb(id)	1220
Canadian Shield rocks (Most of the localities are described by Lang, 1952)			
Bessner mine, Henvey Twp., Ontario (ur) (52.76% U, 5.57% Pb; 0.021, 91.86, 6.71, 1.44)	RSFM (see Section 9.5.c)	Pb^{206}/U^{238} Pb^{207}/U^{235} Pb^{207}/Pb^{206}	690 760 940
—(67.6% U, 1.57% Th, 7.69% Pb; 0.0068, 92.76, 6.24, 0.99)	Nier, 13	Pb^{206}/U^{238} Pb^{208}/Th^{232} Pb^{207}/Pb^{206}	765 787 825
—(microcline) (A^{40}/K^{40} = 0.0537±0.003)	WH	A^{40}/K^{40}	{712 {950
Contact Lake, N.W.T. (pit)	KBE	Pb^{210}	864 ± 35
Renfrew, Ont. (zir) (84α, 30 ppm Pb)	LKH, 1	Pb/α	900
Lac Pied des Monts, Murray Bay, Québec (cleveite) (49.25% U, 6.67% Pb; 0.043, 91.27, 6.94, 1.75)	Nier, 19	Pb^{206}/U^{238} Pb^{207}/Pb^{206}	882 905
Sault Ste. Marie, Ont. (pit)			
Theano Point (0.096, 87.63, 8.18, 4.13)	CFR, 70	Pb^{207}/Pb^{206}	1190 ± 40
—(0.18, 84.40, 8.99, 6.49)	CFR, 69		1190 ± 120
—(0.052, 91.83, 5.74, 2.13)	CFR, 71		400 ± 130
Ranwick (0.10, 87.08, 8.30, 4.53)	CFR, 72		1180 ± 60
Labine-McCarthy (0.19, 82.52, 9.01, 8.31)	CFR, 73		1130 ± 70
Camray (0.20, 84.42, 8.72, 6.65)	CFR, 74	Pb^{207}/Pb^{206}	1000 ± 150
Blackstone Lake pit, Conger Township, Parry Sound, Ont. (ur) (69% U, 2.95% Th, 10.8% Pb; 0.0057, 91.81, 6.79, 1.40)	Nier, 22	Pb^{206}/U^{238} Pb^{208}/Th^{232} Pb^{207}/Pb^{206}	1003 945 1030

Table 9. Age determinations on various materials, selected for geologic importance, and arranged roughly by locality in order of increasing age (*Cont.*)

Locality and Mineral §, ‖	Author ‖ and No.	Method	Age (years × 10^6)
Canadian Shield (*Cont.*)			
Blackstone Lake pit (*Cont.*)			
—(69.3% U, 2.99% Th, 10.72% Pb; 0.007, 91.96, 6.66, 1.38)	WH	Pb^{206}/U^{238}	993
		Pb^{207}/U^{235}	995
		Pb^{208}/Th^{232}	895
		Pb^{207}/Pb^{206}	1000
—(microcline) (A^{40}/K^{40} = 0.055 ± 0.003)	WH	A^{40}/K^{40}	{725 970
Wilberforce, Cardiff Township, Ont. (ur) (53.52% U, 10.37% Th, 9.26% Pb; 0.01, 87.98, 6.59, 5.42)	Nier, 15	Pb^{206}/U^{238}	1077
		Pb^{208}/Th^{232}	983
		Pb^{207}/Pb^{206}	1035
—(0.00, 89.43, 6.60, 3.98)	CRF, 1	Pb^{207}/Pb^{206}	1040 ± 15
—(60.09% U, 7.93% Th, 11.18% Pb; 0.006, 89.67, 6.56, 3.76)	CRF, 2; CFR, 77	Pb^{206}/U^{238}	1150
		Pb^{207}/U^{235}	1110
		Pb^{208}/Th^{232}	1130
		Pb^{207}/Pb^{206}	1032 ± 10
—(0.01, 89.53, 6.72, 3.84)	CFR, 75	Pb^{207}/Pb^{206}	1090 ± 50
—(0.12, 82.34, 7.91, 9.64)	CFR, 76	Pb^{207}/Pb^{206}	1100 ± 130
—(av. of 4)	El	Pb/U(chem.)	1118
—	Lane	Pb/U(chem.)	1075
Concession 16, Cardiff Township (microcline) (A^{40}/K^{40} = 0.059 ± 0.003)	WH	A^{40}/K^{40}	{770 1020
—(ur) (62.29% U, 6.61% Th, 9.92% Pb; 0.0135, 90.12, 6.75, 3.12)	WH	Pb^{206}/U^{238}	1002
		Pb^{207}/U^{235}	1020
		Pb^{208}/Th^{232}	874
		Pb^{207}/Pb^{206}	1026
Calabogie, Ont. (euxenite or samarskite) (4.16% U, 1.11% Th, 0.42% Pb; 0.03, 88.88, 6.66, 4.50)	CFR, 79	Pb^{206}/U^{238}	642
		Pb^{207}/U^{235}	732
		Pb^{208}/Th^{232}	337
		Pb^{207}/Pb^{206}	1010 ± 70
Madawaska, Ont. (fergusonite) (0.01, 90.71, 6.54, 2.77)	CFR, 80	Pb^{207}/Pb^{206}	960 ± 50
Essonville-Tory Hill granite, Haliburton County, Ont.			
(zir) (0.265% U, 0.218% Th, 461 ppm Pb; <0.01, 85.35, 6.39, 8.26)	Car-TPB	Pb^{207}/Pb^{206}	1080 ± 25
		Pb^{206}/U^{238}	1030 ± 25
		Pb^{207}/U^{235}	1060 ± 25
		Pb^{208}/Th^{232}	390

Table 9. Age determinations on various materials, selected for geologic importance, and arranged roughly by locality in order of increasing age (*Cont.*)

Locality and Mineral § ‖	Author ‖ and No.	Method	Age (years × 10^6)
(four splits of the same sample)	LG	Pb/α	
—(1084α, 430 ppm Pb)			952
—(976α, 415 ppm Pb)			1020
—(1100α, 440 ppm Pb)			960
—(1011α, 428 ppm Pb)			1016
(sphene II) (0.2205% Th, 113 ppm Pb; 0.360, 39.07, 7.98, 52.59)	Car-TPB	Pb^{207}/Pb^{206} Pb^{208}/Th^{232}	1090 ± 200 450
(sphene I) (303 ppm U, 240 ppm Pb; 0.732, 28.63, 12.52, 58.10)	TPB	Pb^{206}/U^{238}	910
(whole rock) (A^{40}/K^{40} = 0.054 ± 0.003)	WH	A^{40}/K^{40}	{715 {955
Pegmatite, N. of Tory Hill (microcline) (A^{40}/K^{40} = 0.054 ± 0.003)	WH	A^{40}/K^{40}	{715 {955
Eldorado, Great Bear Lake, N.W.T. (pit)		Pb^{207}/Pb^{206}	
(surface) (0.056, 89.47, 8.69, 1.78)	CFR, 1		1430 ± 40
(underground) (0.021, 90.63, 8.29, 1.10)	CFR, 2		1410 ± 60
(0.07, 88.90, 8.43, 2.61)	CFR, 3		1330 ± 40
(0.07, 89.57, 8.44, 1.90)	CFR, 4		1350 ± 50
(—, 90.30, 8.44, 1.26)	CFR, 5		1460 ± 70
(0.31, 75.67, 11.25, 12.80)	CFR, 6		1480 ± 130
(0.16, 86.21, 8.85, 4.78)	CFR, 7		1130 ± 130
(52.32% U, 10.51% Pb; 0.056, 89.02, 8.69, 2.23)	Nier, 10	Pb^{206}/U^{238} Pb^{207}/Pb^{206}	1251 1420
—	KBE, K-16	Pb^{210}	1208 ± 40
Black Lake, Sask. (pit) (—, 91.81, 7.59, 0.62)	CFR, 67	Pb^{207}/Pb^{206}	1250 ± 50
Nisto Mine (—, 92.27, 7.48, 0.26)	CFR, 68		1230 ± 40
Goldfields, Lake Athabaska, mines, Sask. (pit)			
Bolger (19.20% U, 0.0026% Th, 1.24% Pb; 0.01, 94.43, 5.20, 0.38)	CFR, 58 **	Pb^{206}/U^{238} Pb^{207}/U^{235} Pb^{207}/Pb^{206}	444 437 400 ± 50
Pitch group (0.05, 91.78, 5.86, 2.34)	CFR, 59 **	Pb^{207}/Pb^{206}	490 ± 130
50-CC-61 (0.10, 88.72, 6.89, 4.28)	CFR, 57 **	Pb^{207}/Pb^{206}	680 ± 50

Table 9. Age determinations on various materials, selected for geologic importance, and arranged roughly by locality in order of increasing age (*Cont.*)

Locality and Mineral §· ‖	Author ‖ and No.	Method	Age (years × 10^6)
Canadian Shield (*Cont.*)			
Goldfields (*Cont.*)			
Donaldson (—, 92.95, 6.36, 0.71)	CFR, 56 **	Pb^{207}/Pb^{206}	850 ± 50
ABC group (—, 93.09, 6.45, 0.49)	CFR, 54 **	Pb^{207}/Pb^{206}	920 ± 50
50-AA-14 (32.02% U, 0.0009% Th, 2.83% Pb; —, 92.97, 6.53, 0.53)	CFR, 53 **	Pb^{206}/U^{238}	592
		Pb^{207}/U^{235}	664
		Pb^{207}/Pb^{206}	920 ± 50
Gil group (8.21% U, 0.0097% Th, 1.02% Pb; 0.01, 93.29, 6.52, 0.19)	CFR, 52 **	Pb^{206}/U^{238}	822
		Pb^{207}/U^{235}	850
		Pb^{207}/Pb^{206}	930 ± 20
YY concession (0.916% U, 0.0018% Th, 0.25% Pb; —, 93.14, 6.55, 0.33)	CFR, 51 **	Pb^{206}/U^{238}	190
		Pb^{207}/U^{235}	260
		Pb^{207}/Pb^{206}	940 ± 30
Tam Lake (—, 92.89, 6.61, 0.52)	CFR, 50 **	Pb^{207}/Pb^{206}	945 ± 40
Gully, Beth Zone (—, 92.65, 6.70, 0.67)	CFR, 49 **	Pb^{207}/Pb^{208}	970 ± 50
Cinch Lake (—, 92.48, 7.14, 0.40)	CFR, 43 **		1120 ± 40
—(0.01, 92.69, 6.98, 0.34)	CFR, 44 **		1070 ± 40
—(0.015, 92.20, 6.92, 0.88)	CFR, 45 **		1030 ± 50
49-CC-11 (—, 92.69, 7.19, 0.11)	CFR, 46 **		1140 ± 20
Mic Lake (0.06, 88.86, 7.93, 3.13)	CFR, 47 **		1210 ± 120
—(0.04, 90.41, 7.59, 1.98)	CFR, 48 **		1160 ± 40
Rix (0.165, 83.23, 10.30, 6.30)	CFR, 40		1590 ± 50
—(0.064, 89.16, 8.30, 2.47)	CFR, 41 **		1310 ± 50
—(0.043, 90.92, 7.77, 1.26)	CFR, 42 **		1210 ± 50
50-DD-22 (0.16, 81.54, 10.28, 8.05)	CFR, 39		1630 ± 130
Eagle (—, 89.99, 9.41, 0.63)	CFR, 35	Pb^{207}/Pb^{206}	1700 ± 30
—(—, 90.37, 9.10, 0.55)	CFR, 36		1630 ± 30
—(0.10, 87.64, 9.66, 2.59)	CFR, 37		1620 ± 50
—(—, 91.30, 8.25, 0.45)	CFR, 38		1430 ± 40
—	KBE, K-14	Pb^{210}	1448 ± 35
Martin Lake (4.88% U, 0.0009% Th, 0.30% Pb; 0.03, 89.48, 9.06, 1.45)	CFR, 30	Pb^{206}/U^{238}	400
		Pb^{207}/U^{235}	630
		Pb^{207}/Pb^{206}	1580 ± 60

Table 9. Age determinations on various materials, selected for geologic importance, and arranged roughly by locality in order of increasing age (*Cont.*)

Locality and Mineral §, ‖	Author ‖ and No.	Method	Age (years × 10^6)
—(—, 90.24, 9.27, 0.51)	CFR, 23	Pb^{207}/Pb^{206}	1670 ± 30
—(—, 90.04, 9.21, 0.78)	CFR, 24		1660 ± 40
—(—, 90.54, 9.21, 0.26)	CFR, 25		1660 ± 20
—(—, 90.79, 9.18, 0.28)	CFR, 26		1650 ± 20
—(—, 90.56, 9.01, 0.43)	CFR, 27		1620 ± 30
—(0.14, 87.02, 9.78, 3.03)	CFR, 28		1620 ± 40
—(trace, 89.84, 8.80, 1.41)	CFR, 29		1610 ± 50
—(—, 90.63, 8.85, 0.54)	CFR, 31		1570 ± 30
—(—, 90.79, 8.63, 0.59)	CFR, 32		1530 ± 40
—(—, 91.29, 8.16, 0.58)	CFR, 33 **		1410 ± 30
—(—, 92.33, 7.14, 0.54)	CFR, 34 **		1110 ± 40
—(57.24% U, 7.39% Pb; 0.044, 92.17, 7.32, 0.46, and using a lead similar to N1, Table 9.1, for original lead correction)	KK	Pb^{206}/U^{238} Pb^{207}/U^{235} Pb^{207}/Pb^{206}	860 ± 5 980 ± 5 900 ± 10
Nicholson No. 4 (0.00, 89.49, 9.88, 0.66)	CFR, 19	Pb^{207}/Pb^{208}	1800 ± 40
—(0.03, 90.39, 7.51, 2.10)	CFR, 21 **		1180 ± 80
—(0.04, 90.82, 7.24, 1.90)	CFR, 20 **		1050 ± 90
—	KBE, K-19	Pb^{210}	808 ± 25
Nicholson No. 2 (—, 92.46, 7.25, 0.17)	CFR, 22 **	Pb^{207}/Pb^{208}	1160 ± 20
Ace Mine (0.00, 89.69, 9.96, 0.37)	CFR, 18	Pb^{207}/Pb^{208}	1820 ± 40
Strike Group (Ace Lake) (0.23, 80.18, 11.76, 8.84)	CFR, 17	Pb^{207}/Pb^{208}	1780 ± 40
Fish Hook Bay (Hacker Vein) (6.49% U, 1.63% Pb; 0.03, 88.18, 10.35, 1.46)	CFR, 16	Pb^{206}/U^{238} Pb^{207}/U^{235} Pb^{207}/Pb^{206}	1485 1648 1850 ± 50
Lee Lake, Lac La Ronge, Sask. (0.0355, 87.06, 9.63, 3.34)	CFR, 11		1780 ± 50
East Arm, Great Slave Lake (Stark Lake), N.W.T.		Pb^{207}/Pb^{206}	
Rex (ur) (0.073, 86.83, 10.67, 2.44)	CFR, 13		1850 ± 40
Rag (pit) (0.01, 90.06, 9.46, 0.49)	CFR, 14		1700 ± 30
Nuzone showing, Charlebois Lake, Sask. (ur) (0.044, 85.66, 9.83, 4.47)	CFR, 12	Pb^{207}/Pb^{206}	1780 ± 50

Table 9. Age determinations on various materials, selected for geologic importance, and arranged roughly by locality in order of increasing age (*Cont.*)

Locality and Mineral §, ‖	Author ‖ and No.	Method	Age (years × 10^6)
Sickle Lake, 4 mi. S. of Charlebois Lake, Sask. (ur) (0.071, 84.36, 10.18, 5.37)	CFR	Pb^{207}/Pb^{206}	1800 ± 50
—(biotite)	TD	Sr/Rb(id)	3230
Pegmatite ½ mi. N. of Viking Lake, Beaverlodge, Sask. (ur) (52.9% U, 5.24% Th, 17.14% Pb; 0.005, 87.37, 10.09, 2.53)	WH	Pb^{206}/U^{238}	1850
		Pb^{207}/U^{235}	1880
		Pb^{208}/Th^{232}	1670
		Pb^{207}/Pb^{206}	1910
Bob Ingersoll mine, Keystone, Black Hills, S. Dak. (lep)	TD	Sr/Rb(id)	1390
Black Hills, S. Dak. (lep)	A	Sr/Rb	850–1500
	DA		2000
Las Vegas, Santa Fé, N. M. (monazite) (0.122% U, 9.39% Th, 0.372% Pb; 0.025, 9.07, 1.12, 89.78)	Nier, 29	Pb^{206}/U^{238}	1730
		Pb^{208}/Th^{232}	770
		Pb^{207}/Pb^{206}	1340 ± 200
—(same data, but assuming U loss—U increased to 0.144%)	H	Pb^{206}/U^{238}	1337
		Pb^{207}/U^{235}	1328
		Pb^{207}/Pb^{206}	1330
Harding mine, Dixon, N. M. (lep)	Car	Sr/Rb(id)	1600 ± 100
	A	Sr/Rb	850
Radium Hill, Australia (davidite) (0.21, 78.70, 10.34, 10.78)	CFR, 92	Pb^{207}/Pb^{206}	1540 ± 100
Varuträsk, Sweden (lep)	A	Sr/Rb	2350
			2600
Old African rocks			
Nigel mine, Witwatersrand, S. Afr. (ur) (61.32% U, 14.84% Pb; 0.050, 84.78, 11.57, 3.61)	CFR, 89	Pb^{206}/U^{238}	1340
		Pb^{207}/U^{235}	1650
		(Pb^{208}/Th^{232}	2362 ± 280)
		Pb^{207}/Pb^{206}	2070 ± 50
—	D	Pb^{206}/U^{238}	1377 ± 20
		Pb^{207}/U^{235}	1716 ± 50
		Pb^{208}/Th^{232}	2160 ± 140
		Pb^{207}/Pb^{206}	3712 ± 510
—	KBE, K-20	Pb^{210}	1290 ± 40
Kubuta, Swaziland (lep)	A	Sr/Rb	2200
Lunya, Uganda (lep)	NAD	Sr/Rb(id)	2340
M'bale, Uganda (lep)	NAD	Sr/Rb(id)	2460
	NAD	Sr/Rb(id)	2370

Table 9. Age determinations on various materials, selected for geologic importance, and arranged roughly by locality in order of increasing age (*Cont.*)

Locality and Mineral §·‖	Author ‖ and No.	Method	Age (years × 10^6)
Irumi Hills, Northern Rhodesia (monazite) (0.09% U, 8.15% Th, 0.58% Pb; 0.071, 5.76, 1.85, 92.32; using the Rosetta mine lead, Table 9.1, for original lead correction)	H	Pb^{206}/U^{238}	2040
		Pb^{207}/U^{235}	2330
		Pb^{208}/Th^{232}	1390
		Pb^{207}/Pb^{206}	2620
Southern Rhodesia (monazite)	H		
Jack tin claims, N. of Salisbury (0.19% U, 9.36% Th, 0.95% Pb; 0.037, 7.53, 1.76, 90.68; using the Rosetta lead, as above)		Pb^{206}/U^{238}	2260
		Pb^{207}/U^{235}	2470
		Pb^{208}/Th^{232}	1940
		Pb^{207}/Pb^{206}	2650
Ebonite claims, Bikita (0.074% U, 2.39% Th, 0.34% Pb; 0.007, 9.49, 1.70, 88.80; using the Rosetta lead, as above)		Pb^{206}/U^{238}	2675
		Pb^{207}/U^{235}	2680
		Pb^{208}/Th^{232}	2645
		Pb^{207}/Pb^{206}	2680
—(lep)			
Pope Tantalum mine, east of Salisbury	AM	Sr/Rb	2350
Pope's claims	NAD	Sr/Rb(id)	3740
NNE of Salisbury	AM	Sr/Rb	2400
Lutope tin mine, Wankie dist.	AM	Sr/Rb	2300
Odzi dist.	AM	Sr/Rb	2300
Antelope mine, So. of Al Hayat claims, Bikita dist.	AM	Sr/Rb	2100
Nigel claims, N. of Al Hayat mine	AM	Sr/Rb	2250
Al Hayat mine	AM	Sr/Rb	2500
Mauve Kop, near Ft. Victoria, Bikita dist.	AM	Sr/Rb	3150
Bikita quarry	NAD	Sr/Rb(id)	3160
Hombolo, Tanganyika (lep)	NAD	Sr/Rb(id)	3250
Letaba, Transvaal (lep)	NAD	Sr/Rb(id)	3850
SE Manitoba pegmatites (lep)			
Along Winnipeg River	DA	Sr/Rb(id)	3360
	AG	Sr/Rb	2400
Falcon Island, Lake of the Woods	A	Sr/Rb	2300
Silver leaf mine, Winnipeg River	A	Sr/Rb	2200

Table 9. Age determinations on various materials, selected for geologic importance, and arranged roughly by locality in order of increasing age (*Cont.*)

Locality and Mineral §, ‖	Author ‖ and No.	Method	Age (years × 10^6)
Huron claim, Manitoba (ur)	CFR-Nier, 14	Pb^{206}/U^{238}	1564
(54.25% U, 12.36% Th, 15.47%		Pb^{207}/U^{235}	1985
Pb; 0.018, 81.50, 13.18, 5.31)		Pb^{208}/Th^{232}	1273
		Pb^{207}/Pb^{206}	2475
—(monazite) (0.281% U,	CFR-Nier, 28	Pb^{206}/U^{238}	3217
15.63% Th, 1.524% Pb; 0.010,		Pb^{207}/U^{235}	2839
10.20, 1.86, 87.93)		Pb^{208}/Th^{232}	1827
		Pb^{207}/Pb^{206}	2590
—(lep)	AG	Sr/Rb	2400
Bonneville, Wyo. (lep)	Car	Sr/Rb(id)	3200 ± 300

* From the hundreds of carbon[14] dates available, these have been selected for their value in geologic correlation. No archeologic dates are included, although many useful ones exist. Excluded also are the many dates that consist only of a minimum value, the maximum being unknown. Again, only those horizons are represented whose stratigraphic correlation is reasonably well known; those with floating correlation are excluded even though their absolute dates may be well known. The carbon[14] list was selected in December, 1953, by Richard Foster Flint, Yale University, New Haven, Conn.

† Laboratory-number prefixes:

C = Institute for Nuclear Studies, University of Chicago.
L = Lamont Geological Observatory, Columbia University.
W = U. S. Geological Survey, Washington, D. C.
Y = Geochronometric Laboratory, Yale University.

‡ The errors shown are standard deviations based on counting statistics only (see Section 1.9).

§ Mineral identifications as given by the authors.

‖ Abbreviations and notes:

A = Ahrens, 1949, 1952. Author considers determinations precise within 15–20 percent.
α = alphas/milligram-hour.
AG = Ahrens and Gorfinkle, 1950, 1951.
ALT = Anderson, Levi, and Tauber, 1953.
AM = Ahrens and Macgregor, 1951.
BDG = Blau, Deevey, and Gross, 1953.
BHIP = Begemann, von Buttlar, Houtermans, Isaac, and Picciotto, 1953.
Car = Carnegie Institution (Aldrich, Davis, Graham, Nicolaysen, and Tilton), 1954, and unpublished.
CFR = Collins, Farquhar, and Russell, 1954. (See note under CLRF. The lead:lead ages are considered to be the most reliable by these authors.)
CGW = Chapman, Gottfried, and Waring, unpublished.
CLRF = Collins, Lang, Robinson, and Farquhar, 1952. The authors believe that the younger age values, particularly in the Goldfields region (marked **) date times of solution and redeposition of original deposits. Mineralogical

Table 9. Age determinations on various materials, selected for geologic importance, and arranged roughly by locality in order of increasing age (*Cont.*)

evidence of replacement and working, together with the presence of radiogenic lead in associated galena, supports the hypothesis.

CRF = Collins, Russell, and Farquhar, 1953.

D = Davidson, 1953.

DA = Davis and Aldrich, 1953. Determinations are considered accurate within a few percent.

De = Demay, 1953.

E = Ehrenberg, 1953.

EL = Ellsworth in National Research Council, 1950, pp. 37–38.

GGP = Gentner, Goebel, and Präg, 1954. (Using the decay constant 3.3 gammas/second-gram of potassium.)

H = Holmes, 1946, 1948*a*, *b*, 1950, 1954.

HB = Holmes and Besairie, 1954, recomputed.

HJG = Hutchinson, Jaffe, and Gottfried, unpublished.

HLN = Holmes, Leland, and Nier, 1950.

Ho = Houtermans, 1951.

id = isotope dilution technique.

K = Kulp and coworkers at the Lamont Geological Observatory, unpublished.

KBE = Kulp, Broecker, and Eckelmann, 1953.

KK = Kerr and Kulp, 1952.

Lane = in National Research Council, 1934, p. 21.

lep = lepidolite.

Li = Libby, 1952.

LG = Larsen, Gottfried, Waring, and others, unpublished.

LKH = Larsen, Keevil, and Harrison, 1952.

LWB = Larsen, Waring, and Berman, 1953.

NAD = Nicolaysen, Aldrich, and Doak, 1953.

Ly = Lyons, unpublished.

Nier = Nier, 1939*b*; and Nier, Thompson, and Murphey, 1941.

nm = new mineral.

Ph = Phair, unpublished.

pit = pitchblende.

R = Rodgers, 1952.

RSFM = Russell, Shillibeer, Farquhar, and Mousuf, 1953.

SS = Stieff, Stern, and Milkey, 1953, and unpublished data.

TD = Tomlinson and Das Gupta, 1953.

TPB = Tilton, Patterson, Brown, Inghram, Hayden, Hess, and Larsen (in press).

U = unpublished.

ur = uraninite.

W = Wickman, 1942.

WH = Wasserburg and Hayden, 1954, and unpublished data. [Two ages are shown for each sample. The first, younger, age is computed from an assumed decay rate of 3.5 gammas/second-gram of potassium (branching ratio 0.126, see Table 9.5.1) and the second, older, age from an assumed rate of 2.4 gammas/second-gram (branching ratio 0.085)].

zir = zircon.

9.1 LEAD METHODS

The determination of geological ages by the lead method involves the following nuclear processes:

$$U^{238} \rightarrow \text{emission of 8 alphas} \rightarrow Pb^{206}$$

$$U^{235} \rightarrow \text{emission of 7 alphas} \rightarrow Pb^{207}$$

$$Th^{232} \rightarrow \text{emission of 6 alphas} \rightarrow Pb^{208}$$

The time variation of the relative amounts of parent and daughter atoms in these radioactive processes may be expressed as:

$$(\text{Daughter})_{\text{now}} = (\text{Parent})_{\text{now}}(e^{\lambda t} - 1) \tag{1}$$

9.1.a The chemical lead: uranium method

In an isolated chemical system, a determination of the amounts of parent and daughter and knowledge of the rate of decay λ of the parent leads to a solution for the age t of the system. Considering a uranium mineral and assuming that nothing has been added, nothing removed, and no lead was present when the system originally formed, an age could be found by analyzing for lead and uranium (or thorium) and solving for t. The requisite constants are given in Figure 1.2. The technique is usually referred to as the *chemical lead:uranium (or lead:thorium) method.*

Countless determinations have been made by this method, but it was found that the premises on which the method rests are not valid for most uranium minerals. There is definite evidence of selective uranium leaching by acid waters (Phair and Levine, 1953), and it is now known that most radioactive minerals contained some lead when they were formed. As a result, most of the early lead:uranium age determinations are questionable.

The lead:uranium method has been revived by Larsen and his coworkers who found that a few fairly common minerals (zircon, xenotime, and some monazite) are sufficiently resistant to chemical change and were sufficiently low in lead content at the time that they were formed to satisfy the basic requirements of the method so that age determinations can be made with small enough error to be useful (Larsen, Keevil, and Harrison, 1952).

Larsen's method offers great promise because it is rapid and relatively simple. The minerals to be studied are separated from the rock by standard mineralogic methods (heavy liquids, magnetic separator, flotation, etc.), and their total thick-source alpha activity is determined. The lead content is established spectrochemically (Waring and Worthing, 1953), and the approximate age follows from the relation

$$t = \frac{c\mathrm{Pb}}{\alpha} \tag{2}$$

where t is the age in millions of years, Pb is the lead content in parts per million, and α is the radioactivity in alphas per milligram-hour. Hence the technique is called the *lead:alpha method.* The constant c is 2600 for uranium alone and 1990 for thorium alone. For minerals containing unknown proportions of thorium and uranium, a fairly accurate value for c can be obtained (by difference) from the total alpha activity and a fluorimetric analysis for uranium. Even a large uncertainty in the thorium:uranium ratio, however, produces only a small error in c and in the calculated age. It has been found in practice that in zircon, the most useful mineral for this method, almost all the radioactivity usually is due to uranium and the value of c is about 2400.

9.1.b The isotopic lead:uranium method and the lead:lead method

The end product of uranium^{238} decay is the lead isotope, lead^{206}, and that of uranium^{235} is lead^{207}. The end product of the decay of parental thorium is lead^{208}. Lead^{204} is not derived from the decay of any known long-lived element. The lead present at the time of formation of the earth is believed to have contained lead^{204}, lead^{206}, lead^{207}, and lead^{208}. Analyses of several whole rocks and a large number of lead minerals, associated with little or no radioactive material, show that their lead, generally called *common lead,* is composed of all four of these isotopes. Available isotopic measurements are listed in Table 9.1. The variation in the composition of this common lead is explained as a gradual addition of small amounts of *radiogenic lead* (lead^{206}, lead^{207}, lead^{208} derived from radioactive decay) throughout geologic time.

Experience has shown that some common lead is present in most uranium minerals, just as copper, silver, and other elements are also present. Common lead in a uranium mineral (here called *original lead,* after Holmes) is indicated by the presence of lead^{204} (the lead isotope of non-radiogenic origin) and, in thorium-free districts, by

Table 9.1 Relative isotopic abundances of common leads, arranged by locality and roughly in order of decreasing lead^{206} content

Number *	Source and Mineral †	Geologic Age ‡	Isotopic Abundances (Pb^{204} = 1.00) 206	207	208
GS237	Happy Jack Mine, San Juan County, Utah (79.6% Pb, 0.83% U)	ET	92.62	20.12	37.77
GS261	Monument No. 2 Mine, Apache County, Ariz. (68.7% Pb, 4.8% U)	ET	88.81	18.75	36.36
C90	Witwatersrand, S. Africa	pre Є	58.94	24.10	40.19
K34			59.93	24.11	39.84
GS199	Happy Jack Mine (70.7% Pb, 3.71% U)	ET	46.96	17.25	37.89
GS117	(80.6% Pb, 0.9% U)		33.94	16.75	38.41
GS69	(—)		30.18	15.89	36.96
	Sudbury, Ontario, mines	L pre Є			
C26, R3-12	Worthington		26.00	16.94	52.21
K27	—		26.30	17.38	52.41
R3-13	Hardy (750-ft level)		23.23	16.77	52.64
R3-5	Falconbridge (3300-ft level)		24.29	17.04	45.70
R3-6	Falconbridge (2400-ft level)		23.70	16.92	45.35
R3-7	Falconbridge (1700-ft level)		24.20	16.95	45.58
R3-8	Frood (Disseminated in wall rock, 300-ft level)		15.99	15.84	36.56
R3-9	Frood (Post-ore slip, 400-ft level)		23.10	16.90	45.04
R3-1	McKim (Post-ore slip, 1000-ft level)		22.89	16.72	44.92
R3-2	McKim (Post-ore slip, 960-ft level)		23.03	16.69	45.19
R3-3	McKim (Post-ore slip, 800-ft level)		16.30	15.85	36.97
R3-4	McKim (Post-ore slip, 600-ft level)		16.43	15.96	36.93
C25, R3-10	Garson		22.95	16.69	44.79
R3-11	Garson (Post-ore slip)		23.00	16.61	44.78
K1	Hazel Green, Wis.	—	22.50	16.12	42.34
	Joplin, Mo.	Penn-L Cr			
N14	Galena III		22.28	16.20	41.8
			22.37	16.10	41.8
N14a	—		22.48	16.15	41.3
V23	—		22.42	16.01	41.47

* For footnotes and abbreviations see end of table (page 292).

Table 9.1 Relative isotopic abundances of common leads, arranged by locality and roughly in order of decreasing lead^{206} content (*Cont.*)

Number *	Source and Mineral †	Geologic Age ‡	Isotopic Abundances (Pb^{204} = 1.00) 206	207	208
V24	Joplin, Mo. (*Cont.*)		21.78	15.72	40.76
N7	Galena I		21.65	15.88	40.8
N8	Galena II (average)		21.62	15.74	40.4
N8a	—		21.72	15.74	40.3
N8b	—		21.62	15.74	40.4
K8	—		22.19	15.67	40.49
K3a	Columbia lead mine, Flat River, S.E. Mo.		22.78	16.48	43.06
K3b	(Same crystal)		22.73	16.51	43.12
K2	Central mine, Flat River, S.E. Mo.		20.56	15.84	38.93
P	Alaskite granite, Essonville-Tory Hill, Haliburton County, Ont. (whole rock) (9.3 ppm Pb, 2.74 ppm U, 41.9 ppm Th)	pre Ꞓ	20.25	15.65	48.73
P	Samples from the Pacific Ocean	Q			
	Lomita Marl (0.31 ppm Pb)		19.27	15.61	39.40
	Manganese nodule (3450 ppm Pb)		18.91	15.69	38.68
	Red clay (35.2 ppm Pb)		18.95	15.76	38.92
P	Plateau basalt, Shoshone lava field, Lincoln County, Idaho (whole rock) (6.2 ppm Pb, 0.65 ppm U, 2.02 ppm Th)	Q	18.12	15.45	38.08
B	Vesuvius fumaroles (Cotunnite, $PbCl_2$)	R	19.19	15.80	39.62
			19.14	15.75	39.37
			19.08	15.71	39.24
V27	North Ural, USSR	Dp	20.10	16.08	39.92
V26	West Prebaikal, USSR	D-1 C	18.64	16.46	40.12
V9	North Caucasus, USSR	uJ-Pg	18.84	16.16	38.98
V11	Armenian SSR	J-Pg	18.45	15.80	39.01
V10	Sadon, North Caucasus, USSR	uJ-Pg	18.37	16.00	39.27
V29	Prebalkhash, Central Kazakhstan, USSR	D-P	19.70	15.80	37.68
V14	Kuramen Range, Central Asia, USSR	P	18.79	16.64	38.55

Table 9.1 Relative isotopic abundances of common leads, arranged by locality and roughly in order of decreasing lead^{206} content (*Cont.*)

Number *	Source and Mineral †	Geologic Age ‡	Isotopic Abundances (Pb^{204} = 1.00) 206	207	208
V4	Far Eastern Province, USSR	Pg	18.60	16.11	38.95
V16	Kirgiz SSR	P	18.51	15.79	39.22
V13	South Kirgiziya, USSR	P	18.02	16.26	38.41
V12	Transbaikal, USSR	uJ-Tr	18.22	15.85	39.27
V25	Nagol'nyi Ridge, Ukraine	C	18.49	16.10	39.59
V8	Boleslav, Carpathians	Ng	18.42	15.89	39.21
V18	South mine, Altay, USSR	uC-P	18.03	15.96	37.73
C22	Box Mine, Goldfields, Canada	m pre Є	20.88	15.74	35.39
N9	Metaline Falls, Wash.	Cr	19.30	15.73	39.5
N23	Sonora mine, Arizona	Mio	19.22	16.17	39.15
N17	Casapalca, Peru	Mio	18.86	15.71	38.75
			18.83	15.61	38.5
N16	Casapalca mine, Peru (bournonite)	Mio	18.65	15.49	38.15
			18.69	15.40	38.15
GS198	Drill core, Horse Mesa, Montrose County, Colo.	ET	22.86	15.92	38.96
GS139	Robinson claim, San Miguel County, Colo.	ET	22.31	15.81	38.99
GS165	—		22.21	15.86	39.05
GS192	Lucky Strike mine, Emery County, Utah	ET	20.68	16.01	39.24
GS174	—		19.53	15.51	38.03
GS5	Philadelphia claim, Placerville, San Miguel County, Colo.	ET	19.85	15.34	37.33
GS141	Seven Mile Canyon claim, Grand County, Utah	ET	19.63	15.55	37.89
GS68-2	Cougar mine, Lower Group, San Miguel County, Colo.	ET	19.88	16.12	39.93
GS68-1	—		19.04	15.48	38.01
GS67	Wilson Mesa, Grand County, Utah	ET	19.27	15.58	38.23
GS2	Garfield mine, Garfield County, Colo.	ET	19.03	15.32	37.64
GS9-1	LaSal No. 1 mine, San Juan County, Utah (unknown mineral)	ET	18.99	15.23	37.25

Table 9.1 Relative isotopic abundances of common leads, arranged by locality and roughly in order of decreasing lead²⁰⁶ content (*Cont.*)

Number *	Source and Mineral †	Geologic Age ‡	Isotopic Abundances (Pb^{204} = 1.00) 206	207	208
GS9-2	La Sal (*Cont.*)		18.99	15.26	37.22
GS7-2	Bitter Creek mine, Montrose County, Colo. (descloizite)	ET	18.96	15.42	38.16
GS7-1	—		18.78	15.39	37.82
GS1	Rifle mine, Garfield County, Colo.	ET	18.91	15.20	37.36
GS131	Dirty Devil No. 6 mine, Emery County, Utah	ET	18.90	15.64	38.52
GS195	—		18.54	15.43	38.02
GS197	Blanding water tunnel, Abajo Mts., San Juan County, Utah (unknown mineral)	ET	18.59	15.45	37.95
GS70	—		18.63	15.53	38.38
GS194	Conrad No. 1 mine, Emery County, Utah	ET	18.59	15.50	37.90
GS207	White Canyon claims, Wayne County, Utah	ET	18.89	15.78	38.96
GS208	—		18.67	15.73	38.67
GS191	Temple Mt., Emery County, Utah	ET	18.56	15.60	38.38
GS193	Rex No. 2 mine, Temple Mt., Emery County, Utah	ET	18.47	15.46	38.06
N11	Tucson Mts., Ariz. (wulfenite and vanadinite)	Mio	18.40	15.53	38.1
K36	Deer Trail mine, Marysvale, Utah	T	18.38	15.77	38.46
	Mines in the Colorado Front Range				
GS702	Waldorf, Argentine (86.9% Pb, 5.3 ppm U)	ET	18.51	15.56	39.14
GS267	Stanley, Idaho Springs (74.2% Pb, 10.4 ppm U)	ET	18.29	15.69	38.57
GS270	Wellington, Breckenridge (77.4% Pb, 7.4 ppm U)	ET	18.13	15.49	37.95
GS	Eureka, Central City (83.4% Pb, 8 ppm U)	ET	18.00	15.35	37.68

Table 9.1 Relative isotopic abundances of common leads, arranged by locality and roughly in order of decreasing lead^{206} content (*Cont.*)

Number *	Source and Mineral †	Geologic Age ‡	Isotopic Abundances ($Pb^{204} = 1.00$) 206	207	208
	Colo. Front Range mines (*Cont.*)				
GS275	Bellevue, Lawson (86.3% Pb, 2.7 ppm U)	ET	17.94	15.41	38.23
GS266	Smuggler, Silver Plume (87.0% Pb, 7.1 ppm U)	ET	17.80	15.73	39.62
GS273	Franklin, Central City (74.0% Pb, 3.5 ppm U)	ET	17.73	15.45	37.89
GS276	Yellow Pine, Gold Hill (83.8% Pb, 4.6 ppm U)	ET	17.35	15.32	37.97
GS	Caribou	ET	16.88	15.05	36.93
GS277	Stove Mt. pegmatite, El Paso Co. (84.3% Pb, 3.1 ppm U)	L pre Є	16.52	15.23	36.05
GS268	Cotopaxi (86.2% Pb, 6.9%U)	pre Є	15.73	15.22	34.99
GS272	Blackmoor's, Bergen Park (84.4% Pb, 6.5 ppm U)	pre Є	15.43	15.07	34.60
GS269	Lone Chimney, Guffy (81.1% Pb, 9.2 ppm U)	pre Є	15.41	14.97	34.60
K35	Upper Huronian Iron Formation	pre Є	19.58	16.95	38.24
K11	Darien, Conn.	D	18.87	15.64	38.59
K10	Middletown, Conn.	D	18.81	15.84	38.97
K12	Roxbury, Conn.	D	18.78	15.88	38.96
K13	Pembroke, Mass. (schistose galena)	C	20.69	15.86	39.37
K15	Quincy, Mass.	C	18.34	15.72	37.91
K26	Silver Hill mine, N. Car.	C	18.33	15.79	38.13
N4	Yancey County, N. Car.	C	18.43	15.61	38.2
N21	Durango, Mexico	mT	18.71	15.70	38.5
V3	Seravezza, Italy	LT	18.51	16.05	38.13
	Germany				
G15	Wiesloch 35	T, pm Tr	18.62	15.57	38.79
G14	—		18.55	15.53	38.46
E2	Schapbach, Schwarzwald	eD	18.55	15.58	38.61
G27	Hertmannsweiler, NE of Winnenden, NE of Stuttgart	J	18.52	15.67	38.57

Table 9.1 Relative isotopic abundances of common leads, arranged by locality and roughly in order of decreasing lead^{206} content (*Cont.*)

Number *	Source and Mineral †	Geologic Age ‡	Isotopic Abundances (Pb^{204} = 1.00) 206	207	208
	Germany (*Cont.*)				
G28	Linsenberg, ENE of Rottweil	J	18.50	15.65	38.59
G25	1 km WNW of Altmannshausen near Windsheim, SE of Würzburg	J	18.50	15.63	38.59
N18	Clausthal, Harz Mts.	uC	18.46	15.66	38.6
G23	St. Andreasberg	Ll C	18.47	15.66	38.49
G26	Stiftsberg near Heilbronn	J	18.47	15.64	38.47
E1a	Meggen, Westphalia	eD	18.42	15.91	38.86
E1b	—		18.38	15.81	38.66
G24	—	Ll D	18.37	15.70	38.60
G9	Schauinsland	LuC	18.35	15.47	38.27
G8	—		18.31	15.46	38.28
G6	Oberharz	LlC	18.32	15.53	38.58
G7	—		18.25	15.44	38.32
G18	Ramsbeck	LlC	18.28	15.63	38.48
G19	—		18.28	15.69	38.43
G22	Königstiel	LlD	18.30	15.70	38.35
G4	Chr. Lewin	LuC	18.33	15.66	38.53
G5	—		18.08	15.53	38.03
G21	Maubach	plTr	18.25	15.51	38.25
G20	—		18.20	15.51	38.41
N6	Eifel (cerussite)	uC?	18.20	15.46	37.7
G12	Holzappel	LlD	18.21	15.61	38.11
G13	—		18.15	15.54	37.91
G3	Mühlebach	LlD	18.18	15.58	38.24
G1	—		18.15	15.59	38.15
G2	—		18.15	15.57	38.19
G16	Rammelsberg	LlD	18.17	15.57	38.22
G17	—		18.13	15.58	38.20
G11	Lüderich	LlD	18.17	15.62	38.11
G10	—		18.13	15.56	37.97
V21	Nassau	P-C	18.15	15.69	37.50
N5	—		18.10	15.57	37.85
N24	Freiberg, Saxony	P-C	18.07	15.40	38.0
V22	Saxony	P-C	17.34	15.37	37.60
C10	Katanga, Belgian Congo	pre Є	18.22	15.91	38.27
G30	Broken Hill, N. Rhodesia, Kopje I, Schneiderhöhn 1929, no. 220		18.12	15.83	38.62

Table 9.1 Relative isotopic abundances of common leads, arranged by locality and roughly in order of decreasing lead^{206} content (*Cont.*)

Number *	Source and Mineral †	Geologic Age ‡	Isotopic Abundances (Pb^{204} = 1.00)		
			206	207	208
G29	Mitwaba, Belgian Congo (no. RG 1831 Congo Museum, Tervuren)	pre Є	17.76	15.88	37.58
V1	Monte Negro, Bolivia	Ng	17.75	15.20	37.88
N19	Příbram, Bohemia	uC	17.95	15.57	37.9
V5	Zangezur, Armenian SSR	J-Pg	17.84	15.42	38.16
N25	"Alpine Trias, Austria" (Sample probably invalid. Harvard Min. Mus. records give locality as: Monte Poni, Sardinia)	Tr?	17.75	16.21	38.05
V15	North Kirgiziya, USSR	P	17.68	15.43	38.42
V17	Kuramen Range, USSR	uC-P	17.65	15.45	38.26
V7	Yakutiya, USSR	lCr	17.58	15.09	37.22
V30	Central Kazakhstan, USSR	D-P	17.49	15.13	37.18
V2	Primor'ye, Far Eastern Province, USSR	Pg	17.38	14.91	36.70
V6	"North Caucasus," USSR	uCr	17.32	14.91	36.54
V19	West Tyan'-Shan', USSR	C-P	17.27	15.11	36.89
V20	Karatau, USSR	uC-P	17.04	15.07	37.13
N20	Franklin, N. J.	C-m pre Є	17.15	15.45	36.53
C20	Upper Canada mine, Ont.	pre Є	19.60	15.22	33.62
C12	Frontenac Co., Ont.	pre Є	16.79	15.40	36.49
C16	Rex, Stark Lake, N.W.Terr.	pre Є	16.37	15.65	36.34
N15	Tetreault Montaubon-les-Mines, Qué.	pre Є	16.27	15.16	35.6
R3-14	Fairbank Twp., Ont. (In deformed micropegmatite)	pre Є	16.20	15.76	36.99
N1	Great Bear Lake, N.W.Terr.	pre Є	15.93	15.30	35.3
N10	Wallace, Idaho (cerussite)	Cr	16.10	15.13	35.45
			15.98	15.08	35.07

Table 9.1 Relative isotopic abundances of common leads, arranged by locality and roughly in order of decreasing lead^{206} content (*Cont.*)

Number *	Source and Mineral †	Geologic Age ‡	Isotopic Abundances (Pb^{204} = 1.00) 206	207	208
R1-1	Potgietersrust Dist., Transvaal, S. Africa	pre Є	16.26	15.89	35.64
N2	Broken Hill, N.S.Wales	E pre Є	16.07	15.40	35.5
N3	Broken Hill, N.S.Wales (cerussite)	E pre Є	15.92	15.30	35.3
	—		15.93	15.28	35.2
N22	Langban, Sweden (native lead)	pre Є	15.83	15.45	35.6
V28	Northwest Kazakhstan, USSR	D-P	16.02	14.38	34.44
C24	Delhi Twp., Ont.	pre Є	16.07	15.47	35.17
C23	Matachewan, Ont.	pre Є	15.83	15.41	34.88
C15	Negus mine, Great Slave Lake, N.W. Terr.	pre Є	14.63	15.27	34.46
A	Negus and Con mines (average), Yellowknife, N.W.Terr.	pre Є	14.34	15.26	34.46
C19	Horseshoe Island, Great Slave Lake, N.W.Terr.	pre Є	14.16	15.08	34.28
C17	Sioux Lookout, Ont.	pre Є	14.05	14.92	33.85
A	Steep Rock Lake, Ont.	pre Є	13.94	14.83	33.75
R1-2	Marico Dist., Transvaal, S. Africa	pre Є	15.19	15.50	35.28
R1-7	Ivigtut, Greenland	E pre Є	14.85	14.94	35.07
N13			14.75	14.70	34.5
			14.54	14.60	34.45
R1-5	Phoenix mine, Norseman, W. Australia	pre Є	14.21	15.23	34.19
R1-6	Copperhead mine, Bullfinch, W. Australia	pre Є	14.19	14.92	33.80
V31	Karelo-Finnish SSR	pre Є	14.26	14.77	33.23
V32	Kinon-Koziala, Finland	pre Є	14.27	14.64	32.90
R1-4	Inguladhal, Chitaldrug Dist., Mysore State, India	pre Є	14.17	14.74	33.80
A	Borderland mine, Busia, E. Prov., Uganda	pre Є	14.05	15.10	34.24
A	Risks mine, Kakamega, Kenya	pre Є	14.05	15.05	34.21

Table 9.1 Relative isotopic abundances of common leads, arranged by locality and roughly in order of decreasing lead^{206} content (*Cont.*)

Number *	Source and Mineral †	Geologic Age ‡	Isotopic Abundances (Pb^{204} = 1.00) 206	207	208
C21, R1-3	Rosetta Mine, S. Africa	pre Ꞓ?	12.65	14.27	32.78
P	Canyon Diablo meteorite				
	(troilite) (18 ppm Pb, 0.009 ppm U)		9.41	10.27	29.16
	(metal phase) (0.37 ppm Pb)		9.7	10.5	29.3
P	Henbury meteorite (troilite) (5 ppm Pb)		9.50	10.30	29.26

* Numbers given are those originally assigned by the analyst, preceded by:
A to denote analyses by Allan, Farquhar, and Russell (1953)
B for those by Begemann, Geiss, Houtermans, and Buser (1954)
C for those by Collins, Russell, and Farquhar (1953) and Collins, Farquhar, and Russell (1954)
E for those by Ehrenberg (1953)
G for those by Geiss (1954)
GS for those analyzed by Carbide and Carbon Chemical Co., Y-12 Plant, Mass Assay Laboratory, Oak Ridge, Tenn., for the U. S. Geological Survey
K for those by Kulp, Owen, Eckelman, and Bate (unpublished)
N for those by Nier (1939, 1941)
P for those by Patterson, Brown, Tilton, and Inghram (1953 and unpublished)
R for those by Russell, Farquhar, Cumming, and Wilson (1954)
V for those by Vinogradov, Zadorozhnyi, and Zykov (1952).

† The mineral is galena unless otherwise stated.

‡ The geologic ages are given with varying degrees of accuracy. The following abbreviations are used:

C = Carboniferous	Ng = Neogen (Miocene-Pliocene)
Ꞓ = Cambrian	Q = Quaternary
Cr = Cretaceous	P = Permian
D = Devonian	p = post
E = early	Pg = Paleogen (Paleocene through Oligocene)
J = Jurassic	Penn = Pennsylvanian
L = late	R = Recent
l = lower	T = Tertiary
m = middle	Tr = Trias
Mio = Miocene	u = upper

the presence of $lead^{208}$ (since no thorium is present to form it). It is necessary to correct for the original lead and to determine how much of the $lead^{206}$ and $lead^{207}$ present is due to it.

The error introduced by the variability of common lead will not be serious if most of the lead present is radiogenic. In dealing with uranium minerals that contain much original lead, the error introduced in this way becomes increasingly important, and it becomes necessary to determine, as accurately as possible, the isotopic composition of the particular common lead that was present and included as original lead when the uranium mineral in question was formed. The original lead can be estimated by taking the isotopic composition of a lead mineral in association with the uranium mineral and assuming that they both formed from the same solution. This assumption is not always justified, and the verification must rest on geologic evidence and careful

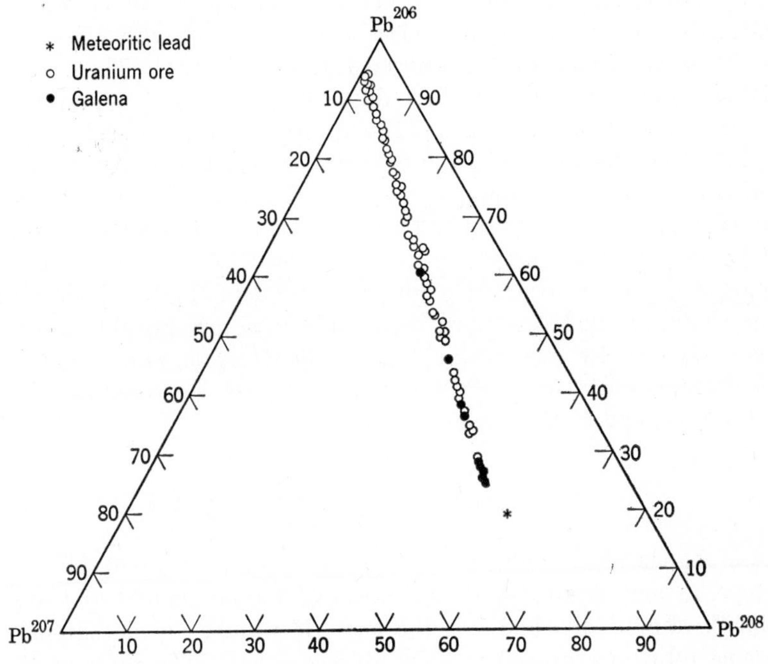

Figure 9.1 Isotopic composition diagram of $leads^{206,\ 207,}$ and ^{208} in galenas and uranium ores from the Colorado Plateau. The lead from the Canyon Diablo meteorite is included for comparison (see Tables 9 and 9.1 for complete data). After Stieff and Stern (unpublished).

study of the isotope picture (Figure 9.1). It is often impossible to obtain a lead mineral associated with an otherwise suitable uranium mineral. In that event, a common lead from the geologic area in question can be selected and used for the accessory lead correction. Houtermans (private communication) suggests two methods of selecting such a lead: First, we may determine the lead:uranium and lead:thorium ratios, correct for the lead^{208} generated by thorium decay in the approximate time indicated, and select a common lead with a lead^{208}: lead^{204} ratio similar to the corrected ratio obtained. The second method applies in localities where different samples of uranium minerals of the same origin contain different ratios of original lead to uranium. If one assumes that the isotopic composition of the original lead is the same in all samples, the composition can be derived from the separate isotopic analyses and uranium contents of several samples.

The corrected values for the radiogenic lead isotopes having been obtained by the subtraction of original lead and the uranium, lead (and thorium) analyses having been made, it is now possible to calculate the age by one of the two *isotopic lead:uranium methods* (lead^{206}:uranium^{238} or lead^{207}:uranium^{235}) by solving equation 1 or, by the *lead:lead method,* from the equation

$$\frac{Pb^{207}}{Pb^{206}} = \frac{U^{235}}{U^{238}} \frac{(e^{\lambda_1 t} - 1)}{(e^{\lambda_2 t} - 1)} \tag{3}$$

where the chemical symbols indicate the number of atoms of each isotope, λ_1 and λ_2 are the decay constants for uranium^{235} and uranium^{238}, respectively, and t is the age. It will be noted that only isotopic ratios are needed to solve this equation. The ratio of the uranium isotopes has been shown to be 1:138 now, and the decay rates are known accurately (Fleming et al., 1952; see Figure 1.2). Nomograms of these functions have been published by Wickman (1939) and by Kulp et al. (1954). Kulp's Pb^{207}/Pb^{206} graph is in error near the low end.

Each of these methods has its advantages and disadvantages. Uranium^{238} and lead^{206} derived from it are the most abundant, so that the lead^{206}:uranium^{238} method is least sensitive to error in analysis or the original lead correction. The chief disadvantages are that hexavalent uranium is readily leached (see Section 2.1) and that radon^{222}, which forms in the decay of uranium^{238}, has a halflife of 3.82 days and, being gaseous, might escape from the system (Wickman, 1942).

Whether such escape actually occurs in many samples and in significant amounts is still a matter of opinion. Many geologists believe that radon loss is high, even in massive pitchblende, deeply buried. Most physicists point out, however, that such loss could take place only by diffusion, and that an atom as heavy as radon cannot be expected to diffuse very far through dense rock in 3.82 days. Some experiments have been made to investigate radon loss, and others are in process, but conclusive results have not yet been obtained because the environment of a mineral in place is difficult to duplicate in the laboratory. The effect of this supposed radon loss would be a low value for lead^{206}, resulting in an apparent age younger than the true age. In order to introduce a significant error, the loss of radon^{222} from the system would have to go on throughout the time since the deposition of the mineral, and not just during the time the rock is exposed to weathering.

The lead^{207}:uranium^{235} method has the advantage that radon^{219} (actinon), formed in this series, has a halflife of only 3.92 seconds and is, therefore, much less likely to escape from the system. The rarity of uranium^{235} is a disadvantage.

The lead^{207}:lead^{206} method seems, at first glance, to be superior in that it deals only in isotopic ratios, and some physicists consider it to be the best of the lead methods. Actually, the method is subject to several errors. Loss of radon^{222} raises the lead:lead ratio and the calculated age. A rather large error may be introduced by the uncertainty in the composition of the original lead. This error may exceed the measured value when dealing with younger uranium minerals containing even small amounts of original lead, as clearly recognized by Holmes (1937) when the method was first proposed. Presence of old radiogenic lead (formed in a prior site of the parent uranium) may cause great error (Stieff and Stern, unpublished). Instrumental errors in mass spectrometry may yield consistently high apparent proportions of lead^{204} and lead^{207}. Redistribution of elements by renewed hydrothermal activity may be a serious source of error in all lead methods.

9.1.c The isotopic lead: thorium method

The isotopic lead:thorium method is analogous to the isotopic lead: uranium method except for the fact that only one parent isotope is involved. Most of the ages obtained by the lead:thorium method disagree with the ages of the same minerals computed by other lead methods (see Table 9). The reasons for this disagreement are largely unknown. Lead:thorium ages of monazite may be low because lead was lost (Holmes, 1948*a*) or because it is difficult to extract lead quantitatively in the presence of phosphate (Ingerson, private communication). The isotope dilution technique circumvents this difficulty and this approach to the problem is being studied (Carnegie Institution, 1954).

9.1.d The lead^{210} method

Another lead method was proposed by Houtermans (1951) and was applied by Begemann et al. (1952, 1953), and Kulp et al. (1953). It is essentially a refinement of the old lead:uranium method. The new procedure is based on the principle that the age of a uranium or thorium mineral can be determined by the ratio of any one of the members of the decay series to the stable end product, as long as the series is in equilibrium. The ratio here employed is lead^{206}:lead^{210}, selected because of the convenient physical and chemical characteristics of lead^{210}.

The isotopic concentration of lead^{206} in the sample is determined by mass spectrometry. If common lead and thorium are absent from the sample, the mass-spectrometric analysis is not necessary and one may simply analyze for total lead (Begemann et al., 1953). The lead^{210} solution may be measured with an immersion beta-gamma counter, after a few weeks storage to allow bismuth^{210}, a good beta emitter, to reach equilibrium with the lead^{210} (see Figure 1.2). (The beta rays from lead^{210} are too weak for convenient measurement.) If sufficient time is available, the lead separated from the sample may be stored for a few months to allow enough polonium^{210} to build up to permit analysis by the thick-source alpha-counting technique (see Figure 1.16). The polonium^{210} alphas are easily counted, but the halflife is too long (138 days) to allow equilibrium to be reached conveniently.

Unfortunately, the lead^{210} method is subject to similar errors as the lead:uranium and lead:lead methods, owing to loss of constituents of the radioactive series by leaching or emanation. The radon loss could be ignored if it were constant throughout the existence of the mineral; such conditions, however, are believed to be rare in nature. Some results obtained by the lead^{210} method are included in Table 9.

9.1.e Lead age of the earth's crust and of the elements *

It has already been said that the composition of common lead varies (see Table 9.1). It is very likely that "primordial lead," or the lead that was made with all the other elements at the time of nucleogenesis, was well mixed. When the earth's crust was formed, the primordial lead was frozen into rocks that also contained uranium and thorium in various ratios to lead. Radiogenic lead was continuously generated in these rocks until at some time and by some geologic process all lead, primordial as well as radiogenic, was extracted from a particular rock and deposited somewhere else as a lead ore. That, at least, is the idealized picture.

Thus, if we knew the age (the time of extraction) and the isotopic composition of a number of lead ores we might calculate the time when the mixing ceased, in other words the time when the solid earth's crust was formed. On the basis of Nier's (1938, Nier et al., 1941) data and with the aid of various assumptions and guesses, such calculations were made by Gerling (1942), Houtermans (1946, 1947), Holmes (1946, 1947), Jeffreys (1948), and Bullard and Stanley (1949). Their results for the "age of the earth" range from 3 to 4×10^9 years. Alpher and Herman (1951) have questioned the validity of some of the calculations and call attention to the fact that both Holmes (1947) and Bullard and Stanley (1949) obtained their results after rejection of part of the data. Without selection, their procedure would have given an age of about two billion years.

With the development of new microanalytical methods it became possible to measure the isotopic constitution of lead in ordinary rocks. The amount of lead in such rocks is very small, and it is most difficult to extract from them enough lead for isotopic analysis without excessive contamination by lead from automobile exhaust fumes, dust in the air, and countless other sources. In a cooperative effort, the isotopic composition of lead has been determined in the Essonville-Tory Hill granite of Ontario, and the Shoshone basalt of Idaho. An isotopic analysis of the lead in Quaternary oceanic deposits and in two meteorites has been made by the same workers (Patterson et al., 1953*a*, *b*, *c*; and private communication, see Table 9.1).

The meteoritic lead contains less of the radiogenic isotopes than any other lead previously analyzed, even though meteorites were

* Prepared by the editor.

thought to be less than about 10^8 years old on the basis of helium measurements by Paneth et al. (1952, 1953; Paneth, 1953; Martin, 1953). If the meteorite lead has the same composition as primordial lead, the age of the earth's crust is greater than 4×10^9 years (Patterson et al. 1953*b*).

The time of the earth's formation must be defined. Considerations of the earth's heat discussed in Chapter 5 imply that the uranium content of the earth's crust is much greater than the average uranium content of the earth as a whole. It follows that the uranium^{238}: lead^{204} ratio of the earth's crust also may be much higher than the same ratio for the whole earth (or the solar system). It is likely that this enrichment of the earth's crust in uranium (relative to lead) occurred very early in the earth's history (see Patterson et al., 1953*b*) although the process is by no means clear (see Chapter 10). The "time of the earth's formation," 4.5 billion years ago, obtained by Houtermans (1953) on the basis of the same meteorite data is effectively the time of this enrichment.

Using all the data in Table 9.1, including the granite, basalt, and meteorite values, Russell et al. (1954) and Cameron (unpublished) have made independent attempts to obtain the best fit to the data now available (Figure 9.2). They propose a method of dating most of the lead ores, but, like the earlier workers, they observe that some lead ores drastically deviate from the idealized model of ore genesis stated above. Altogether, Cameron lists more than a third of the leads in Table 9.1 as "anomalous," i.e., giving an unreasonably young age, presumably due to mixing with radiogenic lead from other reservoirs. The Colorado Plateau leads, the Joplin leads, and the Sudbury leads are good examples of leads contaminated by lead from other reservoirs. Stieff and Stern (unpublished) independently confirm the view that some of the leads from the Colorado Plateau contain quantities of old radiogenic lead. The pattern of Figure 9.2 is a reflection of the increase of radiogenic lead with time, but further interpretation is dangerous. It is unlikely that lead minerals can be dated on the basis of isotopic composition alone, using any simple model (Cannon, private communication). Time variations in the lead:uranium ratio of the host rocks cannot be ignored.

Gerling (1942), Koczy (1943), and Alpher and Herman (1951) have made estimates of the age of the elements (the maximum age of the earth) by extrapolating Nier's (1938, 1941) lead isotope data to a point where the lead^{206} concentration is assumed to be zero. If

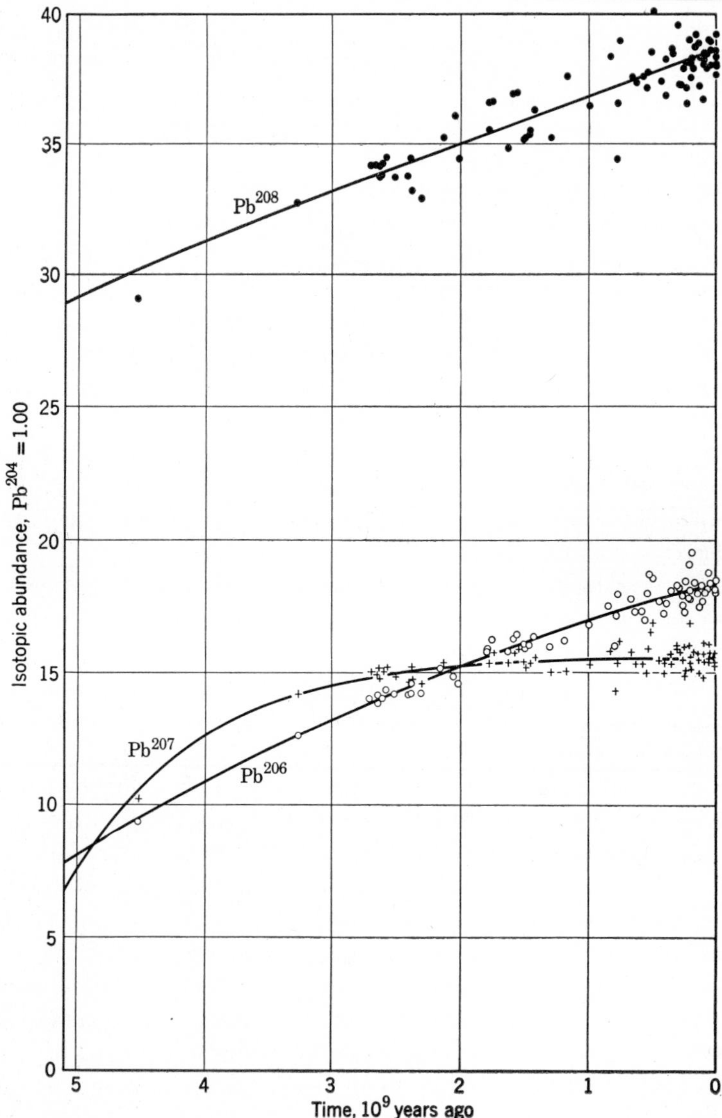

Figure 9.2 Isotopic abundances of lead, relative to lead^{204}, plotted as a function of time. The experimental points are data from Table 9.1 with "anomalous" leads (see text) omitted. The lead sample ages are estimated from the isotopic composition, an age of the elements of 5.1×10^9 years being assumed, Shoshone basalt lead taken as present-day lead, and the lead^{206} and lead^{207} contents of primeval lead taken as 7.85 and 6.54, respectively (see text). The lines are calculated decay curves for lead^{206} and lead^{207}. The lead^{208} line is drawn to fit the data. Redrawn after Cameron (unpublished).

this assumption is correct, if the lead:uranium ratio in the crust has been constant and if no lead^{206} was present when the elements were first formed, that time was about 5.3×10^9 years ago (Koczy, 1943; Alpher and Herman, 1951). Vinogradov, Zadorozhnyi, and Zykov (1952) were the first to add new data to Nier's much-used measurements, and again extrapolating backward obtained 5×10^9 years for the age of the elements. Additional isotopic analyses were made by the Toronto group (Collins et al., 1953; Allan et al., 1953), who calculated the age of the elements to be 5.4×10^9 years. Cameron (unpublished), with the aid of all the currently available data obtained a figure between 5 and 5.3×10^9 years ago for the time of nucleogenesis. All these calculations are based on the highly dubious assumption of a lead:uranium ratio constant with time.

An independent method of estimating the maximum age of the elements is based on the observation that most nuclides of odd A have lower cosmic abundances than neighboring nuclides of even A. If one extrapolates this tendency to uranium, and if one assumes that no disproportionate amounts of uranium^{235} were produced by the decay of transuranic elements, it follows that in primordial uranium, the proportion of the isotope of mass 235 should not have exceeded the proportion of the isotope of mass 238. The proportions were equal about 6×10^9 years ago so that nucleogenesis should not have occurred before that time (Tilton, private communication).

It was already mentioned that most of the earlier Holmes-Houtermans calculations gave roughly 3.5×10^9 years for the age of the earth. In some of these calculations (Alpher and Herman, 1951; Collins et al., 1953), astronomical evidence was cited as confirming the lead isotope results. Since that time, the Hubble constant (related to the rate of nebular recession) has been revised, and new measurements with the Palomar telescope indicate that results of all earlier astronomical age calculations are low by as much as a factor of 2. The most recent astronomical evidence yields the figure of about $5 \pm 1 \times 10^9$ years for the age of the elements (Kuiper private communication).

9.2 THE HELIUM AGE METHOD AND THE DISTRIBUTION AND MIGRATION OF HELIUM IN ROCKS *

PATRICK M. HURLEY †

Helium has a geological occurrence and distribution that are unique among the elements. On the average, it is continuously increasing in amount in the earth's crust, being formed at the expense of the elements of the uranium and thorium series, and samarium[152]. On the other hand, the crust is continuously losing helium at a rate that is less than the amount being formed by radioactive decay, and there has been an increasing flow of helium to the surface throughout geologic time in stable crustal areas. The understanding of the magnitude and distribution of this helium flux in continental areas may be best obtained by a study of the ratios of helium to uranium and thorium in rocks and minerals that has been made during investigations of the helium method of age determination.

As a result, this section will attempt to bring together most of the published analyses that are scattered through the literature, and add new unpublished data that are available. It is hoped that this review will be of value both to the study of the geochemical distribution and upward flow of helium, and to those interested in a summary and report of the present status of the helium method of age determination.

9.2.a Historical review

The work of R. J. Strutt, Arthur Holmes, and others. Helium was not detected in terrestrial materials until 1895 although its presence had been noted previously in the sun's spectrum. At that time Ramsay identified the gas in uranium- and thorium-bearing minerals, and this constant association soon led to the observation that helium was generated by the breakdown of the radioactive elements.

* Grants from the Geological Society of America played an important part in the original construction of the laboratory facilities at the Massachusetts Institute of Technology. The Office of Naval Research has provided continuing support. Some of the new data were obtained in collaboration with Professor E. S. Larsen, Jr., and his associates in the Geochemistry and Petrology Branch of the U. S. Geological Survey, whose work is part of a program undertaken by the Survey on behalf of the Division of Research of the Atomic Energy Commission.

† Department of Geology and Geophysics, Massachusetts Institute of Technology, Cambridge 39, Massachusetts.

Rutherford suggested that the helium accumulation in radioactive minerals might be a means of measuring geological time, and R. J. Strutt (1908*a, b*) soon afterwards began research on the content and accumulation of helium in pitchblende and thorianite. He found that the thorianite contained 280 million times as much helium as was subsequently generated in the same mineral in a year. Tests on leakage of helium from these radioactive minerals, however, indicated that at best only minimum results could be obtained. The results of these investigations are given in Table 9.2.1. The term *helium ratio*

Table 9.2.1 Early helium measurements on various materials

Sample	Helium, 10^{-5} cc/g	Uranium, percent	Thorium, percent	Calculated Helium Ratio, 10^6 years	Reference
Pitchblende, Colo.	30,000	67.0	0	3.9	Ramsay-Travers (1897
Pitchblende, Joachimsthal	10,700	62.33	0	1.4	Strutt (1908*a*)
Pitchblende, Cornwall	10,000	18.0	0	4.9	" "
Pitchblende, Katanga	888,000	77.7	0	77	Davis (1926)
Thorianite, Ceylon	930,000	20.8	57.5	225	Strutt (1911)
Thorianite, Ceylon	780,000	11.1	63.8	242	" "
Shark's teeth, Pliocene, Florida	0.17	0.021	...	0.07	Strutt (1908*a*)
Cetacean bones, Pliocene, Felixstowe	0.16	0.013	...	0.10	" "
Phosphatic nodules, Pliocene, Felixstowe	0.098	0.0040	...	0.21	" "
Phosphatic nodules, Cretaceous, Cambridge	3.03	0.0092	...	2.9	" "
Phosphatic nodules, Cretaceous, Potton, England	2.10	0.0049	...	3.7	" "
Saurian bones, Jurassic, Ely, England	0.36	0.0028	...	1.1	" "
Phosphatic nodules, Jurassic, Knapwell, England	0.67	0.0061	...	0.97	" "
Saurian bones, Jurassic, Whittlesea	0.51	0.00078	...	5.7	" "
Bone, Jurassic, Dorset	0.22	0.0018	...	1.0	" "
Nodules, Ordovician, N. Wales	15.2	0.0027	...	49.0	" "
Phosphatic limestone, Ordovician, Chirbury, England	5.6	0.00067	...	73.5	" "
Phosphatic nodules, Torridon, Scotland	0.83	0.00083	...	0.87	" "

is used instead of *helium age* in this report in all instances where there is a probability of helium loss or where there has been no specific attempt to correct the ratio so that it would refer to absolute age.

Strutt followed up this work by analyses of radium, thorium, and helium in phosphatic deposits, iron ores, titanites, zircons, and some other minerals. The results are shown in Tables 9.2.1 and 9.2.2.

Even more interesting today is the early work on liberation and diffusion of helium in minerals. Strutt (1909), working on monazite and thorianite, showed that some of the helium was released immediately on grinding, but this was followed by a long-continued leakage

Table 9.2.2 Helium measurements on iron ores, zircons, sphenes, beryls, and fluorite

After R. J. Strutt

Sample	Helium, 10^{-5} cc/g	Uranium, 10^{-6} g/g	Thorium, 10^{-6} g/g	Calculated Helium Ratio, 10^6 years	Reference
Iron ores					
Spacrosiderite, Oligocene, Rhine Province	0.16	1.53	1.66	7.3	(1910*a*, *b*)
Pisolitic hematite, Oligocene, Antrim	0.34	2.04	7.67	7.2	"
Hematite, Oligocene, Antrim	1.21	2.24	7.27	25	"
Spathic ore, Jurassic, Yorks	1.07	3.91	11.8	13	"
Oolitic ore, Jurassic, Wurtemburg	0.89	1.91	1.49	34	"
Spathic ore, Jurassic, Cleveland, England	1.39	5.70	34.7	8	"
Hematite, Late Paleozoic, Cumberland	1.65	0.4	0	121	(1908*a*)
Limonite, Late Carboniferous, England	1.50	8.73	4.25	134	(1910*a*, *b*)
Hematite, Devonian, Caen, France	9.84	3.72	13.2	119	"
Zircons					
Recent, Vesuvius, Italy	4	3220	0	0.1	"
Pleistocene, Magen, Germany	11.4	1077	0	1.0	"
Pliocene, New Zealand	8.1	269	700	1.6	"
Miocene, Auvergne, France	21.2	315	0	6	"
Jurassic, N.E. Tasmania	43.4	97	0	40	"
Lower Permian, Urals	3000	538	4090	160	"
Probably Late Carboniferous, Colo.	1930	1085	1000	125	"
" " " N. Carolina	2550	1094	2650	125	"
Devonian, S. Norway	988	1128	2870	45	"
Doubtful Kimberley, S. Africa	3230	916	116	300	"
Ceylon gravels	2100	557	1740	180	"
" "	2830	856	352	260	"
" "	5750	6385	2505	70	"
Renfrew Co., Ontario	1140	155	81	565	"
Sphenes					
Pleistocene, Laacher See	0.6	42	1512	0.9	(1911)
Pre-Cambrian, Cold Spring, N. Y.	1010	159	372	343	"
" " Lewis Co., N. Y.	1660	230	323	476	"
" " Renfrew Co., Ontario	948	365	174	202	"
" " " " "	1760	146	424	595	"
" " Twedestrand, Norway	336	65	416	166	"
" " " "	454	78	72	412	"
" " Arendal, Norway	1230	209	381	347	"
Other minerals					
Fluorite, Devonian, Greenland	1930	25	1600	380	"
Beryl, Mid. Devonian, Norway	240	63	...	334	(1908*a*)
" Paleozoic, Mass.	30	0.8	...	3,250	"
" " Pa.	680	19	...	3,100	"
" " N. H.	1280	1.2	...	94,000	(1911)

of helium from the newly created surfaces. Gray (1909), working also on thorianite, succeeded in liberating 28 percent of the accumulated store of helium by grinding to a size of 1 to 2 microns. It was found that the more finely the mineral was ground, the greater was the amount of helium set free, down to a size limit of about 3 microns. Some 70 percent of the helium appears to be very firmly held in the mineral.

Wood (1911) experimented on the effect of heat in liberating helium. Using monazite and thorianite, he found very little release up to 300° C to 400° C. Following this, helium came off at a steadily increasing rate up to 800° C or 900° C accompanied by development of cracks in the mineral. It must be remembered that the thorianite used contained about one million times more helium than common rocks and minerals. The helium pressure in the mineral may have been as high as 100 or 200 atmospheres. Monazite heated to 720° C lost 68 percent of its helium. Another specimen lost up to 88 percent at 900° C, and up to 98 percent at 1000° C. Thorianite lost 62 percent at 750° C and 100 percent at 1000° C. Strutt in most of his work liberated all the helium by taking the material into solution with acids or fluxes.

Paneth and Peters (1928) demonstrated the diffusion of helium through glass at ordinary temperatures. Lo Surdo (1921) found that in an hour 10^{-9} cc of helium from the air passed through each square centimeter of a hard glass tube, 1.5 mm thick, at 500° C. Williams and Ferguson (1922) worked on the preferential permeability of silica glass to helium at various temperatures. Below 300° C hydrogen does not begin to diffuse through appreciably, but at 500° C the permeability to helium is nearly 30 times as high as that to hydrogen.

For a number of years the loss of helium from radioactive minerals discouraged work on the helium method of age determination, and the lead method was investigated instead. In 1929 the helium method was brought into the light again on the suggestion by Holmes that ordinary igneous rocks which contain radioactivity equivalent to only 10^{-12} gram of radium per gram of rock should have such small accumulations of helium that a much larger fraction of the helium is probably retained. Accordingly, Holmes arranged for determinations of radium and thorium by Dubey and Gunther in the laboratory of Professor Paneth in Berlin. The analyses were made on specimens from Deccan traps and Gwalior dolerites in India, and from the Whin Sill and Cleveland Dyke in England (Dubey, 1930; Holmes and Harwood, 1928; Holmes, 1931). Results are shown in Table 9.2.3. Holmes concluded from the low helium in the first two specimens that acid rocks did not retain helium as well as basic rocks. Later, Holmes and Paneth collaborated on the study of minerals and inclusions in kimberlite from South Africa (Table 9.2.3).

Paneth et al. (1928) failed to find 10 percent loss of helium from iron meteorite material after heating for 5 hours at 500° C. Paneth and Urry in further work (1930*a*, *b*) found that a specimen of the

Table 9.2.3 Helium measurements on some igneous rocks

Sample	Helium, 10^{-5} cc/g	Uranium, 10^{-6} g/g	Thorium, 10^{-6} g/g	Helium Ratio, 10^6 years	Reference
Igneous rocks					
Whin Sill, Carboniferous, Westmorland	3.6	0.81	3.0	182	Dubey-Holmes (1929)
Cleveland Dyke, Tertiary, Durham	1.1	1.83	6.1	26	" " "
Belaki-Bauri, Gwalior Series	5.5	0.51	1.7	466	Dubey (1930)
Santowa-Temak, " "	4.2	0.54	1.5	369	" "
Paniar, " "	3.1	0.69	2.4	190	" "
Acid felsite, Miocene, Mt. Pawagarh, plug	1.1	6.6	41.0	5	Urry (1933)
" " " " " "	1.0	6.6	31.0	6	" "
Kimberlite and its inclusions, S. Africa					
Kimberlite	3.05	3.2	5.3	58	Holmes-Paneth (1936)
Olivine-melilitite	2.13	2.6	3.8	51	" " "
Amphibolite group					
Basic appinite	10.1	2.4	6.0	219	" " "
" "	21.1	2.7	6.1	429	" " "
Appinite	3.7	2.0	4.8	98	" " "
Hornblende-gneiss	8.7	1.8	3.9	265	" " "
Basic granulite	0.4	1.6	3.1	16	" " "
Eclogite nodules					
Eclogite	1.94	1.3	1.3	106	" " "
"	1.9	0.7	0.5	210	" " "
"	9.2	1.5	2.1	398	" " "
Peridotite suite					
Lherzolite	0.37	1.0	1.7	22	" " "
Harzburgite	0.22	1.1	1.7	12	" " "
Saxonite	0.17	0.8	1.1	13	" " "
Phlogopite-glimmerite	0.81	4.2	3.8	14	" " "
Chrome-diopside	0.57	1.9	2.7	19	" " "
Garnet	0.16	0.5	0.6	21	" " "
Zircon xenocrysts					
Zircon	18.0	55.2	8.1	28	" " "
"	27.0	89.7	13.6	25	" " "
"	16.0	29.3	19.5	41	" " "

Mount Ayliff iron meteorite, which was richest in helium and gave the highest "age," lost less than 5 percent of its helium when held for 12 hours at 800° C.

The work of W. D. Urry. Urry (1932) investigated the permeability of various glasses to helium. He recorded the rate of diffusion of helium, neon, and hydrogen at comparatively low temperatures and pressures through various glasses, and concluded that in the process of diffusion helium and hydrogen are first adsorbed on the glass surface and that diffusion proceeds from this layer. Urry (1932) also found that there was no diffusion of helium within his limits of detection (10^{-10} cc) through bismuth or iron under normal conditions and a considerable range of temperatures. He found no passage of helium through a single quartz crystal, but a relative flow rate through basalt and an aggregate of quartz crystals in a ratio of 1 to 10. He considered the flow to occur mainly through intergranular capillary openings. From 1932 to 1936 Urry investigated helium age ratios, and finally drew up a post-Proterozoic time scale (1936*b*). A number of analyses were made also on a suite of rocks of Keweenawan age from the copper mining district in Michigan (Lane and Urry, 1935).

The agreement between Urry's helium age scale and the lead age measurements appeared to be good, and the agreement of the specimens with the sequence indicated by geology was excellent. The time scale, as published by Holmes in his book, *Age of the Earth* (1937), was widely used. Unfortunately it later became apparent to Evans, Keevil, and Goodman, searching for the discrepancy in ages shown by a new direct alpha-counting technique, that Urry's measurements were in error, owing to faulty calibrations. As a result the so-called helium time scale had to be abandoned. The errors for the most part exceeded a factor of 2. The details of the investigation were published in a joint paper by Evans, Goodman, Keevil, Lane, and Urry (1939).

Investigations subsequent to 1936. In 1936 Evans established a laboratory at the Massachusetts Institute of Technology to study the radioactivity of terrestrial materials and methods of age determination. Goodman collaborated with Evans, and in 1937 Keevil joined their ranks. Most of his analyses are listed in Table 9.2.4, together with references to his publications.

His excellent and copious measurements demonstrated the consistently low helium ratios of granitic rocks, usually 20 to 30 percent of the true age of the rock, and the fact that helium ratios on the separate minerals of a single rock sample are different and maintain roughly the same difference in most cases. As a typical example, the averages for the minerals separated from the Cape Ann granite, Massachusetts, are given by Keevil (1942) in the accompanying table.

Sample	Helium, 10^{-5} cc/g	Radium, 10^{-12} g/g	Thorium, 10^{-6} g/g	Helium Ratio, 10^{6} years
Quartz	4.1	0.8	5.7	94
Feldspar	1.5	0.49	3.1	59
Femics	56	6.4	48	159
Whole rock	9.7	1.78	17.1	89

The age of the rock is probably late Paleozoic (roughly 200 million years). These differences were ascribed to a varying retentivity between the minerals, and it was assumed that helium escaped more readily from some minerals than from others. The ferromagnesian

Table 9.2.4 Keevil's helium measurements for rocks and minerals

Igneous rocks and minerals, Keevil (1938*b*, *c*)

Sample	Helium, 10^{-5} cc/g	Radium, 10^{-12} g/g	Thorium, 10^{-6} g/g	Helium Ratio, 10^6 years
Quincy granite, Mass. (Carbonif.)				
Ferromagnesian minerals only	11.4	1.78	25.0	86
Quartz only	2.6	0.61	3.4	86
Feldspar only	1.54	0.41	6.2	49
Granite as a whole	4.33	0.98	12.4	63
Granite 12′ down	3.5	0.91	8.2	67
" 120′ "	4.3	0.98	12.4	65
" 150′ "	4.0	1.20	9.0	65
" 350′ "	3.2	0.95	7.0	65
" 600′ "	4.2	(1.8 alphas/mg. hr)		68
Granite Ry. quarry	4.0	1.06	9.3	65
Dell Hitchcock quarry	5.3	1.25	11.7	72
Xenolith, Fine grained	7.0	1.50	20.8	65
Other rocks				
Granite, Rockport, Mass. (Miss.)	10.5	1.88	16.4	99
Xenolith, " "	11.6	1.95	22.2	93
Granite, Chelmsford, Mass. (Miss.)	17.4	5.30	26.2	72
Pegmatite, " "	0.8	0.61	1.9	33
Granite, Fitchburg, Mass. (Carb.)	3.5	0.78	19.0	45
Pegmatite, " "	0.7	1.08	1.2	20

Pre-Cambrian rocks, Keevil (1943*b*)

Sample	Helium, 10^{-5} cc/g	Activity, α/mg-h	Helium Ratio, 10^6 years
Granite, Taschereau, Que.	1.75	1.01	53
Granodiorite, " "	2.03	0.31	200
" La Motte Lake, Que.	3.55	0.76	143
" Varsan Twp., "	11.0	0.46	710
Quartz Porphyry, Noranda, "	4.08	1.02	123
Diabase, " "	4.9	0.71	210
Granite, Kingston, Ont.	7.5	0.95	242
" " "	6.0	0.72	255
Quartz and feldspar, Kingston, Ont.	1.1	0.173	195
Granite, Gananoque, Ont.	2.8	0.64	134
" Blue Mt.	0.38	0.08	145
" " "	1.31	0.19	215
" " "	0.95	0.055	590
" " "	1.15	0.04	810
Porphyry, Porcupine Area, Ont.	0.85	0.64	41
" " " "	1.18	0,60	60
Quartz, " " "	0.51	0,23	69
Quartz, Dome gold mines	11.7	0.10	3,350
Porphyry pebble, Dome gold mines	1.51	0.40	116
Agglomerate, Tisdale Twp.	0.85	0.49	53
Porphyry, Bristol Twp.	1.27	0.26	150
" " "	0.55	0.5	34
Gold quartz, " "	0.16	0.06	80
Porphyry, Hollinger mine	10.0	0.46	630
" " "	15.3	0.35	1,230
" " "	13.0	0.46	83
" " "	2.37	0.36	202
Granite, Peterson L., Manitoba	17.6	2.34	226
Matavolcanic, " "	1.17	0.02	1,610
" felsic portion	1.97	0.045	1,290
" mafic "	1.66	0.02	2,275
Granite, Tanganyika	0.92	1.40	20
" "	18.3	3.0	191
Gneiss, "	1.15	1.67	21
Granodiorite	1.00	0.12	253

Table 9.2.4 Keevil's helium measurements for rocks and minerals (*Cont.*)

Minerals separated from rocks

Sample	Helium, 10^{-5} cc/g	Activity, α/mg-h	Helium Ratio, 10^6 years
Yellowknife diabase (1), *Keevil, Jolliffe, and Larsen* (1942)			
Magnetite	14.4	0.18	2,460
Pyroxene	5.5	0.10	1,740
Mafic fraction	5.6	0.29	593
Plagioclase	0.45	0.25	55
"	0.35	0.20	54
Whole diabase	4.1	0.11	1,100
Yellowknife diabase (2)			
Magnetite	21.8	0.04	16,700
Pyroxene and olivine	7.9	0.22	1,100
Plagioclase	0.56	0.04	430
"	0.27	0.06	140
Lakeview tonalite, Riverside Co., Calif., Larsen and Keevil (1942)			
Whole rock	2.37	0.95	77
Quartz	0.40	0.12	74
Plagioclase	0.79	0.63	39
"	0.32	0.22	44
"	0.31	0.23	41
Biotite	1.17	0.39	91
Hornblende	5.1	0.78	200
Apatite	79.6	56.2	43
Zircon	305	401	23
Sphene	264	266	30
Bonsall tonalite, S. Calif.			
Whole rock	0.59	1.01	18
Biotite	0.60	0.12	150
Granodiorite, S. Calif.			
Whole rock	0.92	0.43	66
45% quartz, 55% feldspar	0.21	0.125	51
52% " 48% "	0.14	0.12	36
20% " 80% "	0.34	0.15	70
95% biotite, 5% feldspar	0.75	0.44	52
Granodiorite, Flavrian Lake, Que., Keevil (1943*b*)			
Whole rock	3.13	0.43	223
Quartz	0.93	0.30	95
Feldspar	0.87	0.17	166
Hornblende	3.66	0.59	190
Rapakivi granite, Finland			
Quartz	1.47	1.52	30
Green feldspar	3.10	2.46	39
Pink "	1.77	0.2	270
Biotite	10.9	2.74	122
Onas Island granite			
Feldspar	1.54	1.3	36
Hornblende	25.1	2.95	261
Chelmsford granite, Mass., Keevil et al. (1944)			
Microcline	0.8	1.9	13
Quartz and feldspar	1.1	1.5	23
Muscovite	1.43	115	29
Biotite	33.4	13.1	78
Chlorite	1.1	24.5	1
Epidote	320	213	46
Garnet	40.3	3.6	340
Apatite	4,260	710	185
Zircon	120,000	14,000	260
Sphene	248	8	955

minerals generally seemed to retain more helium than the feldspars and quartz. Acid felsitic and glassy rocks were particularly low in helium.

Mafic rocks were found to have generally higher ratios, with some suggestion that this percentage decreased with increasing age. For example, in a list of measurements on diabases and basalts (Keevil, 1943*c*), the helium retentivities were Miocene (0.60), Triassic (0.45), and pre-Cambrian (0.34).

Larsen worked with Keevil during his later work, and provided him with very complete separations of major and minor minerals from igneous rocks. These demonstrate the great differences in activity that exist between the minerals, and also the fact that helium is similarly distributed. Keevil also analyzed a number of less common minerals. It is unfortunate that his principal study of minerals other than the rock-forming ones should have been made on a suite from Franklin and Sterling Hill, New Jersey (1943*c*). Although this geological area is generally accepted as pre-Cambrian, there is considerable evidence that mid-Paleozoic deformation may have caused some recrystallization. There is an interesting coincidence in the helium ratios of various minerals measured by Keevil and samples of zircon and sphene from the same belt measured by this writer. These data are compared and discussed below.

During this period Gerling and his associates at the Radium Institute of the Academy of Sciences of the USSR carried on investigations on the helium method and related subjects. The relationship between helium loss and closeness of packing of the crystal structure was studied (Gerling, 1939*a*), and it was concluded that the bulk of the rock-forming minerals are loose structures and would be least likely to hold helium. Minerals with close packing that were suggested for investigation of helium retention were corundum, polyanite, rutile, chrysoberyl, topaz, cyanite, pyrope, almandine, niobite, magnesite, and spinel. In this group the volume per 1 atom of oxygen was between 14 and 16 cubic angstroms as opposed to the range 16 to 23 for the rock-forming silicates. This was compared with the volume of 13.9 cubic angstroms for the theoretically closest packing per 1 atom of oxygen. Gerling also stated that it was necessary that the mineral be as free as possible from inclusions, have suffered no metamictization, and have no cleavage. Minerals were selected and tested as shown in Table 9.2.5.

Table 9.2.5 Helium measurements by Gerling (1939*a*)

Sample	Geologic Age	Helium Ratio, 10^6 years	Probable Loss of Helium, %
Khlopinite, Transbaikal	Jurassic-Permian	132	12–25
Eschinite, Ural	Permian-Carbonif.	210	<10
Samarskite, Ural	Permian-Carbonif.	237	<10
Loparite, Khibiny	Carbonif.-Devonian	280	<10

Following this, Gerling (1939*b*) measured the rate of diffusion of helium out of selected radioactive minerals, as a function of temperature. He obtained interesting curves of helium effusion that showed not only the change of diffusion coefficient with temperature but also the effect of helium coming out of more than one position in the structure. Using the relationship between temperature and diffusion coefficient, $D = D_0 \exp(-E/Rt)$, he calculated the "heat of diffusion" for helium coming out of different positions in the structure, for several different mineral specimens, as shown in Table 9.2.6.

Table 9.2.6 Gerling's "heat of diffusion" (1939*b*)

Mineral	Helium Ratio, 10^6 years	% Loss of Helium	Heat of Diffusion in cal/gram-atom of Helium			
			I	II	III	IV
Massive loparite, 1–2 mm	280	10	...	34,300	...	...
Poikilitic loparite, 1–2 mm	170	40	22,300	34,000	...	...
Monazite grains, 0.2–0.5 mm	852	47	6,300	27,800	41,400	50,300
Monazite dust, 0.1 mm	852	47	...	28,700	40,500	...
Uraninite grains, 0.2–0.5 mm	48	97	9,600	15,000	...	...

Applying this method to specimens of samarskite and eschinite from pegmatites of the Ilmen Reserve in the Urals, Gerling and Vladimirova (1942) found the helium ages given in Table 9.2.7. In

Table 9.2.7 Helium age of the Ilmen Reserve pegmatites in the Urals (Gerling and Vladimirova, 1942)

Mineral	He, mg/g	U, g/g	Th, g/g	Age in 10^6 years
Samarskite	3.41	0.1038	0.0503	248
Eschinite	0.591	...	0.0901	213

the samarskite for the first process of helium escape the heat of diffusion was found to be 59,000 cal per gram-atom of helium. This value corresponds to a release of 4 to 5 percent of the helium available in the mineral. This quantity of helium was supposed to have evolved by way of diffusion across such disturbances in the lattice as had arisen from the interaction of water with ferrous oxide. The second value of the heat of diffusion was equal to 71,000 cal per gram-atom of helium; in this process the main amount of helium was set free, and it was therefore considered to represent the diffusion of helium across the lattice of the samarskite. This very high value of 71,000 cal for samarskite was believed to exceed by a factor of 2 the least value at which full preservation of helium in the mineral can be guaranteed. Therefore the age of 248×10^6 years was believed to be quite accurate. An attempt to investigate the process of helium evolution from eschinite failed, because this mineral was so retentive that heating up to 1200° C released only 20 percent of the total amount of helium.

Table 9.2.8 Helium analyses of beryllium, boron, and lithium minerals of the USSR (Khlopin and Abidov, 1941)

Mineral	Locality	Geologic Age	Percent Be, B, or Li	Helium, 10^{-5} cc/g
Beryllium minerals				
Beryl	Krasnoyarsky	Pre-Cambrian	4.1	261
"	Dniepropetrovsk	"	4.1	384
"	Tian-Shan	Paleozoic	4.1	643
"	Sarykoy	"	4.1	591
"	Turkestan	"	4.1	402
"	Chatkal	"	4.1	357
Bertrandite	Altai	"	7.4	96
Beryl	Ilmen Mts.	"	4.1	52
"	Urals	"	4.1	30
"	"	"	4.1	27
"	"	"	4.1	23
"	"	"	4.1	20
"	Sverdlov	"	4.1	85
"	"	"	4.1	6
Vorobyevite	"	"	5.0	4
Beryl	Altai	"	4.1	3
Chrysoberyl	Urals	"	7.1	2
Aquam arine	Chita	Mesozoic or Cenozoic	5.0	4
"	"	" " "	5.0	4
Vorobyevite	Transbaikal	" " "	5.0	4
Beryl	"	" " "	4.1	3
Helvite	"	" " "	3.0	1
Boron minerals				
Tourmaline	Karelia	Pre-Cambrian	2.0	0.7
"	Urals	Paleozoic	2.0	6.1
"	Kirghiz, USSR	"	2.0	1.5
Lithium minerals				
Spodumene	Tadjik, USSR	Paleozoic	3.8	1.0
Zinnwaldite	Mongolia	Mesozoic	2.4	3.2

Gerling (1940) also measured the solubility of helium in a silicate melt. He found that 1 g of gabbro-diabase melt dissolved about 2 mm^3 of helium and that approximately this amount was retained by the solid aggregate even after slow cooling and partial crystallization. This would explain the high amounts of helium occasionally found in igneous rocks, as for example in the Sudbury norite and olivine diabase.

Since Strutt's early measurements on beryl there was much discussion on the cause of the anomalously high helium content of this mineral. Khlopin and Abidov (1941) measured the helium content of a number of beryllium, boron, and lithium minerals (Tables 9.2.8 and

Table 9.2.9 Excess helium in beryllium and boron minerals of the USSR. All are Paleozoic except the first beryl, which is pre-Cambrian (Khlopin and Abidov, 1941)

Mineral	Locality	Helium, 10^{-5} cc/g	Radium, 10^{-12} g/g	Thorium, 10^{-6} g/g	Radiogenic Helium, 10^{-5} cc/g	Excess Helium, 10^{-5} cc/g
Beryl	Ukraine	384	0.34	6.9	42.5	341
"	Turkestan	402	0.10	...	0.7	401
"	Urals	52	0.41	1.2	5.1	46
"	"	30	0.02	1.0	0.9	30
"	"	20	0.04	1.0	1.1	19
Vorobyevite	"	4.2	0.02	...	0.2	3
Chrysoberyl	"	2.2	0.04	...	0.3	1.9
Tourmaline	"	6.1	0.05	0.9	1.2	4.9

9.2.9). The analyses indicate that the amount of helium present in beryllium minerals does not depend on the radioactivity of the mineral, the beryllium content, or the age of the mineral. Some of the minerals especially rich in beryllium, for example phenacite, contain practically no helium, although beryl from the same deposit shows a helium content of 85×10^{-5} cc/g. Furthermore, these investigators found that boron and lithium minerals also occasionally contain anomalous amounts of helium. They concluded that the most probable explanation is either the selective occlusion by the minerals of helium dissolved in the magma or else the absorption by the minerals of considerable quantities of relatively short-lived radioactive elements in the course of the mineral's crystallization.

Other minerals have been found that show anomalous helium contents. For example, Keevil (1943*c*) found the accompanying minerals in the suite from Franklin, New Jersey.

	Helium Ratio, 10^6 years
Schefferite	2,200
Calcite	1,600
Calcite	2,360
Calcite	10,200
Barite	1,140
Sussexite	3,550

Other cases appear in the various tables of this chapter and in Table 4.1. Because such minerals as magnetite and quartz also can behave in this way occasionally, it seems likely that occlusion at time of crystallization in a concentrated helium environment is a possible

Table 9.2.10 Helium measurements on the Triassic Palisades diabase and separated minerals (Hurley and Goodman, 1941)

Sample	Helium, 10^{-5} cc/g	Radium, 10^{-12} g/g	Thorium, 10^{-6} g/g	Helium Ratio, 10^6 years
Tests for helium loss on grinding				
Staten Is.—¼ in.	0.82			
—¼ in.	0.95			
—¼ in.	1.03			
—48 + 100 mesh	0.92			
—48 + 100 mesh	0.84			
—48 + 100 mesh	0.99			
—48 + 100 mesh	0.80			
—100 mesh	0.91			
Samples of whole rock				
Staten Is.	0.91	0.24	2.14	62
N. Bergen	0.96	0.19	2.37	72
Guttenberg	0.93	0.16	2.34	75
Edgewater	1.02	0.14	2.08	92
Kingston	1.01	0.17	2.60	76
Feldspar				
Staten Is.	0.25	0.23	2.24	18
N. Bergen	0.31	0.18	1.76	28
Guttenberg	0.57	0.13	1.44	66
Edgewater	0.35	0.12	1.82	37
Kingston	0.30	0.11	1.81	34
Virginia	0.38	0.14	2.10	35
Pyroxene				
Staten Is.	1.57	0.23	2.48	105
N. Bergen	1.46	0.18	2.51	109
Guttenberg	1.29	0.19	2.72	90
Edgewater	1.37	0.14	2.36	119
Kingston	1.46	0.18	3.49	90
Virginia	1.52	0.25	2.22	102

Magnetite associated with Triassic diabase—see Table 9.2.11.

mechanism. The helium content of the beryl may be due to the reaction Be^9 (γ, n) Be^8 (2α) 2 He^4 in agreement with the rather low He^3/He^4 ratio in beryls. It is interesting to note that this ratio for beryls is roughly the same as for natural gas (Table 4.1). This coincidence tends to sustain the occlusion hypothesis. Finally the helium content of native bismuth (Table 9.2.14), that grew in a uranium-rich vein at Great Bear Lake, may represent the mechanism in which the growing mineral occluded short-lived alpha-radioactive atoms.

In 1938 Hurley joined the group at the Massachusetts Institute of Technology, and he and Goodman (1941) continued the study of helium loss in minerals separated from rocks of well-known geological age. Table 9.2.10 gives results on samples of Triassic diabase of a probable true age of 160 million years. This rock contained pyroxene with an average ratio of 103, and feldspar with an average ratio of 36 million years. Magnetite concentrates from the same rocks averaged 160 million years when free from impurities.

This work led to a more general study of helium age ratios in magnetite, since this mineral had exhibited the highest retention of helium. Measurements made by Hurley and Goodman (1943) are given in Table 9.2.11. The helium ratios in most cases showed ages corresponding roughly with ages inferred from the few lead measurements available.

However there were some notable exceptions, and magnetite obtained from rocks of a granitic type seemed unreliable. The best material seemed to be that found in deposits of hydrothermal or contact metamorphic origin. The explanation for the unreliability of these rocks seems to lie at least in part in the presence of acid-soluble radioactive contaminants.

Work on the helium method stopped during the war years. Since that time active investigations of the method have continued in the laboratory of Professor Paneth at Durham, and in this writer's laboratory at the Massachusetts Institute of Technology. Paneth has continued studies on meteorites and on the helium and other rare gases of the upper atmosphere. Work in the M.I.T. laboratory has been concentrated on the problem of helium escape from rocks and minerals and on the distribution of the radioactive elements within rocks. The results of these investigations are discussed in some detail, since they appear to be the key to the possible future use of the helium method as a geological tool.

9.2.b Reasons for low or variable helium ratios

It has commonly been assumed that helium ratios are low because helium atoms diffuse through the crystalline structures of rock minerals, accumulate in the boundary regions of the crystals, and gradually find ways of escape to the surface through openings in the rock.

Table 9.2.11 Helium measurements on magnetite and sulfide minerals (Hurley and Goodman, 1943)

Sample	Helium, 10^{-5} cc/g	Radium, 10^{-12} g/g	Thorium, 10^{-6} g/g	Probable Geologic Age	Helium Ratio, 10^6 years
Desert Mound, Utah	0.60	0.67	4.4	Miocene	17
Chesapeake, "	1.0	1.09	10.5	"	15
Great Western, "	0.80	1.00	6.7	"	15
Blk. Magnetic, "	0.82	0.91	2.6	"	21
Snoqualmie Pass, Wash.	0.21	0.22	0.4	"	25
Sierra de Carrizal	0.43	0.26	0.3	Tertiary	45
Haiti (magnetite)	0.51	0.33	<0.1	Eocene	46
Haiti (sulfide)	0.19	0.13	<0.1	"	43
Fierro, N. M.	0.16	0.07	0.2	Laramide	53
Bingham, Utah (galena)	0.69	0.40	<0.1	"	51
Calumet, Colo.	0.14	0.05	<0.1	"	75
Stoddard, Colo.	0.70	0.27	1.6	"	>51
Whitehall, Mont. (sulf.)	3.31	2.0	0.1	"	50
Magnet Cove, Ark.	0.17	0.08	<0.1	Cretaceous	63
Besshi, Japan	0.78	0.26	<0.1	Mesozoic	90
Texada Is., B. C.	1.77	0.42	0.35	Nevadan	117
" " "	2.35	0.58	<0.1	"	120
Lynn Valley, B. C.	1.70	0.49	0.28	"	100
Butte Co., Calif.	0.22	0.024	0.36	"	120
Juragua, Cuba	0.22	0.07	<0.1	"	100
Clipper Gap, Calif.	0.34	0.08	<0.1	"	132
Pr. of Wales Is., Alaska	5.00	1.08	0.52	"	132
Goose Cr., Va.	1.99	0.24	2.2	Triassic	140
French Cr., Pa.	0.86	0.09	1.10	"	140
Boyertown, Pa.	1.88	0.28	1.03	"	152
Dillsburg, Pa.	0.74	0.12	0.38	"	143
Preakness Mt., N. J.	1.69	0.28	0.58	"	153
Lakeville, N. S.	1.37	0.22	0.30	"	169
Gerrish Mt., N. S.	0.74	0.04	1.1	"	158
Cashtown, Pa.	5.59	0.90	0.55	"	174
Virginia diabase	2.42	0.17	3.10	"	165
Rammelsberg (pyrite)	4.72	0.68	0.41	Upper Carb.	200
Trun, Spain	1.42	0.15	0.62	"	205
Oviedo, "	10.5	0.67	10.6	"	200
Chester, Mass.	0.20	0.02	0.05	"	225
Ducktown, Tenn. (sulf.)	3.50	0.40	1.07	"	215
" " "	2.20	0.22	0.43	"	245
Magnitnaya, Urals	3.78	0.45	0.20	"	240
" "	6.0	0.71	0.29	"	245
Vysokaya, "	0.80	0.05	0.23	Devonian	340
Blagodat "	1.24	0.08	0.23	"	365
" "	1.42	0.11	0.26	"	340
Salem, Mass	0.86	0.05	0.35	Early Paleozoic	>330
Lökken, Norway (sulf.)	3.18	0.22	0.22	Silurian	390
Mellen, Wis.	3.28	0.13	0.72	Keweenawan	500
Eagle R., Mich.	3.04	0.10	0.67	"	550
Sudbury, Ont. (pyrrhotite)	3.59	0.10	1.06	Pre-Cambrian	550
" " "	0.76	0.03	0.13	"	620
Salisbury, N. Y.	7.25	0.23	1.94	"	540
Ford Mine, N. J.	3.95	0.08	1.62	"	550
Ringwood, N. J.	10.6	0.27	5.9	"	410
Mineville, N. Y.	5.33	0.02	3.1	"	560
Salisbury, N. Y.	4.36	0.16	1.15	"	500
Franklin Furnace, N. J.	0.66	0.029	<0.02	"	640
Edwards, Mich.	37.3	0.60	1.95	"	1,300
Republic, "	17.4	0.30	1.13	"	1,200

Table 9.2.11 Helium measurements on magnetite and sulfide minerals (Hurley and Goodman, 1943) (Cont.)

Sample	Helium, 10^{-5} cc/g	Radium, 10^{-12} g/g	Thorium, 10^{-6} g/g	Probable Geologic Age	Helium Ratio, 10^6 years
Spur, Mich.	2.39	0.07	0.15	Pre-Cambrian	800
Michigamme, "	8.65	0.13	0.40	"	1,400
Champion, "	8.52	0.094	0.40	"	1,650
Humboldt, "	66.6	0.98	0.24	"	1,650
Giant's Range, Minn. (impure)	73.3	1.00	18.7	"	>800
Cranberry, N. C.	1.50	0.04	0.18	"	830
" "	2.76	0.06	<0.1	"	1,260
Llano Co., Texas	5.09	0.05	0.95	"	1,050
Kiruna, Sweden	63.0	0.30	18.0	"	1,000
" "	9.6	0.10	1.2	"	1,325
Dungannon, Ont.	2.81	0.03	0.32	"	1,450
Cumberlandite, Cumberland, R. I.	3.7	0.02	0.50	"	1,500
Grangesberg, Sweden	18.0	0.09	2.4	"	1,650
Falun, Sweden	37.9	0.56	<0.1	"	1,650
Greatly discordant cases					
Sudbury olivine diabase	34.8	0.08	0.24	"	10,000
" norite	120.0	0.10		"	<36,000
" pyrrhotite	3.80	<0.01	<0.1	"	>12,000
" "	2.84	0.02	<0.1	"	4,700
Caribou, Colo.	4.10	0.02	<0.1	"	5,700
Bancroft, Ont.	2.49	0.14	1.37	"	300
Craigmont, Ont.	1.03	0.05	<0.1	"	600
Monmouth, Ont.	0.85	0.05	0.25	"	370
Ketchikan, Alaska	1.39	0.13	0.34	Nevadan	270
St. Charles, Que.	0.16	0.02	<0.7	Pre-Cambrian	<200
Broken Hill, N. S. W. (galena)	<1.2	1.0		"	<30
Keewatin Province, Ont., Hurley (1949)					
Larder Lake, Ont.	16.9	Activity	0.19	α/mg-h	2,100
" " "	8.4	"	0.08	"	2,400
Noranda, P. Q.	11.4	"	0.14	"	2,000

If this were known to be true for all minerals, work on the method would have stopped long ago. It is known that the diffusion coefficients for helium in undisturbed crystals of magnetite, zircon, and sphene are so small as to permit no measurable loss of helium in periods of the order of 10^9 years. It is not known, as yet, that the coefficients for common minerals such as quartz and feldspar are significantly higher despite a natural tendency to assume so from measured age ratios. A difference between these two groups of minerals not related to the permeability of their structures to the diffusion of helium is the tolerance of the structures to substitutions of uranium and thorium for their essential constitutents. In the former minerals, such as zircon, the radioactive elements are distributed throughout the structure, whereas in the latter minerals, such as quartz, the content of radioactive elements is believed to occur largely in small inclusions and imperfections and on the surfaces of fractures. Thus, although the helium content of quartz and feldspar can be measured easily, it is impossible to know how much of the radioactivity is contamination. Since quartz and feldspar crystals probably always grow with less radioactive element content than their surroundings, they are probably always subject to radioactive contamination from their surroundings.

Nevertheless, contamination is not the only answer to low helium ratios because helium driven into neighboring crystalline material as alpha particles from surfaces coated with the radioactive elements should still be held as tightly as if the helium originated from uniformly dispersed parent atoms. If the gross content of helium in a granite sample collected 3000 feet below the surface is only one-half of what it should be for its activity and age, this should not mean that the granite has been recently contaminated by meteoric waters to twice its original activity. Another factor which is known to be causing helium loss and which may account for discrepancies not explained by contamination is the damage to the crystalline structure caused by concentration of the radioactive elements into localized centers that become intensely irradiated. Studies of these factors of contamination and radiation damage are reviewed below roughly in chronological sequence.

9.2.c Distribution and possible migration of uranium and thorium in rocks

As seen in the measurements of Larsen and Keevil on the minerals of the Lakeview tonalite (Table 9.2.4), the apatite, zircon, and sphene may account for as much as 50 percent of the rock activity. The principal part of the rock's activity, however, is generally divided between the essential minerals.

In a study of the activity not tied up in the radioactive accessories, Hurley (1950) measured the drop in alpha activity from a crushed sample of granite from Quincy, Mass., after successive acid treatments. The results are given in Table 9.2.12. Most of the activity was removed by hydrochloric acid, showing that the quartz and feldspar grains had low amounts of uranium and thorium in their interior, and that the activity had been superficial. A uranium-lead study of this nature has been made on the Essonville-Tory Hill granite of Haliburton County, Ontario (Tilton and others, in press).

Table 9.2.12 Acid leaching tests on igneous rocks (Hurley, 1950, in part)

Sample	Original activity, α/cm^2-h	Activity after acid treatment, α/cm^2-h	Helium after acid, 10^{-6} cc/g	Helium Ratio, 10^6 years
Granite				
Sudbury Micropegmatite, Pre-Cambrian	3.4	1.14		
Creighton granite, Sudbury, "	15.7	0.73		
Quincy, Mass., Hitchcock Q., Carbonif.				
420–840 microns	9.6	1.0		
250–420 "	7.0	1.0		
125–250 "	7.7	1.0	2.5	115
−125 "	10.8	1.1		
Keene, N. H., "	5.5	0.9		
Quincy, Swingle Q., 3 ft deep, "	17.2	2.7	7.1	120
" " 12 ft "	8.8	1.9		
" " 200 ft "	8.8	2.0	8.4	190
Lighter phase, 200 ft "	11.1	0.9	5.9	310
Quincy, Furnace Cr., "	9.0	1.8	0.8	20
Adams Tunnel, Colo., 3000 ft deep, Pre-C.	3.8	2.1		
" " " 3000 ft "	12.0	6.3	13.2	95
" " " 3000 ft "	6.3	2.7		
" " " 3000 ft "	7.5	4.3		
Butte, Mont., 4000 ft deep, Early Tertiary	4.3	2.0	1.2	26
Diabase and Basalt				
Palisade diabase	0.68	0.27		
" "	0.68	0.43		
Logan Sill	0.76	0.31		
" "	2.0	0.34		
Palisade mafic fraction	0.80	0.14		
" felsic "	0.68	0.14		
Post-Nipissing ol. diabase	0.69	0.92		
Basalt, Mich., Keweenawan	0.27	0.06	0.55 *	440
" " "	0.26	0.16	1.50 *	420
" Wis. "	1.34	1.10		
" Minn. "	1.07	0.47	7.0 *	640
Logan diabase, Minn., "	0.76	0.31	8.0 *	1130
" " " "	2.0	0.34	7.56 *	980
Sudbury ol. diabase, Pre-Cambrian	0.74	0.53	11.3 *	910

* Using helium value before acid treatment.

"The results indicate that uranium and lead exist in the acid-soluble fraction in an entirely different ratio to each other from that in the remaining acid-insoluble ("crystal") portion of the rock. The lead has, moreover, a markedly different isotopic composition in the acid-soluble phase from that in the remaining rock." In order to see if the radioactive soluble material was of supergene deposition, samples of granitic rock were obtained from 3000-feet depth in the Adams Tunnel, Estes Park, Colorado, and from a mine at Butte, Montana. As indicated in Table 9.2.12, less activity was removed by the acid, but enough to suggest that the superficial material was not all due to meteoric deposition. A helium analysis on a sample of the Adams

Tunnel gave a low ratio despite the depth of this rock and its pre-Cambrian age. The table also shows the effect of acid treatment on the helium ratios of the granite. The Quincy granite is probably Carboniferous, or about 240 million years old. The helium ratios, although widely scattered, no longer definitely suggest leakage of helium from the quartz and feldspar when the loss due to radiation damage in the vicinity of radioactive accessory minerals is allowed for.

This led to the thought that surficial contaminations might explain the low ratios in some samples of magnetite. Leaching tests on anomalous magnetite samples were made as shown in Table 9.2.13.

Table 9.2.13 Acid treatment of magnetite

Sample	Weight, g	Activity, α/cm^2-h	Helium, 10^{-5} cc/g	Helium Ratio, 10^6 years
Deep Creek Mine, Adirondacks, Pre-C				
Original sample	101.9	12.8	22.4	100
After first acid leach	88.9	3.2		
" second " "	70.7	2.1	17.5	470
" third " "	48.0	1.6		
" fourth " "	30.9	1.6	18.8	660
" fifth " "	21.7	1.2	19.4	910
			Probable true age	1000
White Mts., N. H.				
Original sample		3.3	2.84	50
After acid leach		0.24	1.10	270
			Probable true age	270

Since magnetite is soluble in hydrochloric acid, the tests were made on initially coarse-grained material, and a record of the weight of the sample indicated the amount dissolved during each acid treatment. In general it was found that the helium ratio increased as the surface layers of the magnetite grains were dissolved away. Although it probably will not be satisfactory to obtain helium ages on magnetite that requires such a treatment, it is possible to determine the amount of surface contamination in a sample and thus gauge its initial suitability for an age measurement. Where a magnetite helium ratio appeared too low for the true age, the thick-source alpha count gave a calculated radium equivalent higher than the radium equivalent measured directly by separate radium and thorium determinations. This is further indication that anomalous magnetite ratios are generally caused by surface contamination, although other factors such as martitization or recrystallization also cause low ratios. It is to be expected that replacement of the magnetite by hematite will release the helium.

With the objective of determining the true retentivity of such minerals as quartz and feldspar, samples were sought that had occluded enough uranium and thorium at the time of origin to take the material well above the level of subsequent environmental contamination. It was decided that gangue minerals from veins bearing pitchblende might have this desired characteristic. Several such samples were obtained from radioactive veins in the western part of the Canadian Shield. Helium ratios are given in Table 9.2.14. The samples were

Table 9.2.14 Helium measurements on minerals and gangues from uranium-bearing veins

Mineral	Locality	Helium, 10^{-5} cc/g	Activity, α/cm^2-h	Calculated Ra Equiv., 10^{-12} g/g	Ra by Rn Method, 10^{-12} g/g	Helium Ratio, 10^6 years
		Ore minerals from veins carrying uranium				
80% Galena	Caribou Mine, Colo.	5.8	30.7		13.8	12
Sulfides	" " "	6.9	21.9		10.1	20
Sulfides	Gilman, Colo.	0.6	1.27		0.60	30
Skutterudite	Gt. Bear L.	152	29.5		4.8	1,000
Native bismuth	" " "	480	8.75		1.26	11,200
		Gangue materials from veins carrying uranium				
Calcite	Eagle M., L. Athabaska	35.5	2.5	1.7		615
Quartz	" " " "	17.8	2.0	1.5		360
Siliceous	Eldorado M., Gt. Bear	13.7	2.1	1.5		265
Calcite	" " " "	119	17	12	6.7	295
Felsitic	" " " "	315	100	71	49	130
Calcite	Ace M., L. Athabaska	29.4	1.6	1.1	0.75	830
Quartz	" " " "	69	49	36	37	60
Calcite	Stark Lake Dist.	25	8.9	6.2		130

high in activity and showed helium contents roughly proportional to this activity, but still only a fraction of the amount produced by the radioactivity. The retentivity of the minerals seems to be definitely low, but the variability of the results and the fact that the radioactivity in the samples is probably concentrated in small grains and inclusions, which would give an unsatisfactory distribution of helium in the samples, still prevent a quantitative or conclusive statement.

Acid leaching tests on basic igneous rocks show that the treatment does not cause much change in the activity. In basalts and other material with glassy base it is probable that the uranium and thorium are not in such concentrated forms as in the holocrystalline rocks, but are disseminated rather uniformly in the glass, and it is certain that the process of devitrification of the glass would expel the helium to grain boundaries whence it could escape. Thus it is probable that lavas containing amorphous matrix material will never yield helium ratios of more than rough qualitative value.

9.2.d Effect of radiation damage

The difficulty of resolving the question of migration of the radioactive elements, and particularly the contamination of the major minerals of granitic rocks which themselves are very low in activity, led to an investigation of minerals that are structurally tolerant to uranium and thorium and contain enough of these elements to place them above any significant contamination. Zircon and sphene were chosen as the most suitable minerals, and helium ratios were measured on a number of samples of different geologic age and occurrence. The results indicated that in some cases the zircon and sphene had retained almost all the helium, and in other cases much or all the helium had been lost. When the retentivity of the helium was correlated with the activity of the sample and its age, it was found that there was a relationship which suggested that radiation damage was the cause of helium loss. Results are listed in Table 9.2.15.

From these results it appears that almost all the helium is retained in the zircons of low activity, and that helium loss is related to the total number of alpha particles per unit volume, which is the alpha activity multiplied by the age of the sample. The results in Table 9.2.15 give rise to a curve of helium loss that differs slightly from that given by Hurley (1952*b*) on more limited data. In that paper a theoretical relationship between helium loss and total alpha irradiation was derived on the assumption that the rate of helium escape was in proportion to the damage of the structure and to the amount of helium present. On this basis,

$$dN/dt = \alpha - K_1 N K_2 \alpha t$$

where N = number of alpha particles (helium atoms) per mg.

t = time in millions of years after the formation of the crystal.

α = number of alpha particles added per mg per million years (assumed to be constant for $t < 1000$ million years).

K_1, K_2 = factors of proportionality in the rate of helium loss: atoms present (K, N) and the openness of the structure $(K_2 \alpha t)$.

Table 9.2.15 Helium retention *vs.* radiation damage in zircon and sphene, listed in order of increasing total irradiation (Hurley, 1952*b*; Hurley and Fairbairn, 1953, in part)

Sample	Estimated True Age, 10^6 years	Measured Helium Ratio, 10^6 years	Total Irradiation, 10^{13} α/mg	Helium Retention
Zircon				
St. Peter's Dome, Colo.	900	860	8	0.95
Idaho batholith	100	83	9	0.83
" "	100	80	9	0.80
Calif. batholith	100	72	14	0.72
" "	100	75	17	0.75
Fredriksvarn, Norway	230	280	19	1.0
Sierra Nevada	100	90	20	0.90
Renfrew, Ont.	1000	880	25	0.88
" "	1000	850	25	0.85
Brudenell, Ont.	1000	850	27	0.85
S. Burgess, Ont.	1000	650	32	0.65
Sierra Nevada	100	75	38	0.75
Lanark, Ont.	1000	940	45	0.94
Rubideoux, Calif.	100	77	54	0.77
Iredell Co., N. C.	350	220	61	0.63
Statesville, N. C.	350	206	64	0.59
Henderson Co., N. C.	350	125	84	0.50
Oklahoma	650	370	95	0.57
Franklin, N. J.	1000	339	156	0.34
Edenville, N. Y.	1000	290	166	0.29
Buncombe Co., N. C.	350	112	176	0.32
York River, Ont.	1000	420	210	0.42
Franklin, N. J.	1000	316	284	0.32
Hammond, N. Y.	1000	160	394	0.16
Glamorgan Tp., Ont.	1000	137	620	0.15
Fraser Mine, Ont.	1000	81	1030	0.09
N. Hastings Co., Ont.	1000	104	1130	0.11
Haliburton Co., Ont.	1000	93	1500	0.10
Sphene				
Williamsbridge, N. Y.	350	335	1	0.96
Tilly Foster, N. Y.	350	300	1	0.85
Eganville, Ont.	1000	670	33	0.67
Nipissing Dist., Ont.	1000	590	45	0.59
Hastings Co., Ont.	1000	650	52	0.65
Nipissing Dist., Ont.	1000	690	59	0.69
Sebastopol, Ont.	1000	690	66	0.69
Hastings Co., Ont.	1000	445	79	0.44
Dwyer Mine, Ont.	1000	410	79	0.41
Watson " "	1000	480	85	0.48
Lanark Co., Ont.	1000	260	105	0.26
Renfrew Co., Ont.	1000	277	125	0.28
Plunketts Mine, Ont.	1000	250	162	0.25
Lyndoch Tp., Ont.	1000	162	223	0.16

The solution of this equation under the specific conditions of the case is

$$N/\alpha t = (1/t) \exp(-K_1K_2\alpha t^2/2) \int_0^t \exp(K_1K_2\alpha t^2/2)\, dt$$

If

$$\sigma = \frac{t}{\sqrt{\dfrac{2}{K_1K_2\alpha}}}$$

$$N/\alpha t = e^{-\sigma^2}/\sigma \int_0^\sigma e^{\sigma^2}\, d\sigma$$

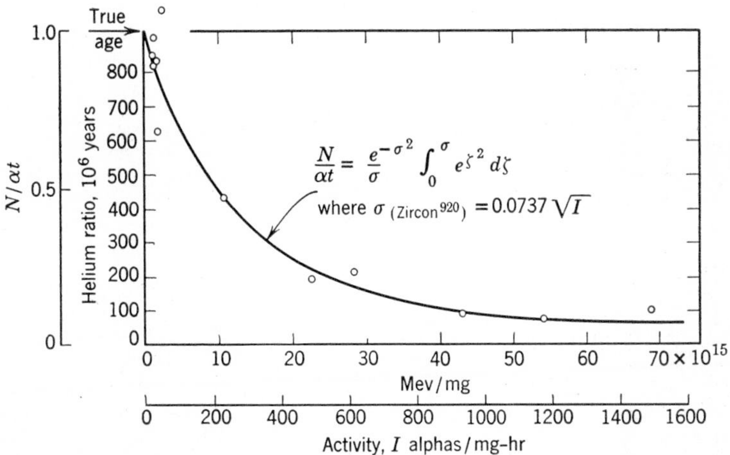

Figure 9.3 Helium ratio of the Essonville-Tory Hill (Ontario) zircons as a function of their alpha activity and total dosage.

In Figure 9.3 a theoretical curve is fitted to the experimental points for zircons of age about 1000 million years only, by taking the point where helium retention is one-half, or $N/\alpha t = 0.5$, at a value for irradiation of 95×10^{13} alphas/mg. A plot of

$$N/\alpha t = e^{-\sigma^2}/\sigma \int_0^\sigma e^{\sigma^2}\, d\sigma$$

as a function of σ is given in Figure 9.4. From this curve $N/\alpha t = 0.5$ when $\sigma = 1.07$. When $t = 920$, $\alpha = 1.03 \times 10^{12}$, and $\sigma = 1.07$, the value of K_1K_2 is 2.62×10^{-18}.

According to the assumptions this curve should apply only to zircons of age about 1000 million years. Zircons of other ages should fall considerably above or below the curve if the value of K_1K_2 remains constant. This does not appear to be true, however, since samples of 350 million years fall together with others of 650 and 1000 million years.

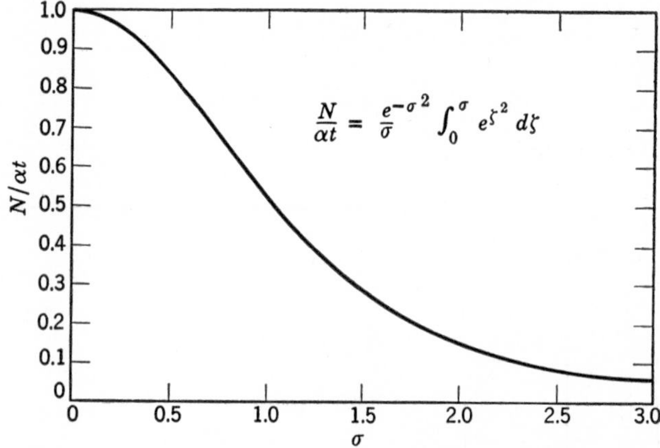

Figure 9.4 Helium retention plotted as a function of sigma (see text).

This is illuminating. It suggests that at any level of damage, if an atom of helium is able to escape through a linkage of damaged volumes, the mean time of escape is small enough to be negligible. On the other hand, if the linkage does not yet exist, the escape probability is essentially zero.

The matter needs a complete restatement with refinements. The relationship between helium loss and irradiation damage appears to be the simple exponential function of αt,

$$N/\alpha t = \exp(-K\alpha t)$$

regardless of the activity of the sample, in the early stages of damage; but the results listed in Table 9.2.15 indicate that when the material has become metamict the level of helium reaches a lower limit below which it does not drop. This indicates the need for keeping a term in the equation that allows for the diffusion rate of helium through metamict material. Not enough data are available to warrant such refinements.

Following these observations on the helium retentivity of zircon, Hurley and Fairbairn (1953) studied the relationship between structural damage and total alpha-particle irradiation in zircon, by measurement of the change of unit cell dimension. In particular the X-ray diffraction angle from the (112) plane was determined to 0.01° by X-ray diffractometer. The angle was found to be 35.635° for completely undamaged material, and it approached 35.1° as the zircon had suffered increasing dosages of radiation. The difference between the measured angle and 35.635° was found to equal 0.535 exp $(-2.31 \times 10^{-16}\alpha t)$. This relationship held only in those cases where the irradiation was less than 400×10^{13} alphas per milligram. Several zircon samples had suffered much greater dosages of radiation, but in these the X-ray peaks were skewed in a way that suggested inhomogeneity of damage, and therefore inhomogeneity in the distribution of uranium in the sample. As a result, it was believed by these authors that zircons that had activities much in excess of 500 alphas per milligram per hour were liable to be radioactively zoned, or else to have small radioactive inclusions which would locally damage the zircon to a greater degree.

Holland working at Princeton University is carrying out a thorough investigation of the metamictization of zircons, using a suite of gem zircons from Ceylon. This excellent work (discussed in Section 6.1) has presented a convincing description of the nature of the lattice distortion that differs from the above. He has investigated the changes that occur in the mineral in the stage following the initial alpha damage, in which the mineral greatly decreases in density. Larsen and Gottfried (unpublished) of the U. S. Geological Survey have also worked on these and other zircons and have measured the change in the refractive index in this degenerative stage that follows a certain dosage of irradiation.

A study of the mechanism of disorder by the action of alpha particles and recoil nuclei has been made by Pellas and reported in a series of papers, the last of which (1953) carries references to the preceding ones. Pellas calculated the number of atoms displaced in minerals that have undergone known bombardments, and related the effects to the nature of the bonds in the structures, and to the quantity of heat liberated during recrystallization.

In a few cases it seems clear that in sphene radiation damage is not the only cause of low helium ratios. A group of samples from the Franklin, N. J., area, and from a crystalline belt in New York that may have suffered metamorphism during the same period, gave results that do not agree with the generalities stated in Table 9.2.15. These sphenes are shown in the accompanying table.

Locality	Helium, 10^{-5} cc/g	Activity, α/mg-h	Helium Ratio, 10^6 years
Franklin, N. J.	310	36	300
Franklin, N. J.	705	87	275
Franklin, N. J., in skarn	1340	179	285
Tilly Foster, N. Y.	24	2.6	300
Pitcairn, N. Y.	238	36	230
Williamsbridge, N. Y.	44	4	335

These results are similar enough to those given by Keevil (1943*b*) on a number of other minerals from Franklin, N. J. Averages of his measurements on minerals that show helium ratios similar to the sphene are tabulated below.

Mineral	Helium, 10^{-5} cc/g	Activity, α/mg-h	Helium Ratio, 10^6 years
Franklinite			270
Willemite	2.7	0.37	225
Fowlerite	2.1	0.28	230
Roepperite	1.66	0.21	240
Garnet	7.33	1.17	193
Vesuvianite	51.9	4.63	344
Siderite with iron olivine	65.5	7.2	280
Apatite	41.5	3.96	322

It would be rather coincidental if all these minerals had lost roughly the same proportion of helium owing to similar retentivities, despite major differences in structure. Furthermore, sphene is known to retain almost all its helium at the irradiations suffered by the minerals in the list. Thus it seems likely that all these minerals have high helium retentivities, but have accumulated helium only since some period of metamorphism in the Paleozoic.

9.2.e Distribution and migration of helium

The amount of helium in rocks of the crust is related to the age of rocks and their content of uranium and thorium. Birch in Chapter 5 estimates that typical granitic, intermediate, and basaltic rocks have radium contents of 1.4, 0.7, and 0.2, respectively, in units of 10^{-12} g/g. If the thorium:uranium ratio is taken as 3.5, this gives a helium production in granitic rocks of 3.5×10^{-3} cc/g in 10^9 years;

in intermediate rocks, 1.7×10^{-3} cc/g in 10^9 years; in basaltic rocks, 0.5×10^{-3} cc/g in 10^9 years.

Normally the helium is driven into the crystal structures of the rock minerals and may be considered as an interstitial solid solution that is tightly held for the most part, except in the vicinity of radioactive concentrations where the alpha radiation damage permits the helium to escape.

As a rough estimate, if the average granitic rock contains zircons averaging 300 alphas/mg-h in activity and half of the activity is concentrated in these accessory minerals, the rock will have one-quarter of its helium released to grain boundaries after 360 million years, or about 1 cubic millimeter of mobile helium per gram in this time. Therefore, in a granitic rock mass starting without any significant helium content at a time 360 million years ago, such as many of the granite bodies in the Southern Appalachians, there will be a mobile helium content of 3×10^6 cc under each square meter for each kilometer of depth. For older rocks the mobile helium content will approach the figure of 10^7 cc for the same volume.

In areas undergoing metamorphism and faulting this helium will have opportunities to migrate toward the surface along channelways of increasing magnitude up to the size of major faults. If these faults enter sedimentary cover near the surface, the helium may become trapped in structures similar to those that form petroleum and natural gas reservoirs. This mechanism may account for some of the helium in the Texas Panhandle field (see Section 4.1.a).

The helium content of the crust to the depth of the Mohorovičić discontinuity in old continental areas is probably of the order 10^9 cc per square meter. From heat flow data the total amount of uranium and thorium in the mantle below a continent appears to be less than that in the crust, so that the helium content in the mantle column will not more than equal this figure. Helium ratios on fresh samples of granitic rock taken from 1 km depth below the surface in the Adams Tunnel showed four-fifths of the radiogenic helium to be lost, so that it appears that the average flow of helium to the surface even in stable crystalline areas must be at least of the order of 10 cc/m^2-year.

It might be pointed out that simple assumptions cannot be made regarding the He^3/He^4 ratios in the helium escaping from rocks, for there is a preferential release of $helium^4$ over neutron-produced $helium^3$, owing to the effect of radiation damage. It is probable that the highly dispersed helium^3 atoms will be among the most tightly held, for they are in undisturbed crystal structures.

9.2.f Cosmic ray production of helium in meteorites (meteoroids)

Arrol, Jacobi, and Paneth (1942) summarized the excellent work on the helium ratios in meteorites that was carried on by Paneth and coworkers for a number of years prior to this date. Since that time the discovery of helium of cosmic-ray origin in meteorites has altered Paneth's earlier age estimates.

Bauer (1947) suggested that an apparent inverse ratio of helium content with mass in meteorites was evidence of the suspected cosmic-ray production of helium, and estimated the probable amount produced. The question of the amount of helium to be expected, its distribution within an object exposed to cosmic radiation, and the proportion of the helium^3 and helium^4 produced by the nuclear reactions was discussed subsequently in the literature. Singer (1952, 1953) concluded that the best estimate for the rate of helium production in an iron meteorite (by a flux of cosmic rays corresponding to the present-day value in the vicinity of the earth's orbit) in the region 2–15 cm beneath the surface of the object is $(5 \pm 1.5) \times 10^{-14}$ cc of helium at standard temperature and pressure per gram of meteorite per year. Of this amount approximately 30 percent was calculated to be helium^3.

Paneth, Reasbeck, and Mayne (1952, 1953; Paneth, 1953) reported measurements on the quantity of helium in five iron meteorites with very different helium contents, and recorded determinations of the He^3/He^4 ratios by mass spectrometer. The results are listed in Table 9.2.16. The following summarizes Paneth's comments and conclusions. From the Mount Ayliff it is seen that the helium^4 produced

Table 9.2.16 Helium content and helium^3:helium^4 ratio in some meteorites (Paneth et al., 1952)

Name of Meteorite	Helium Content, 10^{-6} cm^3/g	He^3/He^4, %
Mount Ayliff	36.8	31.5
Carbo	22.0	28.6
Toluca (Durham)	18.9	29.7
Bethany Amalia (Krantz)	3.4	27.8
Bethany (Harvard)	0.36	17.8
Cape York (Savik)	<0.0002	
Cape York (Ahnighito)	<0.001	
Muonionalusta I	<0.002	

by cosmic rays cannot amount to more than 3.17 times the helium^3. This would give a minimum age for the Bethany (Harvard) of 75 million years. If the cosmic-ray-produced helium^4 was only about equal to the helium^3 (a probable lower limit), the age would be 140 million years. Without considering the cosmic-ray effect, the age calculation would yield 200 million years. If the value for absolute helium^3 production of 5×10^{-14} cc/g-year mentioned above is used, the helium^3 quantity in Toluca, Carbo, and Mount Ayliff would need some 10^8 to 10^9 years for its generation, in general agreement with the age calculated from radiogenic helium production.

The very young ratios reported in the earlier work of Paneth's group (as low as 1 million years), still stand, and are not significantly affected by the contribution of cosmic-ray helium. At least three meteorites (see Table 9.2.12) contain so little helium that they can hardly have solidified more than 1 million years ago. Paneth concludes that a period of about 1000 million years seems sufficient to account for the production of both the helium^4 and the helium^3 content of the oldest (helium-rich) meteorites.

9.3 RADIOACTIVITY AND THE CHRONOLOGY OF THE OCEAN FLOOR

HANS PETTERSSON *

Uranium in sea water decays to thorium^{230} (ionium) which is precipitated on the bottom of the ocean, as discussed in Section 2.4. Thorium^{230} has a halflife of 80,000 years and its separation from its parent offers a potential method of age measurement. In order to realize this possibility, certain conditions must be satisfied:

(*a*) The rate of thorium^{230} deposition per unit of time and bottom surface should remain constant during the span of time to be measured. This obviously presupposes that the content of uranium in sea water, from which the thorium^{230} is derived also should have retained its present value for a considerable length of time, say 300,000 to 400,000 years.

(*b*) The thorium^{230} precipitated onto the sediment surface as well as the radium produced from it should remain immovably together. A migration of either element would obviously upset the radioactive equilibrium assumed to prevail between them.

* Oceanografiska Institutet, Göteborg, Sweden.

(*c*) The quantity of uranium, thorium^{230}, or radium deposited onto the deep-sea bottom by other agencies should be quite small.

Assuming, for the time being, that these conditions are fulfilled, one should be able, from direct measurements of the radium present in different levels of a sediment core, to obtain a chronology extending over say 300,000 to 400,000 years for the deep-sea deposits rich in radium. After 400,000 years the original thorium^{230} content in the layer is reduced through radioactive disintegration to only a few percent, and hence the radium in equilibrium with this residual thorium^{230} would become insufficient for accurate measurement. Thus, even under the most favorable conditions, the radium-thorium^{230} method of age determination is necessarily limited to about half the time commonly ascribed to the Quaternary age.

Piggot and Urry (1939) made age determinations on layers of a deep-sea core by this method. Their first results appeared to confirm the validity of the technique. Their curves are remarkably smooth and conform with the hypothesis. Later measurements on other cores, however, gave more complicated curves which they tried to explain by variations in the rate of sedimentation.

Hundreds of radium determinations made by Kröll and others (unpublished) on cores raised by the *Albatross* expedition do not support the simple hypothesis. Smooth curves are rare exceptions; in most cases the radium content of deep-sea cores shows a maximum at or near the top, and below it a number of secondary maxima separated by deep minima (compare Figure 2.8). It appears that the assumption of constant uniform sedimentation may be invalid and the primary concentration of thorium ^{230} in the sediment seems to change. These problems are discussed by Kröll in a forthcoming paper.

Although the simple radium-thorium^{230} method may be invalid, there are still indirect methods for realizing the same purpose.

From the superficial maximum of radium found near the surface of the red clay (see Figure 2.9) it is possible to estimate the time required for establishing such a value and also the amount of radium derived from the dissolved uranium in the supernatant strata. Taking the maximum of 5×10^{-11} gram of radium per gram of sediment as derived from a water column 5000 m high, Pettersson (1951) estimated the average rate of total sedimentation to be of the order of 0.5 mm in 1000 years. If, on the other hand, the radium maximum is found at a depth of 10 mm below the surface, the time required for establishing radioactive equilibrium between precipitated thorium^{230} and radium (about 10,000 years) leads to approximately the same value for the rate of sedimentation.

Kröll (1953) has made an integration of the radium present in a core of red clay from the central Pacific Ocean down to a level where practically all the thorium^{230} precipitated has had time to disintegrate, so that only very small quantities of uranium-supported radium are present. This allows a comparison between the excess radium in the upper sediment layers and the potential supply of radium derivable from the uranium present in the sea water. Although both figures are of the same order of magnitude, there appears to be a surplus of sediment radium in certain cores over that to be expected from pure thorium^{230} precipitation. This excess factor, about 1½ to 3, falls outside the limits of experimental error. Kröll concluded that it may possibly be due to a considerably higher uranium content in the late Quaternary oceans than the present average value, 1.3×10^{-6} g/L of sea water. However, the discrepancy may be due to the thorium^{230} carried into the sea by rivers as discussed by Koczy in Section 2.4.c.

The total content of thorium^{230}-supported radium in the upper part of the sediment core having been found through such an integration, a theoretical value for the residual thorium^{230} content present near the lower end of the column can be worked out, if it is assumed that the column has accumulated during a certain period of time, say during 320,000 years (four half-value periods of thorium^{230}). The time estimate is adjusted until the calculated thorium^{230} content *in situ* agrees with the measured radium content within certain limits of error. The rate of total sedimentation found in this manner by Kröll is of the order of 1 mm in 1000 years, in fair agreement with other methods of estimation. As already mentioned, the method is liable to error arising from a possible change in the rate of thorium^{230} precipitation.

9.4 THE STRONTIUM METHOD FOR DETERMINING GEOLOGICAL AGE

LOUIS H. AHRENS *

Evidence of beta decay in rubidium was first reported by Thomson (1905) and confirmed by Campbell and Wood (1906). Hemmen-

* Department of Geology and Geophysics, Massachusetts Institute of Technology, (now at Department of Geology and Mineralogy, Oxford University).

dinger and Smythe (1937), Hahn, Strassmann, and Walling (1937), and Mattauch (1937) have shown rubidium^{87} to be the active isotope. The rate of decay has been measured by several observers, as given in Table 9.4.1. Values of measurements made before 1937 have been

Table 9.4.1 Decay constant (λ) and halflife ($t_{1/2}$) of rubidium^{87}

Observers	λ, 10^{-11}/year	$t_{1/2}$, 10^{10} years
Hahn and Rothenbach (1919)	0.93	7.5
Mühlhoff (1930)	0.58	12.0
Orbain (1931)	1.6	4.4
Strassmann and Walling (1938)	1.1 *	6.3
Chaudhury (1942)	0.93	7.5
Eklund (1946)	1.20	5.8
Haxel, Houtermans and Kemmerich (1948)	1.15	6.0
Curran, Dixon, and Wilson (1952)	1.13	6.15 ± 0.3
McGregor and Wiendenbeck (1952)	1.08	6.4 ± 0.3

* Indirect: based on Pb age of 1.99×10^{9} y for southeast Manitoba pegmatite.

recalculated on the basis that $Rb^{87} = 27.85$ percent (Brewer, 1938; Nier, 1950; Herzog et al., 1953). Rubidium^{85} (72.15 percent) is the only other isotope.

General experience in beta counting and improvements of instrumentation combine to make the four modern determinations the most reliable and accurate. Agreement is reasonable, and for our purpose the average of the four modern values ($\lambda = 1.15 \times 10^{-11}$ per year; $t_{1/2} = 6.0 \times 10^{10}$ years) will be used.

The beta decay of rubidium^{87} yields strontium^{87}. Discovery of radiogenic strontium in measurable amount in lepidolite led to the use of the strontium^{87}:rubidium^{87} ratio for measuring geological age (Hahn and Walling, 1938; Goldschmidt, 1937).

9.4.a Outline of geochemistry of rubidium and strontium

Rubidium. Rubidium is a comparatively rare element having an abundance of 0.035 percent by weight in the igneous rocks of the earth's surface. It is very closely associated with potassium in igneous rocks and meteorites (Ahrens, Pinson, and Kearns, 1952); the ratio of percent potassium to percent rubidium averages about 80. Such close association is determined almost solely by the fact that the univalent cations K^+ and Rb^+ are similar in size (1.33A and 1.44A,* respectively) and are both well shielded (screened). Rb^+ is freely accepted in the structures of the potassium host minerals, to such an extent, in fact, that no rubidium minerals ever form. Considerable rubidium enrichment develops in potassium minerals of late-phase replacement crystallization in complex pegmatites. A maximum is reached in lepidolite. Other potassium minerals of late-phase replacement crystallization, namely hydrothermal microcline (notably amazonite), some biotite and muscovite, as well as pollucite and cesium beryl, may show a high enrichment in rubidium.

Nockolds and Mitchell (1948) and Whiting (unpublished thesis, M.I.T., 1951), have investigated the distribution of rubidium in rock-forming minerals; some of their data are given in Table 9.4.2.

Table 9.4.2 Rubidium and strontium contents (in parts per million) in biotite and other rock-forming minerals

Description		Whole Rock	Biotite	K feldspar	Muscovite	Na feldspar	Hornblende
Granodiorite *	Rb	250	1500	140	...	...	...
(Morven-Strontian Complex)	Sr	3000 †	100	2000	...	3000	150
Granite *	Rb	400	2500	1000	...	200	...
(Morven-Strontian Complex)	Sr	1500 †	50	600	...	1500	...
Granite (Moy) *	Rb	500	1000	200	150	200	...
	Sr	1200	70	1500	70	2000	...
Granite ‡	Rb	470	1300	610	...	60	390
	Sr	~200	120	340	...	~340	~10

* Caledonian rocks, Scotland (Nockolds and Mitchell, 1948).
† These strontium concentrations are higher than is usual for rocks of this type.
‡ St. Cloud, Minnesota (F. B. Whiting, unpublished thesis, M.I.T., 1951).

Rubidium is enriched to a greater extent in biotite than in any other common rock-forming mineral. The biotite structure apparently is able to accept Rb^+ more freely than is orthoclase or muscovite. Even so, the rubidium concentration in biotite is only about one-tenth of that in the relatively rare lepidolite.

Strontium. The abundance of strontium in igneous rocks of the earth's surface is 0.022 percent by weight or slightly less than that of rubidium. If 4×10^9 years is assumed as the age of the earth, calculation shows that roughly 1 percent of all strontium in these rocks is radiogenic. This is a small proportion, unlike that of lead,

* Some of the radii used here may be found to differ slightly from those given in commonly used sets (Goldschmidt, Pauling, Ahrens, etc.); they are based on recent minor revisions made by the author which will be published later.

where a comparatively high proportion of all lead in igneous rocks is radiogenic.

Strontium is associated with calcium in much the same way that rubidium and potassium are associated (radii of Sr^{2+} and Ca^{2+} are 1.18A and 1.01A, respectively). Geochemical coherence between these two alkaline earths is, however, not nearly as close as that of the two alkali metals. Potassium and calcium are not closely associated, and, as a result, rubidium and strontium are not closely associated. In igneous rocks, most strontium is taken up by plagioclase and to a lesser extent by potash feldspar. As a result, the strontium concentration is comparatively low in pegmatites, particularly in potassium minerals of late-phase crystallization. As a consequence of these opposing trends, lepidolite, the mineral with the highest rubidium concentration, usually contains an extremely low amount of common strontium, a few parts per million at the very most.

These opposing trends are apparent also in the rock-forming minerals (Table 9.4.2). Biotite shows a maximum concentration of rubidium and a minimum of strontium; plagioclase shows the reverse. The very strongly developed maximum rubidium-minimum strontium relationship in lepidolite, however, gives this mineral pride of place for possible use in age measurements.

9.4.b Use of lepidolite for age measurements

Although lepidolite is restricted to pegmatites, it is fortunately not of extreme rarity. Its resistance to weathering is reasonably high, and lepidolite of excellent quality may be obtained from many pegmatites of all ages. Lepidolite suffers no significant radiation damage from the radioactivity of either $rubidium^{87}$ or $potassium^{40}$. Moreover, radiogenic strontium is probably tightly bound to the oxygen of the structure by an ionic $Sr^{2+}—O^{2-}$ bond, and danger of a loss of either daughter or parent is probably small.

Lepidolites commonly contain about 1.5 percent rubidium. Distribution of concentration about this value is probably lognormal, as in biotite, and it is equally likely, therefore, to find a lepidolite with one-half the most common concentration (0.75 percent) as one with double this concentration (3.0 percent). These amounts are approximate limits; slightly higher or lower concentrations may be found.

Table 9.4.3 shows the amounts of radiogenic strontium produced in a mineral of the rubidium content of average lepidolite (1.5 percent) at different ages. These concentrations are small, even at great ages,

Table 9.4.3 Strontium^{87} generated in a mineral assumed to contain 1.5 percent rubidium (the content of average lepidolite)

Age, 10^9 years	Sr^{87} Generated, ppm
4.0	200
2.0	100
1.0	50
0.5	25
0.1	5

as compared, for example, with the amount of lead produced in uranium minerals.

Analytical methods for determining rubidium, strontium (total), and strontium isotopes in lepidolite. A wide variety of analytical procedures have been used to determine rubidium and strontium and their isotopes for the purpose of making geological age determinations. They are discussed very briefly as follows: (1) the determination of rubidium, (2) a short-cut spectrochemical procedure for determining strontium:rubidium ratios, and (3) the determination of strontium and rubidium by isotope dilution.

The determination of rubidium in lepidolite presents no serious difficulty. In his investigation on the composition of lepidolites, Stevens (1938) used a chemical method described by Stevens and Wells (1934) in which an alkali metal chloride concentrate must be first prepared from a Lawrence Smith fusion. The method is probably accurate, but it is time-consuming. Optical spectrographic methods have been used often to determine rubidium in minerals and rocks. Most such procedures would be classed as semiquantitative with the exception of quantitative methods used by Berggren (1940) and Ahrens and Gorfinkle (1951). The determinations given by Berggren have been made by the Lundegardh method of flame excitation of solutions, and their accuracy appears to be excellent. Ahrens and Gorfinkle (1951) employed direct d-c arc excitation of the mineral powder and made use of the fact that in such methods highest accuracy is attained by using one alkali metal as an internal standard for the determination of another. Reproducibility, calculated as standard deviation, is 3.5 percent. The method is rapid and requires as little as 10 mg of lepidolite per determination.

Flame photometric methods are well adapted to the accurate determination of the alkali metals and may be used for rubidium.

The development of isotope dilution methods for determination of both rubidium^{87} and strontium^{87} (Aldrich et al., 1953*a*, *b*; Tomlinson and Das Gupta, 1953; Section 1.17) is highly significant. Aldrich et al. analyzed a rubidium concentrate which was prepared in two steps: first, enrichment in which use was made of the sparing solubility of $KClO_4$ and $RbClO_4$ in ethanol, followed by further enrichment in an ion exchange column. No enrichment was attempted by Tomlinson and Das Gupta, who preferred to work with extremely small quantities and with a minimum of quantitative chemical treatment. These methods appear to be very accurate and highly reproducible, and determination can usually be made to within 1 percent; such reproducibility is much better than that of the spectrographic methods previously mentioned.

Davis and Aldrich (1953) report 2.6 percent and 1.21 percent rubidium in lepidolite from southeast Manitoba and the Black Hills of South Dakota, respectively; the first determination agrees exactly with the previous value (Ahrens and Gorfinkle, 1951) obtained by optical spectrographic methods (2.64 percent), but the second (1.54 percent) shows a considerable difference. A value of 1.7 percent rubidium in lepidolite from the Black Hills is reported by Tomlinson and Das Gupta (1953). All the Black Hills specimens came from the Bob Ingersoll mine, but they were not cuts of the same sample.

At this stage it should be pointed out that in the procedures developed by Aldrich, Tomlinson, and coworkers not only are both rubidium^{87} and strontium^{87} determined mass spectrometrically but also suitable concentrates of each element, if necessary, may be prepared by similar general methods from the same sample; less than 100 mg of lepidolite are ever required.

Ahrens (1946, 1947, 1949) sought to develop a short-cut procedure which would determine the strontium:rubidium ratio in a single rapid operation. Under appropriate conditions, the intensity of a spectral line is directly proportional to the concentration of the emitting element; therefore, the intensity ratio of a strontium-rubidium line pair should be a function of their concentration ratio and hence of age. The method is rapid, but accuracy is unfortunately not high. Even when the analysis is carried out in quadruplicate, the standard deviation is about 15 percent. Poor reproducibility in the arc discharge and a possible systematic error are due mainly to differences in the distillation rates of strontium and rubidium and to variation in the degree of ionization of strontium.

Although non-radiogenic strontium is often insignificantly low in lepidolite, quantitative isotope information is in any case highly desirable, and we now proceed to discuss strontium determinations: first, methods for determining total strontium; second, the determination of strontium isotope ratios and hence the proportion of radiogenic strontium; and third, the direct determination of radiogenic strontium.

The commonly used chemical methods for determining strontium in silicates (Hillebrand and Lundell, 1953; Groves, 1951) are not sufficiently accurate at the low strontium concentrations encountered in geologic age work. Strassmann and Walling (1938) used a chemical procedure to concentrate and determine strontium in southeast Manitoba lepidolite but were doubtful about completeness of precipitation. Hybbinette (1943) used a combined chemical-spectrochemical procedure in which strontium was first collected in a carrier precipitate of excess calcium oxalate and then determined spectrochemically in the dried powder. Incompleteness of precipitation at low concentrations of strontium, as in comparatively young lepidolites, is a possible source of serious error. Ahrens and Gorfinkle (1951) employed a spectrochemical procedure in which barium was used as an internal standard. A value of 0.021 percent total strontium (about 98 percent radiogenic) was found in southeast Manitoba lepidolite, which is to be compared with a value of 0.026 percent determined mass-spectrometrically by Davis and Aldrich (1953).

Three possible general methods have been discussed for the determination of strontium isotope ratios and hence the proportion of radiogenic strontium. Each is based on the analysis of a spectrum—the first, an optical line spectrum, the second, an optical molecular spectrum, and the third, a mass spectrum.

Heyden and Kopfermann (1938) examined the hyperfine structures of strontium lines emitted from a few milligrams of a strontium salt prepared (Strassmann and Walling, 1938) from southeast Manitoba lepidolite. Isotope components were clearly resolved, and strontium^{87} was found to be dominant. Quantitative or semiquantitative isotope ratio measurements presumably can be made, but accuracy is not likely to equal that attainable by mass-spectrometric procedures.

Ahrens (1948) was able to resolve strontium^{88} F, strontium^{87} F and strontium^{86} F components on a large grating spectrograph. Excessively large quantities (about ½ gram) of strontium salt had to be consumed, and this is a serious drawback.

Mass spectrometric methods are undoubtedly superior, from the point of view both of accuracy and of sensitivity. Mattauch (1947) employed photographic recording and found that a few milligrams or so of strontium salt sufficed to produce an accurately measurable photographic response. Highest sensitivity, however, is achieved with the aid of electronic recording (see Section 1.16). Accurate isotope ratio measurements may be made on as little as a few micrograms or so of a strontium concentrate containing a few percent of strontium. Wiles et al. (1953) describe extremely sensitive mass spectrometric methods for determining isotopes of strontium and rubidium in fission products.

Aldrich, Doak, and Davis (1953*a*), Herzog et al. (1953), and Tomlinson and Das Gupta (1953) describe mass spectrometric procedures for the direct determination of radiogenic strontium. Such direct methods remove the necessity of a two-step strontium analysis—total strontium followed by an isotope ratio determination. The determination appears to be highly reproducible and accurate. Strontium concentrates are prepared in each procedure, and a spike is added, as discussed in Section 1.17. Aldrich and coworkers employed enriched strontium^{84}, whereas Tomlinson and Das Gupta used strontium^{90}. Nicolaysen et al. (1953) made use of direct mass-spectrometric measurement of rubidium^{87} and strontium^{87} for the determination of the ages of African lepidolite.

Age measurements made on lepidolite. Many age determinations of lepidolite are given in Table 9. Those based on mass-spectrometric measurements of rubidium^{87} and strontium^{87} are marked *i.d.* (= isotope dilution) and are probably the most reliable and accurate. Those based on spectrochemical intensity ratio procedures and miscellaneous chemical determinations are probably less reliable.

Age calculations are made by the usual equation for radioactive decay,

$$N = N_0 \exp(-\lambda t)$$

where N_0 is the number of rubidium^{87} atoms originally present in the mineral, and N is the number in existence now. As parent and daughter isotopes have the same mass, the relationship may be expressed in the form

$$C_1/(C_1 + C_2) = \exp(-\lambda t)$$

where C_1 and C_2 are the contents of rubidium^{87} and strontium^{87}, respectively.

The halflife is comparatively long when compared with geological time, and a simplified relationship may be used:

$$t = C_2/\lambda C_1 = 8.7 \times 10^{10} C_2/C_1 \text{ years}$$

The strontium:rubidium method is not well adapted to the determination of comparatively young ages, but it may well become superior to all other methods for reliably dating the earliest pre-Cambrian, once all possible sources of analytical error have been removed. Inconsistencies now apparent in the results of the spectrochemical and mass-spectrometric strontium:rubidium methods (Table 9) are probably due to analytical error, and it should be only a matter of time (not geological, we hope) before such discrepancies are resolved.

In addition to lepidolite, a few other pegmatite minerals undoubtedly may be used. Hydrothermal microline, notably amazonite, and pollucite have been found by Hahn, Mattauch, and Ewald (1943) and Mattauch (1947) to contain significant amounts of radiogenic strontium. Although strontium^{87} does not dominate as completely as in lepidolite, the above authors found it to comprise upwards of 45 percent of total strontium in each specimen that they examined.

9.4.c Possible use of biotite

The value of the strontium method would be much greater if a constituent mineral of a common rock could be used. Table 9.4.2 has shown biotite to have a moderate maximum rubidium-minimum strontium relationship, and Ahrens (1949) and Whiting (unpublished thesis, M.I.T., 1951) have referred to the possibility of using this mineral. Much pertinent information is now available on (1) the determination and abundance of rubidium and total strontium in biotite, and (2) the isotope composition and its measurement in this mineral. Tomlinson and Das Gupta (1953) have actually determined the strontium:rubidium ages of four specimens of biotite (Table 9).

Quantitative spectrochemical methods have been used to determine rubidium and strontium in biotite (Whiting, unpublished; Holyk, unpublished thesis, M.I.T., 1952). These results together with those of Nockolds and Mitchell (1948) indicate a lognormal distribution in which the most common concentration of rubidium is about 0.1 percent with limits of equal likelihood at about 0.03 and 0.3 percent, and that of strontium about 0.01 percent, with limits at about 0.003 and 0.04 percent. Amounts falling outside these limits are occasionally found. It must be emphasized that these values refer to biotite from rocks and that much higher concentrations of rubidium may be found in some specimens of pegmatitic biotite.

Herzog et al. (1953) have mass-spectrometrically determined the isotope composition of strontium from biotite and a few other minerals. A partial chemical enrichment is first carried out, in much the same way as in lepidolite, followed by further enrichment in ion exchange columns (see also Tomlinson and Das Gupta, 1953). Some of the results are shown in Figure 9.5, a histogram of strontium^{87}: strontium^{88} in specimens of biotite, feldspar, and celestite.

The isotope composition of strontium from minerals virtually free of rubidium varies quite considerably; and there is moderate variation

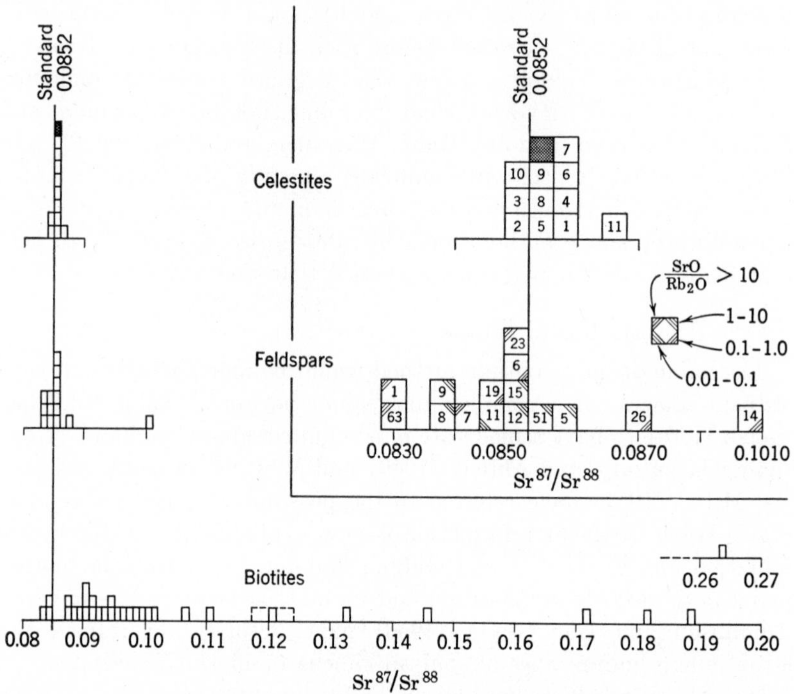

Figure 9.5 Histogram of the strontium^{87}: strontium^{88} ratio in celestites, feldspars, and biotites. The peak region for celestites and feldspars is enlarged in the upper right section of the diagram to show additional detail. After Herzog (private communication).

in the ratio strontium^{86}:strontium^{88}, neither of which has a known radioactive parent. Even if we knew the exact isotopic composition of original non-radiogenic strontium, a simple correction for it could not be made because this composition would not be the same as that of the strontium in the igneous or other material from which the biotite formed. The composition of common strontium varies from rock to rock mainly because of varying contributions of strontium^{87} from rubidium^{87} and also because of some natural isotope variation during the history of the materials from which the rock finally formed.

The available information seems to indicate that, even if reliable age determinations cannot be made on all biotite specimens, it is quite possible that they can be made on a moderately high proportion of those of pre-Cambrian age.

9.5 ARGON^{40}:POTASSIUM^{40} DATING

GERALD J. WASSERBURG *

The element potassium has three naturally occurring isotopes, potassium^{39}, potassium^{40}, and potassium^{41}, with atomic abundances of 93.08, 0.0119, and 6.9, respectively (Nier, 1950). Of these, potassium^{40} is radioactive with a decay constant $\lambda = 0.55 \times 10^{-9}$ year^{-1} (see Birch, 1951; Burch, 1953). Potassium^{40} decays by K-electron capture to argon^{40} with the emission of a gamma and by beta emission to calcium^{40} (see Figure 3.1). The value of the branching ratio is

Table 9.5.1 Determinations of the branching ratio of K^{40}

Author	Branching Ratio
Sawyer and Wiedenbeck (1950)	0.13 ± 10%
Sawyer and Wiedenbeck (1950) Corrected for new value of gamma decay fraction for K^{42} [*Phys. Rev. 91*, 1212 (1953)]	0.102 ± 10%
Inghram et al. (1950)	0.126 ± 4%
Faust (1950)	0.115 ± 10%
Faust (1950) Using mean value for the beta activity (Burch, 1953, 27.4 betas/sec-gK)	0.131 ± 10%
Houtermans et al. (1950)	0.114 ± 10%
Burch (1953) (Assuming 35.0 ev per ion pair)	0.127 ± 4%
Present writer (value suggested by geologic evidence)	0.085 ± 10%

uncertain (see Table 9.5.1). More exact determinations of the decay constants are necessary before argon^{40}:potassium^{40} dating can be developed.

The number of argon^{40} atoms produced after a time t is $A^{40} = \frac{R}{1+R} K^{40}(e^{\lambda t} - 1)$ where R is the branching ratio and K^{40} is the number of potassium^{40} atoms remaining at time t.

The discovery of this long-lived radioactive isotope of potassium has opened up many possibilities in the field of geological dating.

* Institute for Nuclear Studies, University of Chicago.

Because of the ubiquitous nature of potassium minerals and their importance in rock formation, numerous dating problems that were heretofore insoluble may now be approached. The potential applicability of argon^{40}:potassium^{40} dating is much greater than that of the lead:uranium methods. With the exception of zircon and sphene, the rare occurrence of uranium-containing minerals makes it difficult to test the correctness of the dates determined by these methods (see Table 9).

Besides checking the compatibility of lead:uranium ages with argon^{40}:potassium^{40} ages, there are numerous geological criteria that should be used to test the argon^{40}:potassium^{40} dating method. First, a sequence of similar igneous rocks, whose relative ages are established, should be dated. The dates obtained should, within the experimental accuracy, maintain the proper relationships. Since argon^{40}:potassium^{40} ratios can be determined to within 4 percent, it should be quite possible to resolve Paleozoic intrusions separated by one geological period. Confirmatory results of such a nature should be obtained before long-range correlation and dating are attempted.

9.5.a Loss of argon by diffusion

One must, of course, be careful to date individual minerals rather than a piece of rock, as some minerals (perhaps the micas) may have lost a considerable part of their argon, while contributing a significant amount to the potassium content of the rock. It is quite possible that rocks have lost some radiogenic argon by diffusion (Gentner et al., 1953). The amount lost would be critically dependent on the grain size and structure of the potassium minerals. This possibility can be tested by determining the argon^{40}:potassium^{40} ages of coarse- and fine-grained samples of a given mineral from rocks which are cogenetic or from the same rock. This should be done on several rocks of differing ages so as to be able to distinguish between the effects of continual diffusion and metamorphism as the cause of argon depletion.

The effect of argon diffusion on the argon^{40}:potassium^{40} ratio as a function of time in a spherical potassium mineral is shown in Figure 9.6. This is the solution of the problem

$$\frac{\partial C}{\partial t} = D\nabla^2 C + \frac{\lambda R}{1+R} K_0 e^{-\lambda t} \qquad (1)$$

for a sphere of radius a, where C is the argon^{40} concentration, D is the diffusion coefficient, K_0 is the initial concentration of potassium^{40}, λ is the decay constant of potassium^{40}, R is the branching ratio, and t is the time.

$$C(a, t) = 0$$

$$C(r, 0) = 0$$

$$r \leq a$$

$$A^{40}/K^{40} = R/(1 + R) \left\{ -1 + 3/d^2 - 3(\cot d)/d \right.$$

$$\left. + 6d^2/\pi^2 \sum_{m=1}^{\infty} \exp \left[\lambda t \left(1 - \frac{m^2\pi^2}{d^2} \right) \right] \Big/ m^2(d^2 - \pi^2 m^2) \right\} \quad (2)$$

where $d^2 = \lambda a^2/D$.

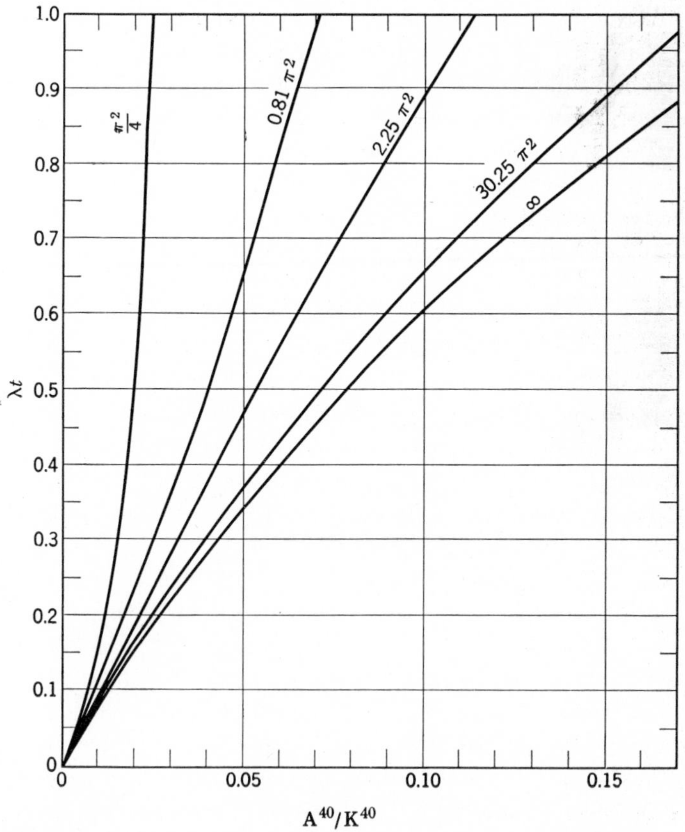

Figure 9.6 Argon^{40}:potassium^{40} ratio as a function of time for different values of d^2, where $d^2 = \lambda a^2/D$, and $d^2 = \infty$ is the limiting case of no diffusion.

9.5.b Previous age determinations

Measuring the small amounts of argon extracted from potassium minerals involves considerable care. Because of the high argon content of the atmosphere, there is a great likelihood of contamination, and it is necessary to determine the amount of normal argon in the sample by mass-spectrometric methods. If the argon measurements are made by volumetric methods, the atmospheric contamination can be determined by measuring either the $argon^{36}$:$argon^{40}$ or the $argon^{38}$:$argon^{40}$ ratio in the sample (Nier, 1950). A mass-spectrometric analysis of the extracted argon is absolutely necessary for the results to be trustworthy.

Several papers have been published on the measurement of $argon^{40}$:$potassium^{40}$ ages (Smits and Gentner, 1950; Gerling and Pavlova, 1951; Gerling and Yashchenko, 1952; Gerling et al., 1952; Mousuf, 1952; Gentner et al., 1953, 1954). The works by Gerling et al. are difficult to evaluate, for the majority of the analyses were not checked for normal argon content. Further, although they obtain agreement between lead:uranium and helium:uranium ages and the $argon^{40}$:$potassium^{40}$ ages, there are no references to the lead and helium determinations and it is not possible to evaluate them. Also, the lead:uranium and helium:uranium ages are not distinguished. Gerling et al. mention the $argon^{36}$ present in some of their samples and give a long discussion of the solubility of argon in a magma. The $argon^{36}$ content which they report is from 0.2×10^{-6} to 0.6×10^{-7} cc at standard temperature and pressure per g. From the $argon^{36}$:$argon^{38}$ values presented in Table 9.5.2 one can see that the amount of $argon^{36}$ is about 0.4×10^{-6} cc at standard temperature and pressure for each sample, regardless of the sample weight (which varies by a factor of 4), indicating that the contamination is atmospheric and not any primordial gas occluded in the sample.

Mousuf (1952) and Russell et al. (1953) have reported $argon^{40}$:$potassium^{40}$ ages for feldspars and compared them with $lead^{207}$:$lead^{206}$ ages determined on uranium minerals from the same localities. The results that they have obtained would be in agreement if a branching ratio of 0.06 were assumed. This value is much lower than any of the values obtained by counting methods and by measuring the $argon^{40}$:$calcium^{40}$ ratio in sylvite (Table 9.5.1). A split sample of one of the minerals that they used was analyzed by Wasserburg and Hayden (1954) who obtained an $argon^{40}$:$potassium^{40}$ ratio larger than the ratio reported by Russell et al. The reason for this dis-

Table 9.5.2 Analyses of No. 4, pink microcline, Bessner Mine, Lot 5, Con. B., Henvey Twp., Ontario

Run	Sample Weight, g	Sieve Size (mesh)	% K	A^{38}/A^{40}	A^{36}/A^{38}	Volume of A^{38} in Tracer, cc (stp)	Radiogenic A^{40}, cc (stp)/g	A^{40}/K^{40}
1	14.522	40 > >80	11.00	1.92 $\pm 0.02 \times 10^{-3}$	0.0506 ± 0.001	1.143 $\pm 0.02 \times 10^{-5}$	4.25 $\pm 0.12 \times 10^{-4}$	0.0565 ± 0.0014
2	27.283	18 > >40	10.92	9.03 $\pm 0.1 \times 10^{-4}$	0.044 ± 0.001	0.997 $\pm 0.02 \times 10^{-5}$	4.27 $\pm 0.12 \times 10^{-4}$	0.0573 ± 0.0004
3	6.902	18 > >40	10.92	3.72 $\pm 0.02 \times 10^{-3}$	0.032 ± 0.001	1.063 $\pm 0.02 \times 10^{-5}$	4.22 $\pm 0.12 \times 10^{-4}$	0.0567 ± 0.0014
4	16.444	180 >	10.43	1.73 $\pm 0.01 \times 10^{-3}$	0.0279 ± 0.0008	1.049 $\pm 0.02 \times 10^{-5}$	3.85 $\pm 0.12 \times 10^{-4}$	0.0542 ± 0.0014

crepancy is not certain, and efforts are being made to find the source of disagreement. The lower argon yields may be due to the method of fluxing used. Furthermore, the various lead:uranium ages do not agree in general.

Gentner et al. (1953, 1954) have determined the argon^{40}:potassium^{40} age of a lower oligocene salt deposit. They found that the argon content of the sylvite was a function of grain size and deduced from this that there was argon loss due to diffusion. From their data they computed $D = 1.5 \times 10^{-19}$ cm^2/sec for argon in KCl. This result would suggest that the branching ratio of 0.126 determined by Inghram et al. (1950) is lower than the true value, which seems unlikely in view of the present data. Gentner et al. analyzed their samples mass-spectrometrically for normal argon contamination.

Fritze and Strassmann (1952) have determined the argon^{40}:potassium^{40} age of the Varuträsk pegmatites. They have made no mass-spectrometric examination of their gas. The age that they calculate disagrees by 40 percent with the data that they present.

9.5.c Isotopic dilution technique

Richard J. Hayden of Argonne National Laboratory and this writer are at present working on the argon^{40}:potassium^{40} method, using an isotopic dilution technique (see Table 9). They also studied stony meteorites and obtained ages of 4.8×10^9 years for Beardsley, a gray chondrite, and 4.57×10^9 years for Forest City, a brecciated spherical bronzite chondrite. These ages were calculated using a branching ratio of 0.085. A vacuum line was constructed for this purpose (see Figure 9.7). Mercury cut-off valves are used in place of stopcocks in order to insure a tight system. All the chemicals in the system are outgassed by baking under vacuum for 48 hours prior to an experiment, and the glassware is torched. With this technique they have been able to keep the amount of normal argon contamination below 3×10^{-4} cc at standard temperature and pressure.

Samples are prepared by taking a coarse-sieve fraction of the crushed mineral. The material is divided into two aliquots, one for the argon analysis and the other for potassium analysis.

The sample to be analyzed for argon, contained in a thin glass envelope, is introduced into the system through the glass side arm of the furnace. The reaction vessel is evacuated and isolated, and a known volume of argon^{38} which was obtained by neutron irradiation of NaCl is introduced (*Natl. Bur. Standards,* 1953, p. 189 ff.). The sample is then pushed into a nickel reaction vessel containing molten

NaOH at 600° C, and the reaction is allowed to proceed for 24 hours. The gases then pass through a $Mg(ClO_4)_2$ drying train and are cycled by means of a Töpler pump through CuO at 450° C. The gas is transferred (either by charcoal traps at liquid nitrogen temperature or by Töpler) to a calcium furnace. The calcium is heated until a mirror is formed, and the pressure is measured by means of a McLeod gauge. The gas is then passed through CuO at 450° C and $Mg(ClO_4)_2$,

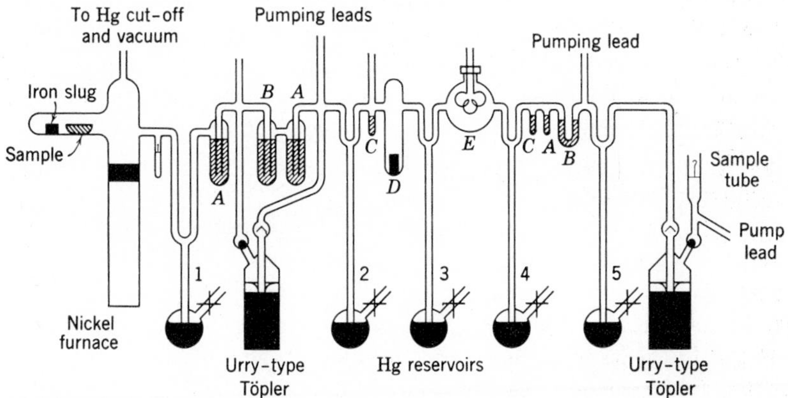

Figure 9.7 Argon extraction and purification system: A = Mg $(ClO_4)_2$ trap; B = CuO furnace; C = charcoal trap; D = calcium furnace consisting of a stainless steel crucible inside a fused quartz tube; E = hot tungsten filament.

and then introduced into a bulb containing a white-hot tungsten filament. The gas is again allowed into the calcium furnace, and the process is repeated until the optimum cleanup is obtained. The purified sample is then collected in a breakoff tube. Purification of the extracted gases is necessary, for large samples tend to increase the mass-spectrometer background and reduce the resolution. HCl and the hydrocarbons $C_3{}^+$, $C_3H_2{}^+$, and $C_3H_4{}^+$ must be eliminated, for they interfere with the measurements in the mass region 36 to 40.

The argon^{36}:argon^{38} and argon^{38}:argon^{40} ratios are then determined on a mass spectrometer with a 12-inch radius of curvature and 60° deflection (see Section 1.16). This instrument can completely resolve equal peaks separated in mass by 1 part in 2000. Thus, possible hydrocarbon peaks could be resolved from the argon. No such peaks were observed when the sample tube was kept at liquid nitrogen temperature.

The amount of radiogenic argon^{40} is given by

$$A^{40} = \frac{\left\{\begin{array}{l}(38)_T[(40/38)_M + (40/38)_T(38/36)_N(36/38)_M \\ \quad - (40/38)_T - (40/36)_N(36/38)_M]\end{array}\right\}}{1 - (36/38)_M(38/36)_N}$$

where M = ratio measured in sample.
T = ratio measured in tracer.
N = value for ratio in normal atmospheric argon.

Table 9.5.2 lists the results obtained for a sample of pink microcline from the Bessner Mine, Lot 5, Con. B, Henvey Twp., Ontario (kindly supplied by R. D. Russell, University of Toronto). The argon^{40}:potassium^{40} age calculated for these data, using a branching ratio of 0.126 and $\lambda = 0.55 \times 10^{-9}$ year^{-1}, is 7.1×10^8 years. The lead^{207}:lead^{206} age obtained by Russell et al. (1953) for a uraninite from this locality is 9.4×10^8 years. Chemical analysis of this uraninite gave 5.57 percent lead and 52.76 percent uranium (Kulp, private communication). Using the isotopic analysis of Russell et al. and computing the contamination from Nier's values on the Great Bear Lake galena (see Table 9.1), we obtain a lead^{206}:uranium^{238} age of 6.9×10^8 years and a lead^{207}:uranium^{235} age of 7.6×10^8 years. Nier (1939*b*) determined the lead:uranium and lead:thorium ages on a sample of Bessner uraninite. He obtained a lead^{206}:uranium^{238} age of 7.65×10^8 years, a lead^{207}:lead^{206} age of 8.25×10^8 years, and a lead^{208}:thorium age of 7.87×10^8 years (see Table 9).

The agreement between the results of runs 1 and 2, Table 9.5.2, where there is a significant difference in the sieve size, indicates that 24 hours is quite sufficient for complete reaction of the feldspar with the NaOH. A run on a different perthite in which the sieve size used was between 4 and 18 mesh, and the reaction time 7 hours, also gave good results. We have not, as yet, been able to prove that all the argon is released by the method of fluxing in NaOH.

In order to determine whether any radiogenic argon is lost by grinding, a sample finer than 180-mesh was run. The reaction and mixing time was 34 hours. The argon^{40}:potassium^{40} ratio obtained (see Table 9.5.2) is 5 percent less than in the other runs. Although the difference is rather small, we believe the effect to be real.

The one critical step in the isotopic dilution method is that there must be complete mixing of the radiogenic argon with the tracer. In order to determine whether 24 hours is sufficient time for mixing, the following experiment was performed. In runs 1 and 2 (see Table

9.5.2), the tracer was added as soon as the reaction started. In run 3, the tracer was added 12 hours after the reaction began and the gases were removed after 12 hours more. The results agree quite well, indicating that the mixing is complete in 12 hours for samples of the size used.

The principal advantages of the isotopic dilution technique (see Section 1.17) are that argon samples as small as 5×10^{-4} cc at standard temperature and pressure can be run with considerable accuracy, and that the final gas sample need only be representative of the radiogenic argon-tracer mixture. Argon^{40}:potassium^{40} ages for potassium feldspars as young as 10 million years could be determined by this method by increasing the size of the sample.

9.6 CARBON^{14} AGE METHOD

JAMES R. ARNOLD *

The carbon^{14} method is the youngest member of the group of radioactive dating techniques discussed in this chapter. Current utility of this technique is perhaps best indicated by the fact that at the time of writing more than a dozen laboratories in this country and abroad are actually making measurements, 7 years after attention was first called to the possibilities of the method by W. F. Libby (1946). Libby's monograph (1952) contains a thorough discussion of the theory and applications of the method, and readers are referred to it for amplification of the points touched on below and a listing and discussion of results obtained prior to September 1, 1951.

Carbon^{14} emits a beta with an energy of 0.155 Mev and has a half-life of approximately 5600 years. It can be made in the neutron pile by the reaction

$$N^{14}(n, p)C^{14} \tag{1}$$

The cross section for this process for thermal neutrons is 1.7 barns. Carbon^{14} is formed in nature in precisely the same way, by reaction between the nitrogen in the atmosphere and neutrons formed by cosmic radiation. This radiation is now known to consist of stripped nuclei, chiefly protons, of energy greater than 10^9 ev. It interacts strongly on entering the atmosphere, producing much nuclear "debris" —protons, mesons, heavier nuclei, and, of course, neutrons. As a re-

* Institute for Nuclear Studies, University of Chicago.

sult, almost all the neutrons that these nuclei release are found high in the atmosphere, above 30,000 feet. Since the cross sections of oxygen, argon, carbon, and hydrogen are much lower than that of nitrogen, reaction 1 will consume nearly all the neutrons formed. Thus the rate of production of $carbon^{14}$ is substantially the rate of production of neutrons, which has been measured by many workers (Libby, 1952; Ladenburg, 1952; Kouts and Yuan, 1952).

If the cosmic radiation has been constant in intensity over the last 30,000 years or more (constant in its long-time average, that is, since short bursts do not affect this result) a steady state will have been reached, exactly analogous to the secular equilibrium among the decay products of radioactive chains. The rate of decay of $carbon^{14}$ will then equal its rate of formation. So far there is no proof, independent of the method, that the cosmic-ray intensity has remained constant, and, however reasonable it may be, we must rank this as a pure assumption.

The $carbon^{14}$ thus formed can be expected to follow a definite geochemical path. In the oxidizing conditions of the upper atmosphere it will be converted rapidly to carbon dioxide, and once in this form will enter the carbon cycle. In time it will be mixed throughout the atmosphere, living and other organic matter, and the carbonate dissolved in the sea. Although it is very difficult to calculate *a priori* the time required for this mixing process, order-of-magnitude estimates indicate that it will be considerably shorter than the halflife, except for small areas under special conditions. It also seems reasonable that the incorporation of $carbon^{14}$ into surface rocks and carbonate sediments will be very slow by comparison. The "exchange reservoir" through which the $carbon^{14}$ is assumed to be mixed uniformly will then consist of the components tabulated.

Ocean carbonate and bicarbonate	7.25 g/cm² earth surface
Dissolved organic matter	0.59
Biosphere	0.33
Atmosphere	0.12
	8.3

The estimates of organic matter are, of course, uncertain; luckily these quantities are small compared to the ocean carbonate.

The average rate of production of neutrons in the atmosphere is 2.4 per cm^2-sec, according to the latest figures (Ladenburg, 1952). (This rate is strongly dependent on geomagnetic latitude, being much higher at the poles.) The disintegration rate of "exchange reservoir" carbon should then be $2.4 \times 60/8.3 = 17.2$ disintegrations per minute. The value actually found is 16.1 ± 0.8 disintegrations per minute, in excellent agreement. A long series of biological samples from various latitudes and altitudes show no evidence of systematic differences, giving general verification to both assumptions. The problem of the contemporary assay is thoroughly discussed by Anderson (1953).

The statements made above neglect the effect of isotopic fractionation. The C^{13}/C^{12} ratio of carbonate in nature exceeds that of organic matter by 2.6 percent (Craig, 1953). (Differences among different types of organic materials are negligible.) We would therefore predict that shells will show a 5.2 percent higher carbon^{14} assay than wood. Early results showed this effect, but results of Blau et al. (1953), confirmed by some unpublished data of others, show a much lower excess of carbon^{14} in shell relative to that in wood. This may have to be ascribed to a small effect of incomplete exchange between the atmosphere and the oceans, from which the shell-forming species obtain their carbon.

A further assumption is required in using carbon^{14} for dating purposes. There must be a fairly sharp dividing line between a time when the carbon is in equilibrium with the reservoir and a time during which no new radiocarbon enters the material. In other words, there must be materials in which, after a definite period, no exchange reactions or gross replacement of materials can take place. This critical time can occur, roughly speaking, at the death of an organism, or at the time of the laying-down of wood or shell, provided that the material is suitably preserved thereafter. Fortunately the lifetime of most organisms is short compared to the error of the method, so that no real ambiguity results from this cause. In such samples the radioactivity will decrease with the halflife of carbon^{14}, and, if a starting value equal to the present-day assay is assumed, an age for the sample can be calculated from its activity.

A series of measurements of samples of known age, extending back about 5000 years, has shown very good agreement with predictions based on this model. A further check on the method has been provided by comparisons among wood, charcoal, shell, peat, antler, dung, etc., of the same age. Alteration of such different materials should proceed at very different rates, and agreement among them is strong evidence for absence of exchange. All the above materials have given good results although evidences of alteration have been seen in some samples, particularly of shell and peat.

The difficulty of reconciling some of the carbon^{14} dates with other evidence has led some geologists, particularly Antevs (1953), to question the applicability of the method to samples stored under moist conditions. The above discussion makes clear that errors in such samples could arise only through exchange with, or replacement by, extraneous carbon. Such exchange is most improbable for polymeric organic molecules, and replacement by extraneous carbon would have to reach an extent of 50 percent in a number of cases to reconcile the carbon^{14} dates with those suggested by these geologists. Aside from the possibility of detecting such gross displacement, the experimental test of comparison among materials from the same site, but of different chemistry, seems definitive. For such different substances as peat and a variety of woods, in a variety of physical locations, to undergo chemical alteration at the same rate within a few percent seems virtually impossible. In short, it is this writer's opinion that the entire structure of the carbon^{14} method must stand or fall with the validity of the Two Creeks and related dates (see Table 9).

The usual technique of measurement can only be sketched here. Further details are given by Anderson, Arnold, and Libby (1951) and by Libby (1952). Samples of organic matter sufficient to yield 8 grams of carbon are first treated with dilute acid to remove carbonates. They are then burned to carbon dioxide, which is purified of radon and gross impurities by a precipitation cycle. The purified carbon dioxide is reduced to carbon with magnesium metal, and the metal and oxide are removed by acid treatment. The resulting highly porous carbon is mounted as a slurry on half of the sample cylinder of a screen-wall counter. The counter and its contents are pumped on, and finally filled with an argon-ethylene counting mixture. By sliding the cylinder from end to end of the counter, "sample" and "background" counts can be alternated without breaking the vacuum. The U. S. Geological Survey (Suess, unpublished) uses a different counting method. The purified carbon is converted to acetylene, and its activity is measured in a proportional counter.

In counting, the instrument is surrounded by an iron or mercury shield to remove the soft component of the cosmic rays and local gamma-ray contamination. A ring of counters in anticoincidence with the screen-wall or proportional counter removes the cosmic-ray mesons. These techniques reduce the background of the counter from 400 counts per minute to 3 to 6 counts per minute. A net effect of 6.7 counts per minute is produced by contemporary carbon.

The usual counting time of 48 hours suffices to give an overall statistical error (standard deviation) of about 1.5 percent for contemporary carbon. This corresponds to an error in age of 120 years. The error in years doubles, roughly, for each halflife in age. It can be seen that the method finds its chief utility in the region of 2000 to 20,000 years. An analysis of the actual deviations of successive runs shows that for a given sample, the statistical error is the dominant one.

A number of other techniques for the measurement of natural radiocarbon have been developed. Ion chambers, gas counting in both the Geiger and proportional regions, and most recently scintillation counting have begun to be used. Table 9.6 (Arnold, 1954), gives a comparison of the important parameters of three methods. The maximum age limit of each method is set arbitrarily to be that age at which the count rate is 4 times the probable error. It can be seen that the newer methods offer the possibility of greatly increased statistical precision. The scintillation counter method in particular, if sufficient sample is available, can be pushed to any desired sensitivity by enlarging the sample cell and adding more tubes.

Table 9.6 Comparison of three methods of C^{14} counting

			Scintillation Counter (100 ml cell volume)		
	Screen-Wall Counter a-c Shielding	Gas Counter (acetylene) a-c Shielding	33% Ethanol, no upper gate	33% Ethanol Pulse Height Disc.	80% Paraffin Pulse Height Disc.
Sample size	8 g	3 g	14.2 g	14.2 g	47 g
Counting efficiency	5.4%	75%	45%	25%	25%
Net sample counting rate	6.7 cpm	34.5 cpm	97 cpm	54 cpm	182 cpm
Net background counting rate	4.0 cpm	30.0 cpm	270 cpm	26 cpm	26 cpm
Statistical error, 2-day count	1.5%	0.7%	0.7%	0.46%	0.20%
Statistical error, in years, 2-day count (contemporary)	120	55	55	37	17
Maximum age limit ($S = 4\sigma$).	25,000 y	30,000 y	29,000 y	34,000 y	44,000 y

It cannot be stressed too strongly that the statistical error will be the largest error only when it is relatively large, and then only when the measurements are made with skill and care. As our statistical precision improves a number of other errors will become important, among them isotopic fractionation, minute amounts of chemical alteration, incomplete mixing of the "exchange reservoir," and, for extremely old samples, the production of carbon^{14} by neutrons in the ground. On the side of archeology and geology, it is very rare that the end of metabolic activity in an organic material can be tied to the chronological problem at hand with a precision of anything like 20 years. In trees and other long-lived organisms the question of when metabolic activity ceases in a given area remains unanswered at this level.

The increased statistical precision will be worth-while, however, both because in some cases it will be possible to exploit it and because the sources of error listed above are themselves geochemical problems of great interest. Where material of uniform biological and geographic origin is available covering a span of years, much new information may be uncovered. For example, Suess (unpublished) used acetylene-gas proportional counting to show a possible decrease in the contemporary assay over the last 50 years, ascribable to the industrial revolution (release of CO_2 from coal).

Hundreds of measurements of radiocarbon age have been published so far. For discussion of these results the reader is referred to the technical literature (Flint and Deevey, 1951; F. Johnson, 1951; Kulp et al., 1951, 1952*d;* Neville, 1953; Roberts, 1952; Zeuner, 1950, 1951, 1952). Because of the convenient halflife and wide availability of materials, most applications of the method to date have been in the fields of archeology and anthropology. Late Pleistocene geology and climatology have contributed a number of results, of which the date of 11,400 years ago for the Two Creeks forest bed and its European equivalents has perhaps aroused the greatest interest. Studies of sedimentation in the deep ocean have also been begun.

The extremely sensitive counting apparatus has now been operated successfully in a number of laboratories. Except for background problems associated with the continuing series of bomb tests all over the world, radiocarbon measurements seem destined to be made in increasing numbers. The technique seems to be reaching maturity.

Chapter 10

THE ORIGIN OF THE EARTH

HAROLD C. UREY *

Since our knowledge of the structure of the solar system was established by the work of Tycho Brahe, Kepler, and Newton, many suggestions have been made relative to the origin of the solar system and thus of the Earth. Each of these theories has been widely discussed and seems to have been confidently accepted often for many years only to be discarded and replaced by another theory which in turn has suffered the same fate.

The problem of the Earth's origin is especially complex, as compared with other scientific problems, because it involves the entire solar system. The origin of Mercury is related to the origin of Jupiter, and it is not even possible to discuss the origin of a chondritic meteorite without attempting to understand the origin of the entire solar system; in fact the latter subject cannot be discussed separately from the problem of the evolution of stars. One of the very great difficulties in proposing a theory for the origin of the Earth arises from this integration of the problem into ever greater problems until it becomes part of the problem of the origin of the universe itself.

As one reads the older discussions of the subject, other difficulties of the problem become apparent. It is evident to the student today that his predecessors lacked sufficient knowledge of the exact physical sciences. Part of this is a personal inadequacy of each author—and who is there that does not have such an inadequacy—and part is the lack of the fundamental scientific knowledge of the time, both theoretical and empirical. To one writing in the middle of the twentieth century, the past scientific knowledge seems to have been hopelessly insufficient for the problem which the investigators attempted to solve. Because of these circumstances, one reads the discussions of the past with a feeling that they are in part logical and physically reasonable and in part obviously impossible and unsound. Those of us

* Institute for Nuclear Studies, University of Chicago.

who may tend to criticize should remember that others who follow us may read what we say with the same critical attitude and that that attitude may be justified.

The origin of a meteorite, the Earth, the sun, or the galaxy was such an exceedingly complicated event that almost any physically possible process did occur. In attempting any discussion of the subject, we must simplify in order to bring the process within our comprehension, and at the same time we are likely to add details that one may judge to be important and another not. As an example, suppose that scientists who lived on a planet on which there was no liquid water were presented with a sample of limestone and they attempted to give a complete discussion of its origin. All theories of the origin of this material which they proposed would be incomplete and would contain incorrect details. In particular, a correct description of its origin in the detail that we can supply would appear utterly fantastic to the reliable scientific students of the subject. I doubt if meteorites owe their origin to as complicated a process as does limestone, but the same difficulty arises when we try to reconstruct the processes. In thinking of the problem of the Earth's origin, we are constantly in great difficulty because the vast expanse, the high temperatures, the long times, the great energies, the low or high gravitational fields, etc., are so far outside our personal knowledge and our physical "intuition" that only mathematical calculations can give reliable answers. On the other hand, the phenomena are so complex that models for which calculations can be made are necessarily very much simpler than the actual processes were or are. We use mathematical methods to correct and justify only qualitatively what appear to be reasonable physical postulates relative to observed regularities.

But can we ever hope to get a satisfactory theory for the Earth's origin in view of these difficulties? No one knows the answer to this question. However, there are certain rules to be followed. The theory for the origin of the Earth that will eventually stand without complete reorganization in time will account for all the astronomical, geological, biological, physical, and chemical data that now exist or will be discovered in the future. This does not mean that suggestions should not be made until this criterion is met, for a given student may not always be able to fill in the facets of a problem which another can.

10.1 REVIEW OF PAST THEORIES

Kant suggested that the planets accumulated from dust clouds, one for each planet, revolving about the sun at approximately the present distances of the planets from the sun. When we remember that the gas laws, the existence of elements and their chemical properties, and the structure and properties of light were all unknown, it would seem that his proposal, which comes nearest to our present ideas, was largely a lucky guess. We can find little wrong with this idea today, but in order to come to this conclusion we must have all the scientific knowledge accumulated during the 200 years after the proposal was made.

Laplace suggested that rings were thrown off at the sun's equator as it contracted under gravitational forces from a radius beyond that of the farthest planet and that these rings collected into the planets. However, it is now evident that such rings would not have separated from such a contracting sun, and it can be shown that, if they did so separate, they would not collect into planets as is evident from the failure of the asteroids to form a planet.

In 1900 Chamberlin and Moulton suggested that the collision of two stars produced a swarm of planetesimals which then accumulated into the planets at low temperatures, and Jeans and Jeffreys proposed a modification of this in which a near approach was substituted for an actual collision. They assumed that the gaseous filament pulled from the sun condensed into the planets at high temperatures. Russell showed that these are impossible assumptions. If the stars were large at the time of collision, the collision may have been a distant one but part of the terrestrial planets would have been inside the sun. On the other hand, if the sun was small, then the relative velocities of the two stars must have been very high. These conditions are imposed by the condition that the angular momentum per gram of the planets must have been supplied by the angular momentum per gram of the colliding stars. Pitzer showed that material drawn from the sun would be at very high temperatures and that light pressure would dissipate this matter and that it would never collect into planets. The literature abounds with chance remarks referring to the high-temperature origin of the Earth, moon, and other planets, due undoubtedly to the very wide acceptance of the Jeans-Jeffreys theory during the last half century. Since the theory is physically impossible, we must again examine the question of the temperature of formation of the earth.

The planetesimal hypothesis of Chamberlin and Moulton is in error on another basis. They postulated that a swarm of planetesimals accumulated into the Earth and other terrestrial planets. Such an accumulation process would not occur in the absence of a viscous medium as is demonstrated by the asteroids. These bodies may collide and break up as they appear to be doing, but they do not agglomerate into larger bodies. The accumulation process requires the presence of gas in order to dissipate the relative energies of such bodies as heat. The importance of the gaseous medium in the formation of the planets is an essential feature of the modern theories of planetary origin. Other hypotheses have been proposed but have not been generally accepted (see Russell et al., 1945, p. 462 ff., and Jeffreys, 1951).

Kant and Laplace assumed that the sun accumulated from more widely dispersed material, whereas those that followed them assumed the existence of stars without attempting to account for their existence. The removal of matter from the sun, or the removal of the moon from the Earth, requires a great supply of energy the source of which is not obvious, whereas accumulation processes dissipate energy and are thus spontaneous. It seems doubtful that the process of forming planets is as difficult energetically as it has been generally believed to be for the past half century, and it is likely that the probability of planet formation in the neighborhood of stars is greater than has been assumed.

Vast dust clouds exist in interstellar space, and there is considerable evidence indicating that stars are even now being produced from such clouds. Blaauw (1952) has shown that the stars of the ζ Persei star cluster are moving away from each other at 12 km per second and that, 1.3 million years ago, these stars were very near each other. It seems probable that they originated at that time and at the position of the center of the cluster; remnants of the dust clouds still exist in this region of space. We expect that stars should form spontaneously from more widely dispersed matter because of the decrease of potential energy in the process, but it is not so easy to understand the high velocity of recession of the stars of this cluster. The stars of this cluster are *B* type stars with luminosities about 10,000 times that of the sun. Blaauw also shows that the larger Scorpio Centaurus cluster has a similar structure. It is probable that some explosive process produced it. Stars seem to originate in clusters from very massive dust clouds within very short periods of time—say less than 1.3 million years. Conditions some 4.5 billion years ago may have been considerably different from what they are now, but still this process for the formation of stars would seem probable for that time, and somehow such stars as the type G_0 sun may well have originated by some modification of the process that is now producing these B-type stars, and it may once have been part of a cluster though it seems not to be so at the present time. It seems reasonable to believe that the planets originated from such dust clouds by some process incidental to the formation of the sun as a star. The assumption that the sun first originated as a star and then was disrupted by some process to produce the planets seems to us today to be less probable.

10.2 GENERAL EVIDENCE RELATIVE TO THE ORIGIN OF THE SOLAR SYSTEM

It has long been recognized that there are regularities in the solar system that cannot be due to some chance, but must give clues to the process of origin. The planets and their satellites mostly move eastward around the sun in orbits which make only small angles with their median plane, which is approximately the plane of the ecliptic. Triton, satellite of Saturn, is an important exception, and there are small satellites which also are retrograde. The planets and their satellites also rotate eastward on their axes with only moderate angles between their axes and the plane of the ecliptic. Uranus is an exception with an axis making a 98° angle with the plane of its orbit. Approximately 98 percent of the angular momentum of the solar system is in the orbital angular momenta of the planets. Most of this is carried by Jupiter, but the angular momentum per unit mass is greater for Pluto than for any other known object in the system. This circumstance long has been a mystery to all students of the problem of the origin of the system. Since angular momentum cannot be created or destroyed, this angular momentum must have been present from the beginning and its distribution resulted from some circumstance during the origin of the system.

The low abundance of the inert gases in the Earth's atmosphere was pointed out by Aston. Russell and Menzel (1933) suggested that the low abundance of neon on the Earth as compared to astronomical sources was due to the loss of this element as well as other volatiles from the Earth's atmosphere during an early high-temperature period at the terminus of the Earth's formation. They suggested that the water and nitrogen were retained in chemical combination while these other volatiles were lost. The loss of gases of molecular weights from 16 to 130, i.e., methane to xenon, must have occurred while the mass of the Earth was distributed through a large volume since it is otherwise difficult to account for their loss. Helium is now escaping from the Earth's atmosphere, which is estimated to be at some 2000° K at the escape layer. In order for xenon to escape at a comparable rate from the present Earth, the temperature would have to be $130/4 = 32.5$ times as high. It is difficult to suggest how such a high temperature could have been produced during the terminal stage of the Earth's formation and not during the earlier stages when the volatiles now on the Earth's surface were incorporated into the body of the forming Earth.

Many data exist relative to planets other than the Earth which are significant to the Earth's origin. The moon's surface is ancient and records the fall of objects of substantial size on its surface. These objects contained masses of high-density material, presumably iron-nickel. The intense bombardment ended in a surprisingly short time, 10^4 or 10^5 years. Gilbert (1893) published a very important paper on this subject. Baldwin (1949) reviewed the evidence, and both he and Urey (1952, Chapter 2) add some new points to the discussion and give reference to other literature. Mars does not have a well-developed core as shown by its value for the Clairaut constant, namely $\epsilon MG/a^3\Omega^2$, equals 1.19–1.22, which is very near the value 1.25 required for a planet of uniform density (M is the mass; G, the gravitational constant; a, the radius; ϵ, the oblateness; and Ω, the angular velocity of rotation). Apparently, terrestrial planets can originate by a process that does not produce a core, and the planet can exist throughout the age of the solar system without a core being formed.

The dynamics of the moon's motion indicate that it is not in equilibrium with the gravitational and mechanical forces acting on it. The moments of inertia about its polar axis and about an axis pointing toward the Earth can be explained if there are excess masses on its surfaces toward and away from the Earth corresponding to about a 1-kilometer thickness of lunar material of average density in these regions, whereas the equilibrium values should be less than one-tenth of this. This difference is definitely outside the limits of error. These observations indicate that the center of the moon has great strength, about that of building bricks, and this indicates that the center of the moon is now rigid. It is doubtful if the moon was ever molten.

This was the conclusion reached by G. K. Gilbert some 60 years ago and quite independently by the present writer.

Chemical evidence relative to the Earth's origin has been largely neglected by astronomers and physicists who have considered this problem in the past (Urey, 1952). Rabe's new determination (1950) of the mass of Mercury showed that there is an unmistakable variation in density of the terrestrial planets. This is shown by the data of Table 10. It is difficult to estimate the densities of the Earth and

Table 10 Characteristic parameters of the moon and some planets

Planet	Mass (Earth = 1)	Radius (Earth = 1)	Mean Density	Mean Density at Zero Pressure	Percent Iron-Nickel Phase	Oblateness ϵ	$\epsilon MG/a^3\Omega^2$
Moon	0.012304	0.2728	3.34	3.31	0		
Mercury	0.0543	0.38	5.46	5.4	72		
		0.403	4.58	4.5	50		
Venus	0.8136	0.961	5.06	4.4(?)	45		
Earth	1	1	5.515	4.4	45	0.0033659	0.976
Mars	0.1080	0.520	4.24	4.02	30	0.00520	1.22
		0.523	4.17	3.95	27	0.00520	1.19

This table differs slightly from a similar one in *The Planets*, p. 60. Kuiper's values of the radii of Mercury and Mars are included instead of the Russell, Dugan, and Stewart values. The 0.38 and 0.523 values for the radii of Mercury and Mars, respectively, are Kuiper's values; the 0.403 value for Mercury is Rabe's average, and the 0.520 value for Mars is Trumpler's result. The percent of iron is calculated assuming a density of silicate and iron of 3.3 and 7.23, respectively.

Venus at zero pressure, but there is no doubt of the large differences between the densities of Mercury, Mars, and the moon, which have low pressures in their interiors. The Earth and Venus have intermediate densities. This means that the metallic and silicate fractions characteristic of the meteorites have been partially separated and one fraction has been partially lost to differing degrees during the formation of the several terrestrial planets. A mechanism for this separation and loss must be provided for in any acceptable model for the origin of the solar system.

Since Mars has no core, it appears that this planet is solid throughout and was never molten. It has not been possible to draw any conclusions relative to the temperature of formation of Venus and Mercury. However, elements that are volatile at the melting points of silicates are not concentrated at the surface of the Earth, indicating that no such high temperatures existed during the late stages of the Earth's formation (Urey, 1953). There appears to be considerable evidence favoring low average temperatures during the formation of the terrestrial planets.

On the other hand, the work of Patterson et al. (1953*a*) on the isotopic composition of lead in the iron meteorites and the igneous rocks of the Earth (see Table 9.1) gives some very interesting information on this question. The lead of the iron meteorites has changed its isotopic composition only very slightly due to the low concentrations of uranium and thorium in these objects. We can conclude that this is close to primordial lead (see Section 9.1.e). The isotopic composition of the lead from granite and basalt differs from that of the primordial lead by amounts that indicate an age of 4.5×10^9 years. However, the primordial abundance of lead and uranium and thorium are such that the latter elements must have been concentrated relative to lead by a large factor if the additional radiogenic leads have been supplied by these elements. Since lead is definitely chalcophile, it appears that the primordial lead, that is, lead formed before the iron meteorites were chemically separated from the uranium and thorium, was removed from the mantle by the removal of the iron sulfide phase early in the Earth's history. Undoubtedly, proponents of the completely molten primitive Earth will regard this as proof for their view, and it is certainly important evidence favoring this view.

10.3 RECENT THEORIES FOR THE EARTH'S ORIGIN

Weizsäcker suggested that the sun during its early history acquired a nebula of gas and dust about it which rapidly became flattened into a disk in what is now the plane of the ecliptic, and that this nebula broke up into turbulent eddies in which the planets accumulated. It was assumed that the pattern of eddies was very regular with five eddies in a ring, that the entire disk consisted of a succession of such rings, and that the planets accumulated in "roller bearing" eddies between the larger ones. This pattern was assumed in order to account for the Titius Bode law for the spacing of the planets. Weizsäcker's ideas stimulated much thought on this subject, although his detailed model has not been accepted. Turbulent eddies are irregular in size and arrangement rather than so uniform as he supposed.

Kuiper (1951) has modified Weizsäcker's ideas into a far more acceptable model. He has shown that a disk of dust cloud would break up into turbulent eddies of irregular sizes but of dimensions increasing as the distance from the sun. Such eddies would coalesce as they collide until only one mass of gas remained at successive radii from the sun, one for each planet. These "protoplanets" were initially so large that they nearly touched each other. Kuiper shows that they would be stable under the tidal forces of the sun if they possessed enough mass to form the planets. He accounts for the breakup of the solar nebula at the Roche density which determined the size and distribution of the protoplanets and their spacing relative to the sun. Tidal effects compelled these masses to rotate in the same sense as their orbital rotation about the sun. These rotational periods were the same as the orbital periods, and, as their gas was lost, the residue retained the sense of rotation and part of the angular momentum so that the planets rotate with much shorter periods.

Kuiper follows Eucken's (1944) ideas relative to the actual accumulation of the planets. Eucken proposed a model for the accumulation of the planets. He assumed an Emden gas sphere in quasi-equilibrium; i.e., the temperature, pressure, and density throughout was an equilibrium one. As gas was lost from this sphere, condensation of the least volatile constituents began at the center of the sphere. These he showed would be iron and nickel. The more volatile constituents would condense next, and he showed that the more abundant constituents of the silicates would condense at this stage. He showed that it was possible to account for the iron core of the earth and the silicate mantle in this way. Eucken assumed that only the substances volatile at ordinary temperatures and below escaped from the Earth, but he did not consider the problem of removing a substantial part of the entire silicate fraction in order to account for the varying densities of the Earth and other planets.

The volatilities of the constituents of the silicate fraction of cosmic material differ greatly. Mercury is a very volatile element, and other elements are far more volatile than the magnesium silicate which must be one of the most important constituents. If the process of condensation and loss of the low-temperature volatiles only occurred as Eucken assumed, then mercury and other higher temperature volatiles should be concentrated at the Earth's surface, which is contrary to observation. On the other hand, if we modify the Eucken model by assuming a loss of the silicate fraction in order to retain a larger fraction of iron and hence increase the mean density of the Earth, then mercury and other elements should have been preferentially lost from the Earth to a high degree, which again is contrary to observation. Eucken's model applied to Mars should have produced a planet with an iron core, again contrary to observation. The model was an important attempt to understand the origin and structure of the terrestrial planets, but it does not conform to more detailed chemical and physical evidence which has now become available (Urey, in press).

In the writer's opinion Kuiper's theory for the development of the solar nebula is correct and is a definite step toward the understanding of the origin of the solar system. It accounts for the Titius Bode law and the other mechanical regularities of the solar system, and it includes the necessary gaseous mechanism for the accumulation of solid objects into the terrestrial planets.

At the time that this theory was being developed, the writer began a consideration of physical chemical evidence relative to the problem, hoping that it would supplement the astronomical theory. This it did for the most part. It was immediately evident that Eucken's theory overlooked important chemical problems.

The meteorites contain the "non-volatile" elements in relative amounts which are very similar to those expected from astronomical studies for most of the stars The data for the Earth's surface are more difficult to interpret since much chemical differentiation has occurred during geologic time, but it has been generally supposed that the differences in elementary abundances relative to the meteorites can be accounted for and that it is not necessary to assume any important primitive differences in composition. It is recognized that the volatiles, hydrogen, the inert gases, carbon as methane, nitrogen as the element or ammonia, and oxygen as water were lost to a large extent though not completely during the process of formation of both the Earth and meteorites. At the same time the variation in densities of the terrestrial planets became clearly established through the work of Rabe (1950) on the mass of Mercury. Hence the necessity for some fractionations of the metallic and silicate fractions during the formation of the planets became apparent.

In order that the elements be retained on the Earth and meteorites in approximately cosmic proportions, it is necessary that some process of complete condensation of the elements less volatile than mercury shall have been available and that the elements so condensed should at no stage be largely evaporated and lost again. The chemical properties show that low temperatures are required for the condensation of the more volatile constituents such as water and mercury. The presence of carbon compounds of low volatility in the carbonaceous chondrites containing the elements carbon, hydrogen, nitrogen, oxygen, sulfur, and chlorine, indicates a method by which these elements may have been condensed in non-volatile form during the condensation of dust in the primordial dust cloud. This writer originally suggested water, ammonia, hydrated silicates, ammonium salts, iron carbide and graphite, etc., for this purpose but both these (except iron carbide and graphite) and carbon compounds require a low initial temperature. The retention of mercury also requires such temperatures.

There is evidence indicating that these materials were subjected to high temperatures sufficient to melt silicates and iron while they were part of substantial bodies. (1) Massive iron objects occur as meteorites and there is strong evidence for the presence of such masses in the large objects that fell on the moon. Such separation of silicate and metallic iron requires the presence of gravitational fields of perhaps 10 dynes such as would be present on a body 100 km or greater in radius. (2) Not all the iron of the meteorites and the Earth is in the reduced state. At the temperature of melted iron all iron compounds would be reduced to the elementary state in the presence of cosmic proportions of hydrogen, water, and hydrogen sulfide. Thus heating in the presence of such gases must have occurred with limited access of such gases for limited times, such as would occur if the material were incorporated into objects of asteroidal size. (3) The more volatile elements such as mercury, arsenic, zinc, and cadmium have been retained in approximately cosmic proportions, and even water has been retained in appreciable amounts. This shows that heating processes could only have been applied to large objects and for lengths of time such that extensive fractional distillation did not occur. (4) The volatile gases, even xenon, did escape as did also some of the silicate fraction as gas or solid particles This must have occurred while the mass of the present Earth was distributed over a large volume, and the very great depletion of the inert gases relative to the oxygen as water indicates a very complete loss of gas at some stage before any important fraction of the Earth had accumulated into a compact body. (5) The variation in density of the terrestrial planets requires a loss of either the high-density metallic phase or more probably the low-density silicate phases in varying amounts for the different terrestrial planets, and yet this occurred without an important loss of the more volatile constituents of the silicate fraction. This is a limiting condition on the course of events during the Earth's formation.

All these chemical conditions can be understood providing the primordial dust accumulated into substantial objects, some hundreds of kilometers in diameter, at low temperatures so that the elements less volatile than mercury were included in about cosmic proportions, and providing that the heating processes followed this accumulation and did not last so long that these objects evaporated or that their more volatile constituents were lost. These conditions are not met by the Eucken model, and a modified model incorporating these planetesimals or satellites is necessary.

10.4 A SUMMARY OF THE PROBABLE COURSE OF EVENTS WHICH LED TO THE EXISTENCE OF THE SOLAR SYSTEM

Early in the history of our galaxy clouds of dust and gas of cosmic composition contracted to smaller volume. At some stage this cloud condensed into a large number of stars, of which the sun was one. Some residues of the dust cloud remained and collided with the sun and were partially captured by it. This assemblage rapidly contracted into the solar disk of Weizsäcker and Kuiper. This disk broke up into masses of protoasteroidal or protolunar magnitude because of the gravitational instability of such masses. Within these masses the accumulation of substantial bodies of asteroidal and perhaps lunar dimensions occurred at low temperatures as indicated particularly by the chemical studies of this author. These objects and their gaseous envelopes collided with each other and formed protoplanets consisting of these solid bodies and part of their gaseous elements. Tidal effects of the sun determined their spacings and sizes as derived by Kuiper. At this stage high temperatures originating from the adiabatic compression of their gases or from some temporary high temperature of the sun or both raised the surface temperatures of these objects, partially evaporated silicate materials from their surfaces, and increased their metallic iron content. Or collisions of smaller objects with the surfaces splashed the silicate materials from these objects as suggested by the brecciated structures of the chondritic meteorites. The gases of the protoplanets and the evaporated shattered silicates were lost owing to light pressure from the sun. Subsequently the planetesimals, or, better, satellite objects since they moved within the Earth-moon system, accumulated into the Earth. The moon itself appears to be one such object that was not captured by the Earth and which itself has captured smaller objects of similar origin. The moons of Mars and the asteroids also are objects of this kind.

10.5 THE ACCUMULATION OF THE EARTH

In order to account for the absence of the inert gases in the Earth's atmosphere it is necessary to conclude that the cosmic mixture of gases was lost from the Earth's protoplanet before the materials of the

Earth had become consolidated into an object of the present mass or even before the growing Earth had reached a mass and radius equal to those of Mars. It seems necessary to conclude that the protoplanet became a miniature globular cluster type of object with most of the gases dispersed into space, and with objects some hundreds of kilometers in radius moving in their own gravitational fields. In order to account for the amount of neon in the Earth's atmosphere only about 10^{19} grams of cosmic mixture of gases could have been captured by the Earth. If this occupied a volume equal to that of a sphere of radius equal to the moon's orbital radius, the mean density of the gas would be only 5×10^{-14} g/cm^3. Following such very complete loss the satellite objects accumulated into the Earth. Rapid radiation of the energy of accumulation through the gas cloud was possible. If this calculation is made for the other inert gases, argon exclusive of A^{40}, krypton, and xenon, one gets 3×10^{21}, 1.4×10^{23}, and 1.2×10^{23} grams, respectively. The heavier inert gases have been retained to a larger extent than the lighter ones.

Satellite objects such as those indicated would accumulate slowly into a planet and probably not completely at all, as has occurred in the case of the Earth's moon and the moons of Mars, unless some residual gas was present. Assuming that the objects moved relative to the gas at supersonic velocities, the back pressure would be ρv^2, where ρ is the density of gas and v the velocity of the object relative to the gas. The rate of loss of energy is then

$$-dE/dt = \pi r^2 \rho v^3$$

and the total energy of an object in an inverse square field of force moving in a circular orbit is equal to the negative of the kinetic energy, namely $\frac{4}{3}\pi\rho_0 r^3 v^2$ where ρ_0 is the density of the object and r is its radius. Substituting, we secure

$$\frac{4}{3}\frac{\rho_0}{\rho} r \frac{dv}{v^2} = dt$$

This integrates to

$$t - t_0 = \frac{4}{3}\frac{\rho_0 r}{\rho}\left(\frac{1}{v_0} - \frac{1}{v}\right)$$

The linear velocity of the moon is 10^5 cm/sec and of an object in a circumsurface orbit about the earth is 7.9×10^5 cm/sec. Using values for ρ_0, and r for the moon and ρ equal to 5×10^{-14} g/cm^3, the time is 1.5×10^{17} sec, which is equal to the age of the solar system.

Since the velocity of sound in hydrogen gas is greater than 10^5 cm, the calculation does not apply and the moon would lose energy more slowly than has been calculated. But, if the density of gas was larger, if the objects were smaller, and especially if they began this fall from orbits nearer the Earth, a very small density of gas would suffice to make them spiral into the Earth. It should be noted that objects of low density and smaller radius should fall more rapidly than those of larger size and density. As energy is transferred to the gas from the accumulating objects the gas should be moved away from the Earth, and in this way the low-density gas cloud could be maintained. The inert gases could be swept away by water, ammonia and carbon arriving with the objects and being pumped away as gaseous hydrogen, water, nitrogen or ammonia, and methane.

The mean temperature of the Earth during the period of accumulation may have been either low or high, depending on the rate of accumulation and the rate of loss of energy by radiation. It is a common assumption that the temperature was high, though no careful arguments seem to have been advanced in favor of this view (see Chapter 5). If the initial temperature was high, the core of the Earth would have formed during this process, and, if it is not possible for the core to form by any process in an Earth of lower temperature, then the existence of a core in the Earth conclusively proves a high-temperature origin of the Earth. Kuhn and Rittman (1941) argued that this was true and that a core could not have formed except in a molten Earth, but the present writer doubts the validity of their arguments. Solid iron in small masses would not sink through solid silicates, but larger masses could move through them, and liquid iron might move comparatively rapidly through silicates by dissolving constituents from the bottom and depositing the silicates at the top of a liquid iron pool. Molten iron sulfide wets silicates and should move more readily than iron. We shall regard the question of the primitive temperature of the Earth as an open one and consider evidence relative to this question.

As is well known, a mixture of the oxides of the lithophile elements does not melt or solidify at one temperature and without fractionation of the elements. It is generally believed that the crust of the Earth, some 10 km thick under the oceans and some 30 km thick under the continents, has been differentiated from the underlying materials of the mantle by partial melting. This process is evidently going on at the present time at a rate which indicates that most of the crust has been produced continuously throughout geologic time and not entirely at the beginning. If the Earth was completely molten at the end of its formation period and then solidified, it would seem that a substantial crust would have been formed at that time. Bowen (unpublished; see Slichter, 1950) maintained that a much thicker crust should have been expected had this been true, assuming that the mantle has the average composition of meteorites. If it does not have such a mean composition, it would be a really difficult problem to explain such a difference. Countercurrent fractionation between sinking crystals and rising liquid should have concentrated silica and other constituents at the surface to a high degree. This does not seem to have happened.

Urey (1953) has shown that the elements that have been concentrated to a high degree in the oceans and sediments, i.e., chlorine, bromine, iodine, and boron, have the common property of being soluble in water at low temperatures, that no other elements have this property under natural conditions, and that elements that are markedly volatile at high temperatures are not concentrated systematically at the Earth's surface. These facts indicate that the prevailing temperature of the Earth's surface during the terminal stage of its formation was low, probably not higher than 200° C. In fact, the lack of systematic fractionation of elements less volatile than mercury in the Earth and meteorites indicates that all heating processes that existed during the formation of these bodies occurred under such conditions that volatiles were neither lost nor concentrated relative to other elements.

Vening Meinesz (1950, 1951, 1952) has pointed out an interesting regularity in Prey's expansion of the Earth's surface in spherical harmonics. The first to the fifth harmonics inclusive are very prominent. The first harmonic merely states that the continents are in one hemisphere. He interprets this to mean that convection with the entire Earth acting as a single cell occurred early in the Earth's history before a core had formed. Following this, more complicated convections occurred in the mantle after the core had formed and these convections produced the continents which are described by the higher harmonics. This postulate requires that the core grew during geologic time and that the Earth was formed at such a temperature that the iron core was not formed as the Earth grew, for the single-cell convection is not possible in an Earth with a core. Segregation of the continents on one side of the Earth could not occur until the Earth was completely formed. Again, a low temperature of formation is indicated,

Patterson et al. (1953*b*) have shown that the primordial lead was early separated from the uranium and thorium of the Earth. As mentioned previously, this can be explained by a formation of the core early in the Earth's history. We should attempt to postulate a course of events which is consistent with all the evidence, and perhaps it is too soon to expect that this can be done now. However, a tentative suggestion may be made. Great pools of lava, probably 10 or 20 km deep, have existed on the moon, and probably similar pools existed on the Earth during its period of formation even if the general temperature was not high. The iron, iron sulfide, and silicate phases separated in such pools, and the more dense phases were separated from the silicate phases by distances of the order of kilometers. They were partially mixed together again in subsequent collisions of satellite objects as the Earth accumulated. Finally differentiation of the Earth occurred with the iron and iron sulfide forming the core and the separated silicate phase forming the outer mantle of the Earth. The lead has moved into the core with the iron sulfide. Finally this outer mantle may be assumed to supply the granites and basalts of the Earth's crust.

H. Hess (private communication) argues that the dunitic bombs in the throats of old volcanoes are samples of the Earth's mantle, but points out that the crust of the Earth if mixed with a mantle of the composition of these dunitic materials would not give a material of the composition of the stone meteorites. However, a mixture of the crust with a thickness of a few hundred kilometers of this dunitic material would approximate cosmic matter in composition. Holyk and Ahrens (1953) point out that their determinations of potassium in the ultramafic rocks and in meteorites indicate that the crust has been produced from 10^{27} g of the Earth. This is approximately the mass of the outer mantle of the Earth. Rubey (unpublished) has proposed essentially this structure for the present Earth and its development with time.

It seems to this writer that the Earth is differentiating its substance at the present time and has been doing so continuously throughout geologic time. This process is much more easily understood if the Earth was initially more homogeneous than it is now. In view of this process, the argument that even greater differentiation of crustal materials should have occurred, if the original completely molten Earth hypothesis is assumed, should be given careful consideration. The absence of a systematic concentration of volatile elements at the

Earth's surface is an important argument against a completely molten Earth.

The outline of events given in the first part of this Chapter could be consistent with either hypothesis relative to the physical state of the Earth when it was formed.

10.6 CONCLUSION

During the first part of this century great confidence was felt and expressed relative to the origin of the Earth. This confidence was not justified in the opinion of this writer. During the past decade great progress has been made in the understanding of the origin of stars in general and the solar system in particular. It is most probable that we have much more to learn before a definite and lasting model of the origin of the solar system and the Earth is devised. It is a fascinating study and to an active scientist the journey is far more interesting than the ultimate arrival.

LITERATURE CITED *

Ahrens, L. H. (1946) Determination of the age of minerals by means of the radioactivity of Rb, *Nature 157,* 269.

Ahrens, L. H. (1947) The determination of geological age by means of the natural radioactivity of rubidium: A report of preliminary investigations, *Trans. Geol. Soc. S. Africa 50,* 24–54.

Ahrens, L. H. (1948) Molecular spectroscopic evidence of the existence of strontium isotopes Sr^{88}, Sr^{87} and Sr^{86}, *Phys. Rev. 74,* 74–77.

Ahrens, L. H. (1949) Measuring geologic time by the strontium method, *Bull. Geol. Soc. Amer. 60,* 217–266.

Ahrens, L. H., and L. Gorfinkle (1950) Age of extremely ancient pegmatites from south-eastern Manitoba, *Nature 166,* 149.

Ahrens, L. H., and L. Gorfinkle (1951) Quantitative spectro-chemical analysis of rubidium in lepidolite, *Am. J. Sci. 249,* 451–456.

Ahrens, L. H., and A. M. Macgregor (1951) Probable extreme age of pegmatites from Southern Rhodesia, *Science 114,* 64–65.

Ahrens, L. H. (1952) The oldest rocks, *Trans. Am. Geophys. Union 33,* 193–195.

Ahrens, L. H., W. H. Pinson, and M. M. Kearns (1952) Association of rubidium and potassium and their abundance in common igneous rocks and meteorites, *Geochim. et Cosmochim. Acta 2,* 229–242.

Ahrens, L. H. (1954) The lognormal distribution of the elements, *Geochim. et Cosmochim. Acta 5,* 49–73.

Alderman, A. R. (1936) Eclogites in the neighbourhood of Glenelg, Inverness-shire, *Quart. J. Geol. Soc. London 92,* pt. 4, 488–530.

Aldrich, L. T., and A. O. Nier (1948*a*) The occurrence of $helium^3$ in natural sources of helium, *Phys. Rev. 74,* 1590–1594.

Aldrich, L. T., and A. O. Nier (1948*b*) $Argon^{40}$ in potassium minerals, *Phys. Rev. 74,* 876–877.

Aldrich, L. T., J. B. Doak, and G. L. Davis (1953*a*) The use of ion exchange column in mineral analysis for age determination, *Am. J. Sci. 251,* 377–387.

Aldrich, L. T., L. F. Herzog, J. B. Doak, and G. L. Davis (1953*b*) Variations in strontium abundances in minerals, Part 1: Mass spectrometric analysis of mineral sources of strontium, *Trans. Am. Geophys. Union 34,* 457–460.

Alexandrov, S. P. (1927) Radiographien tüjamujunscher Erze [Radiographs of ores from Tuya Muyun], *Z. Krist. 65,* 141–148.

Allan, D. W., R. M. Farquhar, and R. D. Russell (1953) A note on the lead isotope method of age determination, *Science 118,* 486–488.

* Reports, releases, preprints, and similar material of restricted circulation are denoted as *unpublished* in the text and listed here only when the subject is of unusual interest and not treated in regular published sources. All titles are given in the original language, with translations, where necessary [in brackets].

Allen, E. T., and A. L. Day (1935) Hot springs of the Yellowstone National Park, *Carnegie Inst. Wash. Publ. 466,* 525 pp.

Alpher, R. A., and R. C. Herman (1951) The primeval lead isotopic abundances and the age of the earth's crust, *Phys. Rev. 84,* 1111–1114.

American Petroleum Institute (1943, 1944–1945, 1946–1947, 1948–1949, 1950–1951, 1952) *Annual report of progress: Fundamental research on occurrence and recovery of petroleum,* New York.

Anderson, B. W., and C. J. Payne (1937) Recent work on zircon, III: Research in measurement of physical properties, *Gemmologist 7,* 298–301.

Anderson, C. C., and H. H. Hinson (1951) Helium-bearing natural gases of the United States, *U. S. Bur. Mines Bull. 486,* 141 pp.

Anderson, E. C., J. R. Arnold, and W. F. Libby (1951) Measurement of low level radiocarbon, *Rev. Sci. Instr. 22,* 225–230.

Anderson, E. C. (1953) The production and distribution of natural radiocarbon, *Ann. Rev. Nuclear Sci. 2,* 63–78.

Anderson, E. C., Hilde Levi, and H. Tauber (1953) Copenhagen natural radiocarbon measurements, *Science 118,* 6–9.

Antevs, Ernst (1953) Geochronology of the deglacial and neothermal ages, *J. Geol. 61,* 195–230.

Arnold, J. R. (1954) Scintillation counting of natural radiocarbon, I: The counting method, *Science 119,* 155–157.

Arrol, W. J., R. B. Jacobi, and F. A. Paneth (1942) Meteorites and the age of the solar system, *Nature 149,* 235–238.

Asayama, T. (1936) Radioaktive Untersuchung des Hiei-Granitgebiets [Study of the radioactivity of the Hiei granite region], *Japan. J. Astron. Geophys. 14,* 19–26.

Bain, G. W. (1950) Geology of the fissionable materials, *Econ. Geol. 45,* 273–323.

Bainbridge, K. T., M. Goldhaber and Elizabeth Wilson (1953) Influence of the chemical state on the lifetime of a nuclear isomer, Tc^{99m}, *Phys. Rev. 90,* 430–438.

Baldwin, R. B. (1949) *Face of the Moon,* University of Chicago Press, 239 pp.

Baranov, V. I., and S. I. Kretschmer (1935) Verwendung von Lichtplatten mit dicker Emulsionsschicht zur Erforschung der Verteilung radioaktiver Elemente in Naturobjekten [Thick emulsions for the study of the distribution of radioactive elements], *Compt. rend. acad. sci. U.R.S.S. 1,* 546–549.

Barnard, G. P. (1953) *Modern Mass Spectroscopy,* The Institute of Physics, London, 326 pp.

Barnes, R. B., and D. J. Salley (1943) Analysis for potassium by its natural radioactivity, *Ind. Eng. Chem. Anal. Ed. 15,* no. 1, 4–7.

Barrett, J. H. (1950) Upper limit on the cross section for the scattering of neutrinos, *Phys. Rev. 79,* 907–908(L).

Barth, T. F. W. (1938) Radium and the petrology of certain granites of Finland, *Am. J. Sci. (5) 35,* 231–245.

Bateman, H. (1910) The solution of a system of differential equations occurring in the theory of radioactive transformations, *Proc. Cambridge Phil. Soc. 15,* 423–427.

Bauer, A. (1939) Untersuchungen zur Kenntnis der spezifisch leichten Zirkone [Study of zircons of low specific gravity], *Neues Jahrb. Mineral. Beilage Bd. A75,* no. 2, 159–204.

Bauer, C. A. (1947) Production of helium in meteorites by cosmic radiation, *Phys. Rev. 72,* 354–355.

Becquerel, H. (1896) Sur les radiations émises par phosphorescence [Phosphorescent radiations]; Sur les radiations invisibles émises par les corps phosphorescents [Invisible radiations emitted by phosphorescent substances]; Sur les radiations invisibles émises par les sels d'uranium [Invisible radiations emitted by salts of uranium], *Compt. rend. 122,* 420, 501, 689.

Beers, R. F., and C. Goodman (1944) Distribution of radioactivity in ancient sediments, *Bull. Geol. Soc. Amer. 55,* 1229–1253.

Beers, R. F. (1945) Radioactivity and organic content of some Paleozoic shales, *Bull. Am. Assoc. Petroleum Geol. 29,* 1–22, see p. 11.

Begemann, F., H. v. Buttlar, F. G. Houtermans, N. Isaac, and E. Picciotto (1952) Les résultats préliminaires des mesures d'âge de la pechblende de Shinkolobwe par la méthode du RaD [Preliminary results of age measurements of Shinkolobwe pitchblende by the $lead^{210}$ method], *Bull. soc. belge géol. paléontol. et hydrol. 61,* 223–226.

Begemann, F., H. v. Buttlar, F. G. Houtermans, N. Isaac, and E. Picciotto (1953) Application de la méthode du RaD à la mesure de l'âge "chimique" d'un minerai d'Uranium [Application of the $lead^{210}$ method to the measurement of the "chemical lead" age of a uranium mineral], *Geochim. et Cosmochim. Acta 4,* 21–35.

Begemann, F., J. Geiss, F. G. Houtermans, and W. Buser (1954) Isotopenzusammensetzung und Radioaktivität von rezentem Vesuvblei [Isotopic composition and radioactivity of recent lead from Vesuvius], *Nuovo cimento 11,* 663–673.

Belcher, D. J., R. C. Herner, T. R. Cuykendall, and H. S. Sack (1953) Use of radioactive material to measure soil moisture and density, *Am. Soc. Testing Materials, Special Tech. Publ. 134,* 10–22.

Bell, K. G., C. Goodman, and W. L. Whitehead (1940) Radioactivity of sedimentary rocks and associated petroleum, *Bull. Am. Assoc. Petroleum Geol. 24,* 1529–1547.

Benfield, A. E. (1939) Terrestrial heat flow in Great Britain, *Proc. Roy. Soc. (London) A173,* 428–450.

Benfield, A. E. (1947) A heat flow value for a well in California, *Am. J. Sci. 245,* 1–18.

Benfield, A. E. (1948) Thermal consequences of the capture of neutrinos by the Earth, *Phys. Rev. 74,* 621(L), erratum, 1192.

Berbezier, J., R. Chaminade, and C. Lallemant (1952) Description de l'équipement d'un véhicule de radiosondage gamma [Description of the equipment in a gamma-ray logging vehicle], *Ann. géophys. 8,* 260–263.

Berbezier, J., and C. Lallemant (1952) Description du matériel simplifié de radiosondage gamma employé sur les exploitations minières [Description of simplified equipment for gamma-ray logging in mineral exploration], *Ann. géophys. 8,* 314–315.

Berggren, T. (1940) Minerals of the Varuträsk pegmatite, XV: Analyses of the mica minerals and their interpretation, *Geol. Fören. i Stockholm Förh. 62,* 182–193.

Bernert, Traude (1951) Radiumbestimmungen an Tiefseesedimenten [Determination of radium in deep sea deposits], *Österr. Akad. Wiss., math.-naturw. Kl., Sitzber., Abt. IIa, 160,* 99–111.

Berriman, R. W. (1948) Recording of charged particles of minimum ionizing power in photographic emulsions, *Nature 162,* 992–993.

Bethe, H. (1930) Zur Theorie des Durchgangs schneller Korpuskular-strahlen durch Materie [Theory of transmission of fast particles through matter], *Ann. Physik 5,* 325–400.

Billings, M. P., and N. B. Keevil (1946) Petrography and radioactivity of four Paleozoic magma series in New Hampshire, *Bull. Geol. Soc. Amer. 57,* 797–828.

Birch, Francis, and Harry Clark (1940) The thermal conductivity of rocks and its dependence upon temperature and composition, *Am. J. Sci. 238,* 529–558, 613–635.

Birch, Francis, and Harry Clark (1945) An estimate of the surface flow of heat in the West Texas Permian basin, *Am. J. Sci. 243-A,* 69–74.

Birch, Francis (1948) The effects of Pleistocene climatic variations upon geothermal gradients, *Am. J. Sci. 246,* 729–760.

Birch, Francis (1950) Flow of heat in the Front Range, Colorado, *Bull. Geol. Soc. Amer. 61,* 567–630.

Birch, Francis (1951) Recent work on the radioactivity of potassium and some related geophysical problems, *J. Geophys. Research 56,* 107–126.

Birch, Francis (1952) Elasticity and constitution of the Earth's interior, *J. Geophys. Research 57,* 227–286.

Birch, Francis (1954) Thermal conductivity, climatic variation, and heat flow near Calumet, Michigan, *Am. J. Sci. 252,* 1–25.

Birks, J. B. (1953) *Scintillation Counters,* McGraw-Hill, New York, 148 pp.

Blaauw, A. (1952) The age and evolution of the Zeta Persei group of O- and B-type stars, *Bull. Astron. Inst. Neth. 11,* 405–413.

Blanchard, A., and J. T. Dewan (1953) The calibration of gamma ray logs, *Petroleum Engr. 25,* August, B76–B80.

Blatt, J. M., and V. F. Weisskopf (1952) *Theoretical Nuclear Physics,* John Wiley & Sons, New York, 864 pp.

Blau, M., and H. Wambacher (1933) Über den Einfluss des Kornzustands auf die Schwärzungsempfindlichkeit bei Exposition mit Alpha-Partikeln [The effect of grain condition on the sensitivity to alpha-particle exposure], *Z. wiss. Phot. 31,* 243–250.

Blau, M., E. S. Deevey, Jr., and M. S. Gross (1953) Yale natural radiocarbon measurements, I: Pyramid Valley, New Zealand, and its problems, *Science 118,* 1–6.

Blifford, I. H., L. B. Lockhart, Jr., and J. Rosenstock (1952) On the natural radioactivity in the air, *J. Geophys. Research 57,* 499–509.

Boato, G., G. Careri, and M. Santangelo (1952) Argon isotopes in natural gases, *Nuovo cimento 9,* 44–49.

Boltwood, B. B. (1904) Relation between uranium and radium in some minerals, *Nature 70,* 80.

Boltwood, B. B. (1905) On the ultimate disintegration products of the radioactive elements, *Am. J. Sci. (4) 20,* 253–267.

Boltwood, B. B. (1907) On the ultimate disintegration products of the radioactive elements, *Am. J. Sci. (4) 23,* 77–88.

Bonét-Maury, P., and M. Lefort (1948) Formation of hydrogen peroxide in water irradiated with X- and alpha-rays, *Nature 162,* 381–382.

Borkowski, C. J., and R. L. Clark (1953) Gamma-ray energy resolution with NaI-TlI scintillation spectrometers, *Rev. Sci. Instr. 24,* 1046–1050.

Bousquet, A. G. (1949) Counting rate meters *versus* scalers, *Nucleonics 4,* no. 2, 67–76.

Bowen, N. L. (1937) Recent high-temperature research on silicates and its significance in igneous geology, *Am. J. Sci. (5) 33,* 1–21.

Bragg, W. H. (1907) On the ionization of various gases by the alpha particles from radium, *Phil. Mag. (6) 13,* 333–357.

Breger, I. A., and V. L. Burton (1946) The effects of radioactivity on a naphthenic acid, *J. Am. Chem. Soc. 68,* 1639–1642.

Breger, I. A. (1946–1947) Effects of electrical discharge and radiation on organic compounds *in Am. Petroleum Inst. Report of progress: Fundamental research on occurrence and recovery of petroleum,* 214–233.

Breger, I. A. (1948) Transformation of organic substances by alpha particles and deuterons, *J. Phys. & Colloid Chem. 52,* 551–563.

Breger, I. A., and W. L. Whitehead (1951) Radioactivity and the origin of petroleum, *Proc. 3rd World Petroleum Congr., Hague, Sec. I,* 421–427.

Brewer, A. K. (1938) A mass-spectrographic determination of the isotope abundance and of the atomic weight of rubidium, *J. Am. Chem. Soc. 60,* 691–693.

Brooks, B. T. (1931) Chemical considerations regarding the origin of petroleum, *Bull. Am. Assoc. Petroleum Geol. 15,* 611–627.

Brooks, B. T. (1948) Role of active surface catalysts in origin of petroleum, *Bull. Am. Assoc. Petroleum Geol. 32,* 2269–2286.

Brown, H. (1949) A table of relative abundances of nuclear species, *Revs. Mod. Phys. 21,* 625–634.

Brown, H. (1952) Rare gases and the formation of the earth's atmosphere *in* G. P. Kuiper (ed.), *The Atmospheres of the Earth and Planets,* rev. ed., 258–266, University of Chicago Press.

Brown, H., W. J. Blake, A. A. Chodos, R. Kowalkowski, C. R. McKinney, G. J. Neuerburg, L. T. Silver, and A. Uchiyama (1953*a*) Geochemical aspects of interstitial material in igneous rocks (abstract), *Bull. Geol. Soc. Amer. 64,* 1400.

Brown, H., W. J. Blake, A. A. Chodos, R. Kowalkowski, C. R. McKinney, G. J. Neuerburg, L. T. Silver, and A. Uchiyama (1953*b*) Leaching studies of interstitial material in igneous rocks (abstract), *Bull. Geol. Soc. Amer. 64,* 1400.

Brown, J. C. (1936) *India's Mineral Wealth,* Oxford University Press, London, 271 pp.

Brown, S. C. (1948) Theory and operation of Geiger-Müller counters, *Nucleonics 2,* no. 6, 10–22; *3,* no. 2, 50–64; *3,* no. 4, 46–61.

Brownell, G. M. (1950) Radiation surveys with a scintillation counter, *Econ. Geol. 45,* 167–174.

Bryant, J., and M. Michaelis (1952) The measurement of micromicrocurie amounts of radon by a scintillation counting method, *Ministry Supply (Brit.) Radiochemical Centre Rept. R.CC/R.26.*

Buck, W. L., and R. K. Swank (1953) Preparation and performance of efficient plastic scintillators, *Nucleonics 11,* no. 11, 48–52.

Buddington, A. F. (1933) Correlation of kinds of igneous rocks with kinds of mineralization *in Ore Deposits of the Western States (Lindgren volume),* 350–385, American Institute of Mining and Metallurgical Engineers, New York.

Bullard, E. C. (1939) Heat flow in South Africa, *Proc. Roy. Soc. (London) A173*, 473–502.

Bullard, E. C. (1942) Radioactive heat generation in rocks, *Monthly Notices Roy. Astron. Soc., Geophys. Suppl. 5*, 41–47.

Bullard, E. C., and J. P. Stanley (1949) The age of the earth, *Suomen Geodeettisen Laitoksen, Julkaisuja; Veröffentl. Finnisch. Geodät. Inst.*, no. 36, 33–40.

Bullard, E. C., and E. R. Niblett (1951) Terrestrial heat flow in England, *Monthly Notices Roy. Astron. Soc., Geophys. Suppl. 6*, 222–238.

Bullard, E. C. (1952) Heat flow through the floor of the eastern North Pacific Ocean, *Nature 170*, 199–200.

Bullard, E. C. (in press) Oceanic heat flow, *Proc. Roy. Soc. (London)*.

Bumstead, H. A., and L. P. Wheeler (1904) Properties of a radioactive gas found in the soil and water near New Haven, *Am. J. Sci. (4) 17*, 77–111.

Burch, P. R. J. (1953) Specific gamma-activity, the branching ratio and the half-life of potassium-40, *Nature 172*, 361–362.

Burton, M. (1947) Radiation chemistry, *J. Phys. & Colloid Chem. 51*, 611–625, 786–797.

Burton, V. L. (1949) The effects of radioactivity on oleic acid, *J. Am. Chem. Soc. 71*, 4117–4119.

Burton, V. L., and G. R. Sullivan (1951) Carbon content and radioactivity of marine rocks, *Trans. Am. Geophys. Union 32*, 881–884.

Bush, R. E., and E. S. Mardock (1950) Some preliminary investigations of quantitative interpretations of radioactivity logs, *J. Petroleum Technol. 2*, January; also, *Trans. Am. Inst. Mining Met. Engrs. 189*, 19–34.

Bush, R. E., and E. S. Mardock (1951) The quantitative application of radioactivity logs, *J. Petroleum Technol. 3*, July; also, *Trans. Am. Inst. Mining Met. Engrs. 192*, 191–198.

Cady, H. P., and D. F. McFarland (1907) The occurrence of helium in natural gas and the composition of natural gas, *J. Am. Chem. Soc. 29*, 1525–1526.

Campbell, N. R., and A. Wood (1906) The radioactivity of the alkali metals, *Proc. Cambridge Phil. Soc. 14*, 15–21.

Carnegie Institution, Washington (1954) Age of rocks, *Year Book 53*, 78–84.

Carslaw, H. S., and J. C. Jaeger (1947) *Conduction of Heat in Solids*, Clarendon Press, Oxford, 386 pp.

Chackett, K. F., P. Reasbeck, and E. J. Wilson (1953) Recent studies on iron meteorites, II: Determination of the helium content, *Geochim. et Cosmochim. Acta 3*, 261–271.

Chamberlin, T. C. (1899) Lord Kelvin's address on the age of the earth as an abode fitted for life, *Science 9*, 889–901; *10*, 11–18.

Charrin, Paul, and J. H. Russell (1953) Application of radiation logs in oil fields, *Petroleum Engr. 25*, April, B59–B68.

Chaudhury, P. K. Sen (1942) Radioactivity of rubidium, *Proc. Nat. Inst. Sci. India 8*, 45–54.

Chudoba, K. F., and M. von Stackelberg (1936) Dichte und Struktur des Zirkons [Density and structure of zircons], *Z. Krist. 95*, 230–246.

Chudoba, K. F. (1937) Hardness and density of zircons, *Gemmologist 7*, 548–549.

Clark, H. (1941) The effects of simple compression and wetting on the thermal conductivity of rocks, *Trans. Am. Geophys. Union*, 543–544.

Clarke, H. T., and A. Mazur (1941) The lipids of diatoms, *J. Biol. Chem. 141,* 283–289.

Clewell, D. H., R. A. Broding, G. B. Loper, S. N. Heaps, R. F. Simon, R. L. Mills, and M. B. Dobrin (1953) Instrumentation for geophysical exploration, *Rev. Sci. Instr. 24,* 243–266.

Collins, C. B., A. H. Lang, S. C. Robinson, and R. M. Farquhar (1952) Age determination for some uranium deposits in the Canadian shield, *Proc. Geol. Assoc. Can. 5,* 15–41.

Collins, C. B., R. D. Russell, and R. M. Farquhar (1953) The maximum age of elements and age of the earth's crust, *Can. J. Phys. 31,* 402–418.

Collins, C. B., R. M. Farquhar, and R. D. Russell (1954) Isotopic constitution of radiogenic leads and the measurement of geological time, *Bull. Geol. Soc. Amer. 65,* 1–22.

Condit, R. I., and J. D. Graves (1952) Locating buried radioactive sources, *Nucleonics 10,* no. 6, 18–21.

Cooke-Yarborough, E. H., and E. W. Pulsford (1951) A counting-rate meter of high accuracy, *Proc. Inst. Elec. Engrs. (London) 98,* Pt. II, 191–195.

Coon, J. H. (1949) Helium^3 isotopic abundance, *Phys. Rev. 75,* 1355–1357.

Coppens, René (1953) Sur la radioactivité des ampélites [Radioactivity of black shales], *Compt. rend. 236,* 600–601.

Coppens, René, and Goulven Vernois (1953) Détermination expérimentale du coefficient d'absorption des rayons alpha d'un corps de composition chimique inconnue et recherche de la teneur en uranium et en thorium d'un corps radioactif par autoradiographie [Experimental determination of the absorption coefficient of alpha rays from an unknown source and autoradiographic study of the uranium and thorium content of radioactive matter], *Compt. rend. 234,* 1974–1976.

Coster, H. P. (1947) Terrestrial heat flow in Persia, *Monthly Notices Roy. Astron. Soc., Geophys. Suppl. 5,* 131–146.

Cowper, G. (1954) Aerial prospecting with scintillation counters, *Nucleonics 12,* no. 3, 29–32.

Craig, Harmon (1953) The geochemistry of the stable carbon isotopes, *Geochim. et Cosmochim. Acta 3,* 53–92.

Curie, I., H. v. Halban, Jr., and P. Preiswerk (1935) Sur la création artificielle d'éléments appartenant à une famille radioactive inconnue, lors de l'irradiation du thorium par les neutrons [Artificial formation of elements of an unknown radioactive series by irradiation of thorium with neutrons], *J. phys. radium* (7) *6,* 361–364.

Curie, I. (1946) Sur la possibilité d'étudier l'activité des roches par l'observation des trajectoires des rayons alpha dans l'émulsion photographique [The possibility of studying activity of rocks by observing the tracks of alpha particles in the photographic emulsion], *J. phys. radium* (8) *7,* 313–319.

Curie, M. S. (1898) Rayons émis par les composés de l'uranium et du thorium [Rays emitted by uranium and thorium compounds], *Compt. rend. 126,* 1101.

Curie, M. S. (1910) *Traité de radioativité* [Treatise on radioactivity], Gauthier-Villars, Paris, 2 vols., *1,* 426 pp., *2,* 548 pp.

Curie, M. S., A. Debierne, A. S. Eve, H. Geiger, O. Hahn, S. C. Lind, St. Meyer, E. Rutherford, and E. Schweidler (1931) The radioactive constants as of 1930, *Revs. Mod. Phys. 3,* 427–445.

Curie, M. S., and F. Joliot (1934) Sur la radioactivité du samarium [The radioactivity of samarium], *Compt. rend, 198,* 360–362.

Curie, P., and M. Curie (1899) Effets chimiques produits par les rayons de Becquerel [Chemical effects of Becquerel's rays], *Compt. rend. 129,* 823–825.

Curie, P., and A. Laborde (1903) Sur la chaleur dégagée spontanément par les sels de radium [Heat spontaneously evolved by radium salts], *Compt. rend. 136,* 673–675.

Curran, S. C., D. Dixon, and H. W. Wilson (1952) The natural radioactivity of rubidium, *Phil. Mag. 43,* 82–92.

Curtiss, L. F. (1949) Measurements of radioactivity, *Nat. Bur. Standards (U. S.) Circ. 476,* 84 pp.

Curtiss, L. F. (1950) The Geiger-Müller counter, *Nat. Bur. Standards (U. S.) Circ. 490,* 25 pp.

Dalton, J. C., J. Golden, G. R. Martin, E. R. Mercer, and S. J. Thomson (1953) Recent studies on iron meteorites, III: Determination of the uranium and thorium contents, *Geochim. et Cosmochim. Acta 3,* 272–287.

Daly, R. A. (1933) *Igneous Rocks and the Depths of the Earth,* McGraw-Hill Book Co., New York, 598 pp.

Damon, P. E. (1950) Radioactivity and mineralization in rhyolite porphyry, *Geophysics 15,* 94–101.

Damon, P. E., and H. I. Hyde (1952) Scintillation tube for the measurement of radioactive gases, *Rev. Sci. Instr. 23,* 766.

Daniels, F., Ch. A. Boyd, and D. F. Saunders (1953) Thermoluminescence as a research tool, *Science 117,* 343–349.

Davidson, C. F. (1951) Distribution of radioactivity, *Mining Mag. (London) 85,* 329–340.

Davidson, C. F. (1953) The gold-uranium ores of the Witwatersrand, *Mining Mag. (London) 88,* 73–85.

Davidson, C. F., and D. Atkin (1953) On the occurrence of uranium in phosphate rock, *Compt. rend. 19e Congr. Géol. Intern. Alger, Sec. 11,* 13–31.

Davis, C. W. (1926) The composition and age of uranium minerals from Katanga, S. Dakota and Utah, *Am. J. Sci. (5) 5,* 201–217.

Davis, F. J. (1947) Factors affecting operation of apparatus for counting alpha particles in an ion-counting chamber, *Nat. Bur. Standards (U. S.) J. Research 39,* 545–549.

Davis, G. L. (1947) Radium content of ultramafic igneous rocks, I: Laboratory investigation, *Am. J. Sci. 245,* 677–693.

Davis, G. L., and H. H. Hess (1949) Radium content of ultramafic igneous rocks, II: Geological and chemical implications, *Am. J. Sci. 247,* 856–882.

Davis, G. L. (1950) Radium content of ultramafic igneous rocks, III: Meteorites, *Am. J. Sci. 248,* 107–111.

Davis, G. L., and L. T. Aldrich (1953) Determination of the age of lepidolites by the method of isotope dilution, *Bull. Geol. Soc. Amer. 64,* 379–380.

Demay, André (1953) Détermination de l'âge absolu d'une pechblende du gisement filonien de la Crouzille dans le massif granulitique de St-Sylvestre, au nord de Limoges [Absolute age of a pitchblende from the Crouzille vein in the St. Sylvestre granulites, north of Limoges], *Compt. rend. 237,* 48–50.

Demers, Pierre (1947) New photographic emulsions showing improved tracks of ionizing particles, *Can. J. Research A25,* 223–251.

DeMille, John B. (1947) *Strategic Minerals,* pp. 349–354, McGraw-Hill Book Co., New York, 626 pp.

Dewan, J. T., and L. A. Allaud (1953) Experimental basis for neutron logging interpretation, *Petroleum Engr. 25,* September, B49–B54.

Dienes, C. J. (1953) Radiation effects in solids, *Ann. Rev. Nuclear Sci. 2,* 187–220.

DiGiovanni, H. J., R. T. Graveson, and A. H. Yoli (1953) Scintillation unit for drill-hole logging, *Nucleonics 11,* no. 4, 34–39.

Dubey, V. S., and A. Holmes (1929) Estimates of the ages of the Whin Sill and Cleveland Dyke by the helium method, *Nature 123,* 794–795.

Dubey, V. S. (1930) Helium ratios of the basic rocks of the Gwalior series, *Nature 126,* 807.

DuMond, J. W. M., and E. R. Cohen (1953) Least-squares adjustment of the atomic constants, *Revs. Mod. Phys. 25,* 691–708.

Ehrenberg, H. Fr. (1953) Isotopenanalysen an Blei aus Mineralen [Isotopic analyses of lead from minerals], *Z. Physik 134,* 317–333.

Eichholz, G. G., J. W. Hilborn, and C. McMahon (1953) The determination of uranium and thorium in ores, *Can. J. Phys. 31,* 613–628.

Einarsson, T. (1949) *The Eruption of Hekla, 1947–1948,* Pt. IV, 2: Rate of production of material during the eruption, Visindafelg Islandinga, Reykjavik.

Eklund, S. (1946) Studies in nuclear physics. Excitation by means of x-rays. Activity of Rb^{87}, *Arkiv Mat., Astron. Fysik. 33A,* no. 14.

Ellis, C. D., and W. A. Wooster (1927) The average energy of disintegration of radium E, *Proc. Roy. Soc. (London) A117,* 109–123.

Elmore, W. C., and M. Sands (1949) *Electronics: Experimental Techniques,* McGraw-Hill Book Co., New York, 417 pp.

Elster, J., and H. Geitel (1901) Über eine fernere Analogie in dem elektrischen Verhalten der natürlichen und der durch Becquerelstrahlen abnorm leitend gemachten Luft [Analogy in the electrical behavior of natural air and air made abnormally conducting by Becquerel's rays], *Physik Z. 2,* 590–593.

Elster, J., and H. Geitel (1902*a*) Beschreibung des Verfahrens zur Gewinnung vorübergehend radioaktiver Stoffe aus der atmosphärischen Luft [Process for obtaining ephemerally radioactive materials from atmospheric air], *Physik Z. 3,* 305–310.

Elster, J., and H. Geitel (1902*b*) Über die radioaktivität der im Erdboden enthaltenen Luft [The radioactivity of soil air], *Physik Z. 3,* 574–577.

Erickson, R. L., T. A. Myers, and C. A. Horr (in press) The association of uranium and other metals with crude oils, asphalts and petroliferous rocks, *Bull. Am. Assoc. Petroleum Geol.;* see also *Bull. Geol. Soc. Amer. 64* (1953), 1505 (abstract).

Erlenmeyer, H., W. Oppliger, K. Stier, and M. Blumer (1950) Die Bestimmung von Uran in Gesteinen [Determination of uranium in rocks], *Helv. Chim. Acta 33,* 25–26.

Eskola, P. (1921) On the eclogites of Norway, *Videnskapsselskapets-Skrifter,* no. 8.

Eucken, A. (1944) Physikalisch-chemische Betrachtungen über die früheste Entwicklungsgeschichte der Erde [Physico-chemical considerations of the earliest history of the earth], *Nachr. Akad. Wiss. Göttingen, math.-physik. Kl., Heft 1.*

Evans, R. C. (1948) *An Introduction to Crystal Chemistry,* Cambridge University Press, 388 pp.

Evans, R. D. (1934) The measurement of natural alpha particles ejected from solids, *Phys. Rev. 45,* 29–37.

Evans, R. D., and H. Williams (1935) The radium content of lavas from Lassen Volcanic National Park, California, *Am. J. Sci.* (*5*) *29,* 441–452.

Evans, R. D., A. F. Kip, and E. G. Moberg (1938) The radium and radon content of Pacific Ocean water, life and sediment, *Am. J. Sci.* (*5*) *36,* 241–259.

Evans, R. D., C. Goodman, N. B. Keevil, A. C. Lane, and W. D. Urry (1939) Intercalibration and comparison in two laboratories of measurements incident to the determination of the geologic ages of rocks, *Phys. Rev. 55,* 931–946.

Evans, R. D., and C. Goodman (1941) Radioactivity of rocks, *Bull. Geol. Soc. Amer. 52,* 459–490.

Ewald, H., and H. Hintenberger (1953) *Methoden und Anwendungen der Massenspektroskopie* [Methods and Applications of Mass Spectroscopy], Verlag Chemie, Weinheim, 288 pp.

Faessler, A. (1942) Untersuchungen zum Problem des metamikten Zustandes [Study of the metamict state], *Z. Krist. 104,* 81–113.

Fano, Ugo (1953) Gamma ray attenuation, *Nucleonics 11,* no. 8, 8–12; no. 9, 55–61.

Faul, Henry (1948) Radioactivity exploration with Geiger counters, *Trans. Am. Inst. Mining Met. Engrs. 178,* 458–478.

Faul, Henry, and C. W. Tittle (1951) Logging of drill holes by the neutron-gamma method, and gamma ray scattering, *Geophysics 16,* 261–276.

Faul, Henry, G. B. Gott, G. E. Manger, J. W. Mytton, and A. Y. Sakakura (1954) Radon and helium in natural gas, *Compt. rend. 19e Congr. Géol. Intern. Alger, Sec. 9,* 339–348.

Faust, W. R. (1950) Specific activity of potassium, *Phys. Rev. 78,* 624.

Fearon, R. E., and E. S. Mardock (1951) The quantitative interpretation of radioactivity logs, *World Petroleum Congr., Proc. 3rd Congr., Hague, Sec. II,* 418–435.

Feldman, K., and G. M. Wright (1949) Diamond drill hole G-M counter, *Can. J. Research 27,* 23–27.

Fermor, L. L. (1935) Monazite, *Records Geol. Survey India, 70,* 260–263.

Fersman, A. (1930) Geochemische Migration der Elemente, Pt. 2, I: Die Uran-Vanadium Grube Tuja Mujun in Turkestan [Geochemical migration of the elements, Pt. 2, I: The uranium-vanadium mine at Tuya Muyun, Turkestan], *Abhandl. prakt. Geologie Bergwirtsch., Halle, 19,* 1–52.

Finaly, S. S. de (1932) The radium content of some Hungarian rocks, *Am. J. Sci.* (*5*) *24,* 306–310.

Flanagan, F., and F. Senftle (in press) Tables for evaluating Bateman's equation coefficients for radioactivity calculation.

Fleming, E. H., A. Ghiorso, and B. B. Cunningham (1952) Specific alpha activities and half-lives of U^{234}, U^{235} and U^{236}, *Phys. Rev. 88,* 642–652.

Fleming, W. H., and H. G. Thode (1953) Neutron and spontaneous fission in uranium ores, *Phys. Rev. 92,* 378–382.

Flerov, G. N., and K. A. Petrzhak (1940) Spontaneous fission of uranium, *J. Phys.* (*U.S.S.R.*) *3,* 275–280.

Fletcher, A. L. (1911) The radioactivity of the Leinster granite, *Phil. Mag.* (*6*) *21,* 102–106.

Flint, R. F. (1947) *Glacial Geology and the Pleistocene Epoch,* John Wiley & Sons, New York, 589 pp.

Flint, R. F., and E. S. Deevey, Jr. (1951) Radiocarbon dating of late Pleistocene events, *Am. J. Sci. 249,* 257–300.

Ford, I. H. (1951) Radioactivity of rocks: An improvement in the photographic technique, *Nature 167,* 273–274.

Føyn, E., B. Karlik, H. Pettersson, and E. Rona (1939) The radioactivity of seawater, *Göteborgs Kgl. Vetenskaps-Vitterhets-Samhäll. Handl. Ser. B. 6,* no. 12, 44 pp.; also, *Nature 143,* 275–276.

Føyn, E., E. Gleditsch, and I. T. Rosenquist (1941) The determination of radium in some igneous rocks, *Am. J. Sci. 239,* 805–808.

Franklin, E., and W. R. Loosemore (1951) A survey equipment using low-voltage halogen-quenched Geiger-Müller counters, *Proc. Inst. Elec. Engrs.* (*London*) *98,* Pt. II, 237–244.

Frederickson, A. F. (1948) Some mechanisms for the fixation of uranium in certain sediments, *Science 108,* 184–185.

Friedman, Herbert (1949) Geiger counter tubes, *Proc. Inst. Radio Engrs. 37,* 791–808.

Friedmann, Hans (1951) Potash content by Geiger counter, *Eng. Mining J. 152,* no. 10, 90–91, 119.

Fritze, K., and F. Strassmann (1952) Zur geologischen Altersbestimmung nach der Kalium-Argon-Methode [Determination of geologic age by the potassium-argon method], *Naturwissenschaften 39,* 522–523.

Garrigue, H. (1934) Radioactivité de l'air de l'habitation de l'Observatoire du Pic du Midi [Radioactivity of the air in the dormitory of the observatory on the Pic du Midi], *Compt. rend. 198,* 494–496.

Garrigue, H. (1935) Radioactivité de l'air en montagne [Radioactivity of air in the mountains], *Compt. rend. 200,* 414–415; also, *Thèse Ser. A.,* no. 1627 (1936), Masson et Cie, Paris, 83 pp.

Garrigue, H. (1950) Sur la radioactivité naturelle de l'atmosphère [Natural radioactivity of the atmosphere], *Compt. rend. 230,* 1272–1274.

Garrigue, H. (1951) Recherches sur la radioactivité de l'air libre [Study of the radioactivity of free air], *Compt. rend. 232,* 722–724.

Gaudin, A. M., and J. H. Pannell (1948) Radioactive determination of potassium in solids, *Anal. Chem. 20,* 1154–1156.

Geiger, H., and W. Müller (1928, 1929) Das Elektronenzählrohr [The electron counter tube], *Physik Z. 29,* 839–841; *30,* 489–493.

Geiss, J. (1954) Isotopenanalysen an "gewöhnlichem Blei" [Isotopic analyses of "ordinary lead"] *Z. Naturforsch. 9a,* 218–227.

Gentner, W., R. Präg, and F. Smits (1953) Argonbestimmungen an Kalium-Mineralien, II: Das Alter eines Kalilagers im Unteren Oligozän [Determinations of argon in potassium minerals, II: The age of a lower-Oligocene potash deposit], *Geochim. et Cosmochim. Acta 4,* 11–20.

Gentner, W., K. Goebel, and R. Präg (1954) Argonbestimmungen an Kalium-Mineralien, III: Vergleichende Messungen nach der Kalium-Argon- und Uran-Helium-Methode [Determinations of argon in potassium minerals, III: Comparative measurements by the potassium-argon and uranium-helium methods], *Geochim. et Cosmochim. Acta 5,* 124–133.

Gerling, E. K. (1939*a*) Part taken by close packing of crystals in the diffusion of helium, *Compt. rend. acad. sci. U.R.S.S. 24,* 274–277.

Gerling, E. K. (1939*b*) Diffusionswärme des Heliums als Kriterium für die Brauchbarkeit von Mineralien für Altersbestimmungen nach der Heliummethode [Diffusion temperature of helium as a criterion for the usefulnes of minerals for helium age determination], *Compt. rend. acad. sci. U.R.S.S. 24,* 570–573.

Gerling, E. K. (1940) On the solubility of helium in melts, *Compt. rend. acad. sci. U.R.S.S. 27,* 22–23.

Gerling, E. K. (1942) Age of the earth according to radioactivity data, *Compt. rend. acad. sci. U.R.S.S. 34,* 259–261.

Gerling, E. K., and M. E. Vladimirova (1942) Age of pegmatite veins of the Ilmen Reserve in the Urals, *Compt. rend. acad. sci. U.R.S.S. 37,* 179–184.

Gerling, E. K., and T. G. Pavlova (1951) Determination of the geological age of two stone meteorites by the argon method, *Doklady Akad. Nauk S.S.S.R. 77,* 85–86.

Gerling, E. K., and M. L. Yashchenko (1952) O vozraste tektitov [On the age of tectites], *Doklady Akad. Nauk S.S.S.R. 83,* 901–902.

Gerling, E. K., G. M. Ermoline, N. V. Baranovskaia, and N. E. Titov (1952) Pervii opit primeneniya argonovogo metoda opredeleniya vozrasta mineralov [First results in the application of the argon method to determination of the age of minerals], *Doklady Akad. Nauk S.S.S.R. 86,* 593–596.

Gilbert, G. K. (1893) The moon's face: A study of the origin of its features, *Bull. Phil. Soc. Wash. 12,* 241–292.

Gimenez, C., and J. Labeyrie (1952) Fabrication et propriétés des compteurs de Geiger remplis à la vapeur de brome et destinés à la prospection beta et gamma [Manufacture and properties of bromine-filled Geiger counters intended for beta and gamma ray prospecting], *Nuovo cimento 9,* 169–183.

Goldschmidt, V. M. (1937) Geochemische Verteilungsgesetze der Elemente, IX [Geochemical distribution laws of the elements, 9], *Skrifter Norske Videnskaps-Akad. Oslo. I. Mat. Naturv. Kl.,* no. 4.

Goodman, Clark, and R. D. Evans (1941) Age measurements by radioactivity, *Bull. Geol. Soc. Amer. 52,* 491–544.

Goodman, Clark (1942) Geological application of nuclear physics, *J. Appl. Phys. 13,* 276–289.

Gottfried, D. (1953) The age and relationships of radioactivity, lead content, and physical properties of zircon crystals from Ceylon (abstract), *Trans. Am. Geophys. Union 34,* 342.

Gray, J. A. (1909) Liberation of helium from radioactive minerals by grinding, *Proc. Roy. Soc. (London) A82,* 291–306.

Grimaldi, F. S., I. May, and M. H. Fletcher (1952) U. S. Geological Survey fluorimetric methods of uranium analysis, *U. S. Geol. Survey Circ. 199,* 20 pp.

Grimaldi, F. S., Irving May, M. H. Fletcher, and Jane Titcomb (1954) Collected papers on methods of analysis for uranium and thorium, *U. S. Geol. Survey Bull. 1006,* 184 pp.

Gross, W. H. (1952) Radioactivity as a guide to ore, *Econ. Geol. 47,* 722–742.

Groven, C., J. Govaerts, and G. Guében (1938) Photographic action of artificial radio-elements, *Nature 141,* 916–917.

Groves, A. W. (1951) *Silicate Analysis,* 2nd ed., Thomas M. Murby, London, 336 pp.

Guelke, R., J. C. R. Heydenrych, and F. Anderson (1948) Instruments for measuring radioactivity and temperature in boreholes, *S. African Sci. 2,* 68–70.

Guelke, R., J. C. R. Heydenrych, and F. Anderson (1949) Measurement of radioactivity and temperature in narrow boreholes, and the development of instruments for this purpose, *J. Sci. Instr. and Phys. in Ind. 26,* 150–153.

Hahn, O., and M. Rothenbach (1919) Über die Radioaktivität des Rubidium [Radioactivity of rubidium], *Physik Z. 20,* 194–202.

Hahn, O., and L. Meitner (1935) Über die künstliche Umwandlung des Urans durch Neutronen [Transmutation of uranium by neutrons], *Naturwissenschaften 23,* 37–38.

Hahn, O., F. Strassmann, and E. Walling (1937) Herstellung wägbarer Mengen des Strontiumisotops 87 als Umwandlungsprodukt des Rubidiums aus einem kanadischen Glimmer [Preparation of weighable amounts of strontium^{87} as conversion product of rubidium from a Canadian mica], *Naturwissenschaften 25,* 189.

Hahn, O., and E. Walling (1938) Über die Möglichkeit geologischer Altersbestimmungen Rubidiumhaltiger Mineralen und Gesteine [Possibility of absolute age determination on rubidium-bearing minerals and rocks], *Z. anorg. u. allgem. Chem. 236,* 78–82.

Hahn, O., J. Mattauch, and H. Ewald (1943) Geologische Altersbestimmungen mit der Strontium Methode [Geologic age determinations by the strontium method], *Chem. Ztg. 67,* 55–56.

Hahn, O. (1950) *New Atoms; Progress and Some Memories,* a collection of papers edited by W. Gaade, Elsevier, Houston, 184 pp.

Halsted, R. E., and A. O. Nier (1950) Gas flow through the mass spectrometer viscous leak, *Rev. Sci. Instr. 21,* 1019–1021.

Harrison, F. B. (1952) Large-area liquid scintillation counters, *Nucleonics 10,* no. 6, 40–45.

Hatsuda, Z. (1934) see Jeffreys (1936).

Haxel, O., F. G. Houtermans, and M. Kemmerich (1948) On the half-life of Rb^{87}, *Phys. Rev. 74,* 1886–1887.

Hecht, F. (1952) Minerale und Gesteine: Radioaktive Eigenschaften. Altersbestimmung [Minerals and rocks: Radioactive properties. Age determination], *in* Landolt-Börnstein, *Zahlenwerte und Funktionen,* 6th ed., *3,* 284–312, Springer-verlag, Berlin-Göttingen-Heidelberg.

Hée, A. (1948) Recherches sur la radioactivité d'un granite des Vosges par la méthode photographique [Studies of the radioactivity of a Vosges granite by the photographic method], *Compt. rend. 227,* 356–358.

Hée, A., M. Wack, and M. Jarovoy (1952) Étude du rayonnement beta des roches [Study of beta radiation from rocks], *Ann. géophys. 8,* 323–327.

Hée, A., and M. Jarovoy (1953) Autoradiographie des rayons beta du potassium [Autoradiography of potassium beta rays], *Ann. géophys. 9,* 153–157.

Heisig, G. B. (1932) Heats of formation and *M/N* ratios, *J. Phys. Chem. 36,* 1000–1005.

Hemmendinger, A., and W. R. Smythe (1937) The radioactive isotope of rubidium, *Phys. Rev. 51,* 1052–1053.

Henderson, G. H., and S. Bateson (1934) A quantitative study of pleochroic haloes, I, *Proc. Roy. Soc. (London) A145,* 563–581.

Henderson, G. H., and L. G. Turnbull (1934) A quantitative study of pleochroic haloes, II, *ibid. A145,* 582–591.

Henderson, G. H., C. M. Mushkat, and D. P. Crawford (1937) A quantitative study of pleochroic haloes, III, *ibid. A158,* 199–211.

Henderson, G. H., and F. W. Sparks (1939) A quantitative study of pleochroic haloes, IV and V, *ibid A173,* 238–264.

Hernegger, F., and B. Karlik (1935) Uranium in sea water, *Göteborgs Kgl. Vetenskaps-Vitterhets-Samhäll. Handl. Ser. B. 4,* no. 12, 15 pp.

Hersey, J. B., C. B. Officer, H. R. Johnson, and S. Bergstrom (1952) Seismic refraction observations north of the Brownson Deep, *Bull. Seis. Soc. Amer. 42,* 291–306.

Herzog, L. F., L. T. Aldrich, W. K. Holyk, F. B. Whiting, and L. H. Ahrens (1953) Variations in strontium isotope abundances in minerals, Part 2: Radiogenic Sr^{87} in biotite, feldspar, and celestite, *Trans. Am. Geophys. Union 34,* 461–470.

Hess, F. L., and R. C. Wells (1920) Brannerite, a new uranium mineral, *J. Franklin Inst. 189,* 225–237, 779–780.

Hess, F. L. (1933) Uranium, vanadium, radium, gold, silver and molybdenum sedimentary deposits *in Ore Deposits of the Western States (Lindgren volume),* 473–476, American Institute of Mining and Metallurgical Engineers, New York.

Hess, F. L. (1937) Monazite, *Industrial Minerals and Rocks,* 523–526, American Institute of Mining and Metallurgical Engineers, New York.

Hevesy, G. (1935) Artificial radioactivity of scandium, *Kgl. Danske Videnskab. Selskab., Mat. fys. Medd. XIII (3),* 17 pp.

Heyden, M., and H. Kopfermann (1938) Über die Kernspinänderung beim radioaktiven Zervallsprozess $Rb^{87} \rightarrow Sr^{87}$ [The change in nuclear spin in the radioactive disintegration process $Rb^{87} \rightarrow Sr^{87}$] *Z. Physik 108,* 232–243.

Hill, R. D. (1941) Production of helium^3, *Phys. Rev. 59,* 103.

Hillebrand, W. F. (1890, 1891) On the occurrence of nitrogen in uraninite and on the composition of uraninite in general, *Am. J. Sci. (3) 40,* 384–394; also, *U. S. Geol. Survey Bull. 78,* 43–79.

Hillebrand, W. F., and F. L. Ransome (1905) On carnotite and associated vanadiferous minerals in western Colorado, *U. S. Geol. Survey Bull. 262.*

Hillebrand, W. F., and G. E. F. Lundell (1953) *Applied Inorganic Analysis,* John Wiley & Sons, New York, 1034 pp.

Hoffmann, J. (1942) Über in Süsswasser gelöste und von Sedimenten mitgerissene Uranmengen [On the uranium content of fresh waters and their sediments], *Chem. Erde 14,* 239–252.

Holland, H. D., and J. L. Kulp (1950) Geologic age from metamict minerals, *Science 111,* 312.

Holland, H. D., D. A. Schulz, and M. N. Bass (1953) The effect of nuclear radiation on the structure of zircon (abstract), *Trans. Am. Geophys. Union 34,* 342.

Holland, H. D., and J. L. Kulp (1954*a*) The mechanism of removal of ionium and radium from the oceans, *Geochim. et Cosmochim. Acta* (in press).

Holland, H. D., and J. L. Kulp (1954*b*) The transport and deposition of uranium, ionium and radium in rivers, oceans and ocean sediments, *ibid.* (in press).

Hollander, J. M., I. Perlman, and G. T. Seaborg (1953) Table of isotopes, *Revs. Mod. Phys. 25,* 469–651.

Holmes, Arthur, and R. W. Lawson (1926) The radioactivity of potassium and its geological significance, *Phil. Mag.* (7) *2,* 1218–1233.

Holmes, Arthur, and H. F. Harwood (1928) The age and composition of the Whin Sill and the related dikes of the north of England, *Mineralog. Mag. 21,* 493–542.

Holmes, Arthur (1931) Radioactivity and geological time, Physics of the Earth, IV, *Nat. Research Council (U. S.) Bull. 80,* 124–459.

Holmes, Arthur (1933) The thermal history of the Earth, *J. Wash. Acad. Sci. 23,* 169–195.

Holmes, Arthur, and F. A. Paneth (1936) Helium-ratios of rocks and minerals from the diamond pipes of South Africa, *Proc. Roy. Soc. (London) A154,* 385–413.

Holmes, Arthur (1937) *The Age of the Earth,* Thomas Nelson and Sons, London, 287 pp.

Holmes, Arthur (1946) Estimate of the age of the earth, *Nature 157,* 680–684.

Holmes, Arthur (1947) A revised estimate of the age of the earth, *Nature 159,* 127–128.

Holmes, Arthur (1948*a*) The oldest known minerals and rocks, *Trans. Edinburgh Geol. Soc. 14,* Pt. 11, 176–194.

Holmes, Arthur (1948*b*) Monazite as a geological timekeeper, *Proc. Roy. Soc. Edinburgh B63,* Pt. II, 115–124.

Holmes, Arthur (1950) The age of uraninite from Gordonia, S. Africa, with an isotopic analysis of lead, *Am. J. Sci. 248,* 81–94.

Holmes, Arthur, W. T. Leland, and A. O. Nier (1950) Age of uraninite from a pegmatite near Singar, Gaya district, India, *Am. Mineralogist 35,* 19–28.

Holmes, Arthur (1954) The oldest dated minerals of the Rhodesian shield, *Nature 173,* 612–614.

Holmes, Arthur, and H. Besairie (1954) Sur quelques mesures de géochronologie à Madagascar [Geologic age measurements in Madagascar], *Compt. rend. 238,* 758–760.

Holter, N. J., and W. R. Glasscock (1952) Tracing nuclear explosions, *Nucleonics 10,* no. 8, 10–13.

Holyk, W. K., and L. H. Ahrens (1953) Potassium in ultramafic rocks, *Geochim. et Cosmochim. Acta 4,* 241–250.

Honig, R. E. (1946) Radiochemical changes in some fatty acids, *Science 104,* 27–28.

Honig, R. E., and C. W. Sheppard (1946) An experimental comparison of the chemical effects of deuterons and of alpha particles on methane and *n*-butane, *J. Phys. Chem. 50,* 119–143; see also Sheppard and Honig, *ibid.* 144–152.

Hoogteijling, P. J., and G. J. Sizoo (1948) Radioactivity and mineral composition of soil, *Physica 14,* 357–366.

Hopkins, J. I. (1951) Electron energy studies with the anthracene scintillation counter, *Rev. Sci. Instr. 22,* 29–33.

Horwood, J. L., and C. McMahon (1950) Assays of uncrushed ore samples using a high-pressure ionization chamber, *Can. Mining J. 71,* 56–60.

Houtermans, F. G. (1946) Isotopenhäufigkeiten im natürlichen Blei und das Alter des Urans [Isotopic constitution of common lead and the time of the formation of uranium], *Naturwissenschaften 33,* 185–186.

Houtermans, F. G. (1947) Das Alter des Urans [Time of the formation of uranium], *Z. Naturforsch. IIa,* 322–328.

Houtermans, F. G., O. Haxel, and J. Heintze (1950) Die Halbwertszeit des K^{40} [Halflife of potassium^{40}], *Z. Physik 128,* 657–667.

Houtermans, F. G. (1951) Über ein neues Verfahren zur Durchführung chemischer Altersbestimmungen nach der Blei-Methode [A new procedure for chemical age determinations by the lead method], *Sitzber. heidelberg. Akad. Wiss., math.-naturw. Kl., Abt. II,* 123–136.

Houtermans, F. G. (1953) Determination of the age of the Earth from the isotopic composition of meteoritic lead, *Nuovo cimento* (*9*) *10,* 1623–1633.

Hudgens, J. E., R. O. Benzing, J. P. Cali, R. C. Meyer, and L. C. Nelson (1951) Determination of radium or radon in gases, liquids or solids, *Nucleonics 9,* no. 2, 14–21.

Hughes, D. S., and H. J. Jones (1950) Variation of elastic moduli of igneous rocks with pressure and temperature, *Bull. Geol. Soc. Amer. 61,* 843–856.

Hughes, H. (unpublished) The electrical conductivity of the Earth's interior, Thesis, Cambridge University, 1953; see also Jeffreys, 1952, p. 373.

Hurley, P. M., and Clark Goodman (1941) Helium retention in common rock minerals, *Bull. Geol. Soc. Amer. 52,* 545–560.

Hurley, P. M., and Clark Goodman (1943) Helium age measurement, I: Preliminary magnetite index, *Bull. Geol. Soc. Amer. 54,* 305–324.

Hurley, P. M. (1949) Age of Canada's principal gold-producing belt, *Science 110,* 49.

Hurley, P. M. (1950) Distribution of radioactivity in granites and possible relation to helium age measurements, *Bull. Geol. Soc. Amer. 61,* 1–7.

Hurley, P. M. (1952*a*) Heat production in basalts and their origin (abstract), *ibid. 63,* 1265.

Hurley, P. M. (1952*b*) Alpha ionization damage as a cause of low helium ratios, *Trans. Am. Geophys. Union 33,* 174–183.

Hurley, P. M., and H. W. Fairbairn (1952) Alpha-radiation damage in zircon, *J. Appl. Phys. 23,* 1408.

Hurley, P. M., and H. W. Fairbairn (1953) Radiation damage in zircons: A possible age method, *Bull. Geol. Soc. Amer. 64,* 659–674.

Hursh, J. B., and A. A. Gates (1950) Body radium content of individuals with no known occupational exposure, *Nucleonics 7,* no. 1, 46–59.

Hushley, W., and W. R. Dixon (1947) The gamma-ray measurement of radium ore concentrates, *Can. J. Research A25,* 210–222.

Hybbinette, Anna-Greta (1943) Bestämning av låga halter strontium i några svenska pegmatitmineral [Determination of low strontium contents in some Swedish pegmatite minerals], *Svensk Kem. Tidskr. 55,* 151–154.

Iimori, S. (1938) Samarskite found in the placer of Ryujomen, Korea, *Sci. Papers Inst. Phys. Chem. Research* (*Tokyo*) *34,* 922–930.

Immelman, M. N. S. (1934) A determination of the radium content of some South African granites, *Phil. Mag.* (*7*) *17,* 1038–1047.

Ingerson, E. (1953) Nonradiogenic isotopes in geology: A review, *Bull. Geol. Soc. Amer. 64,* 301–374.

Ingham, W. N., and N. B. Keevil (1951) Radioactivity of the Bourlamaque, Elzevir, and Cheddar batholiths, Canada, *Bull. Geol. Soc. Amer. 62,* 131–148.

Inghram, M. G. (1948) Modern mass spectroscopy *in* L. Martin (ed.), *Advances in Electronics, 1,* 219–268, Academic Press, New York.

Inghram, M. G., H. S. Brown, C. C. Patterson, and D. C. Hess (1950) The branching ratio of K^{40} radioactive decay, *Phys. Rev. 80,* 916–917.

Isaac, N., and E. Picciotto (1953) Ionium determination in deep-sea sediments, *Nature 171,* 742–743.

Jeffreys, H. (1936) On the radioactivities of rocks, *Gerlands Beitr. Geophys. 47,* 149–170.

Jeffreys, H. (1942) On the radioactivities of rocks, *Monthly Notices Roy. Astron. Soc., Geophys. Suppl. 5,* 37–40.

Jeffreys, H. (1948) Lead isotopes and the age of the earth, *Nature 162,* 822–823.

Jeffreys, H. (1951) The origin of the solar system in Beno Gutenberg (ed.), *Internal Constitution of the Earth,* 2nd ed., 8–22, Dover Publications, New York.

Jeffreys, H. (1952) *The Earth,* 3rd ed., Macmillan, Cambridge University Press, 392 pp.

Jensen, M. L. (1953) Geologic importance of variations in stable isotopic abundances, *Econ. Geol. 48,* 161–176.

Johnson, F. (1951) Radiocarbon dating, *Mem. Soc. Am. Archaeology,* no. 8; also, *Am. Antiquity 17,* 65 pp.

Joly, J. J. (1908) On the radium content of deep-sea sediments, *Phil. Mag.* (*6*) *16,* 190–197.

Joly, J. J. (1909) *Radioactivity and Geology,* Archibald Constable, London, 287 pp.

Joly, J. J. (1910) The amount of thorium in sedimentary rocks, II: Arenaceous and argillaceous rocks, *Phil. Mag.* (*6*) *20,* 353–357.

Joly, J. J. (1923) Pleochroic haloes of various geological ages, *Proc. Roy. Soc.* (*London*) *A102,* 682–705.

Joly, J. J., and J. H. J. Poole (1924) The radioactivity of basalts and other rocks, *Phil. Mag.* (*6*) *48,* 819–832.

Jones, C. (1896) The optical effects of intensification, *Phot. J. 21,* 233.

Kallmann, H., M. Furst, and M. Sidran (1952) Scintillation counting techniques, *Nucleonics 10,* no. 9, 15–17.

Kandiah, K. (in press) A scaling unit employing multielectrode cold cathode tubes, *Proc. Inst. Elec. Engrs.* (*London*).

Katcoff, S., O. A. Schaeffer, and J. M. Hastings (1951) Half-life of I^{129} and the age of the elements, *Phys. Rev. 82,* 688–690.

Keevil, N. B. (1938*a*) Thorium-uranium ratios of rocks and their relation to lead ore genesis, *Econ. Geol. 33,* 685–696.

Keevil, N. B. (1938*b*) The distribution of helium and radioactivity in rocks, I: Mineral separates from the Quincy granite, *Am. J. Sci.* (*5*) *36,* 406–416.

Keevil, N. B. (1938*c*) The application of the helium method to granites, *Trans. Roy. Soc. Can. Sec. IV, 32,* 123–150.

Keevil, N. B. (1942) The distribution of helium and radioactivity in rocks, II: Mineral separates from the Cape Ann granite, *Am. J. Sci. 240,* 13–21.

Keevil, N. B., A. W. Jolliffe, and E. S. Larsen, Jr. (1942) The distribution of helium and radioactivity in rocks, IV: Helium age investigations of diabase and granodiorites from Yellowknife, Northwest Territories, *Am. J. Sci. 240,* 831–846.

Keevil, N. B. (1943*a*) Radiogenic heat in rocks, *J. Geol. 51,* 287–300.

Keevil, N. B. (1943*b*) The distribution of helium and radioactivity in rocks, V: Rocks and associated minerals from Quebec, Ontario, Manitoba, New Jersey, New England, New Brunswick, Newfoundland, Tanganyika, Finland, and Russia, *Am. J. Sci. 241,* 277–306.

Keevil, N. B. (1943*c*) Helium indexes for several minerals and rocks, *ibid.*, 680–693.

Keevil, N. B., and W. E. Grasham (1943) Theory of alpha-ray counting from solid sources, *Can. J. Research A21,* 21–36.

Keevil, N. B., A. R. Keevil, W. N. Ingham, and G. P. Crombie (1943) Causes of variations in radioactivity data, *Am. J. Sci. 241,* 345–365.

Keevil, N. B. (1944) Thorium-uranium ratios in rocks and minerals, *ibid. 242,* 309–321.

Keevil, N. B., E. S. Larsen, Jr., and F. J. Wank (1944) Distribution of helium and radioactivity in rocks, VI: The Ayer granite-migmatite at Chelmsford, Mass., *ibid.*, 345–353.

Kelvin, (Lord) W. T. (1899) The age of the earth as an abode fitted for life, *Phil. Mag.* (*5*) *47,* 66–90.

Kerr, P. F., and H. D. Holland (1951) Differential thermal analysis of davidite, *Am. Mineralogist 36,* 563–572.

Kerr, P. F., and J. L. Kulp (1952) Pre-Cambrian uraninite, Sunshine Mine, Idaho, *Science 115,* 86–88.

Khlopin, V. G., and Sh. A. Abidov (1941) Radioactivity and helium content of beryllium, boron, and lithium minerals of the U.S.S.R., *Compt. rend. acad. sci. U.R.S.S. 32,* 637–640.

Kimura, K. (1936) Chemical investigations of Japanese minerals bearing the rarer elements, *J. Chem. Soc. Japan 57,* 1195–1207.

King, Clarence (1893) The age of the earth, *Am. J. Sci.* (*3*) *45,* 1–20.

Kirchheimer, F. (1953) Weitere Untersuchungen über das Vorkommen von Uran im Schwarzwald [Further studies of uranium occurrence in the Schwarzwald], *Geol. Landesamt Baden-Württ., Abh. Heft 1,* 1–60.

Knopf, A., C. Schuchert, A. F. Kovarik, A. Holmes, and E. W. Brown (1931) The age of the earth, *Nat. Research Council* (*U. S.*) *Bull. 80,* 487 pp.

Koczy, F. F. (1943) The "age" of terrestrial matter and the geochemical uranium/lead ratio, *Nature 151,* 24.

Koczy, F. F. (1949*a*) The thorium content of Cambrian alum shales of Sweden, *Sveriges Geol. Undersökn., Ser. C, Avhandl. och Uppsat. no. 509; Årsbok. 43,* no. 7, 12 pp.

Koczy, F. F. (1949*b*) Thorium in seawater and marine sediments, *Geol. Fören. i Stockholm Förh. 71,* 238–242.

Koczy, G. (1950) Weitere Uranbestimmungen an Meerwasserproben [Further uranium determinations on samples of sea water], *Österr. Akad. Wiss., math.-naturw. Kl., Sitzber., Abt. IIa, 158,* 113–121.

Kolb, H. J., and J. J. Comer (1945) Habit modifications of ammonium dihydrogen phosphate crystals during growth from solution, *J. Am. Chem. Soc. 67,* 894–897.

Korff, S. A. (1946) *Electron and Nuclear Counters,* Van Nostrand, New York, 212 pp.

Korff, S. A. (1954) Effects of the cosmic radiation on terrestrial isotope distribution, *Trans. Am. Geophys. Union 35,* 103–106.

Kouts, H. J., and L. C. L. Yuan (1952) The production rate of cosmic-ray neutrons and carbon^{14}, *Phys. Rev. 86,* 128–129.

Kovach, E. M. (1944) An experimental study of the radon-content of soil-gas, *Trans. Am. Geophys. Union 25,* 563–571.

Kovach, E. M. (1945) Meteorological influence upon the radon content of soil-gas, *Trans. Am. Geophys. Union 26,* 241–248.

Kovach, E. M. (1946) Diurnal variations of the radon-content of soil-gas, *Terrestrial Magnetism and Atm. Elect. 51,* 45–56.

Kovarik, A. F., and L. W. McKeehan (1925, rev. 1929) Radioactivity, report of committee on X-rays and radioactivity, *Nat. Research Council* (*U. S.*) *Bull. 51,* 203 pp.

Kraushaar, J. J., E. D. Wilson, and K. T. Bainbridge (1953) Comparison of the values of the disintegration constant of Be^7 in Be, BeO BeF_2, *Phys. Rev. 90,* 610–614.

Krige, L. J. (1939) Borehole temperatures in the Transvaal and Orange Free State, *Proc. Roy. Soc.* (*London*) *A173,* 450–474.

Kröll, V. (1953) Vertical distribution of radium in deep-sea sediments, *Nature 171,* 742.

Kuhn, W., and A. R. Rittman (1941) Über den Zustand des Erdinnern und seine Enstehung aus einem homogenen Urzustand [State of the earth's interior and its development from an originally homogeneous mass], *Geol. Rundschau 32,* 215–256.

Kuiper, G. P. (1951) On the origin of the solar system *in* J. A. Hynek (ed.), *Astrophysics,* 357–424, University of Chicago Press.

Kulp, J. L., H. W. Feely, and L. E. Tryon (1951) Lamont natural radiocarbon measurements, I, *Science 114,* 565–568.

Kulp, J. L., and L. E. Tryon (1952) Extension of the carbon^{14} age method, *Rev. Sci. Instr. 23,* 296–297.

Kulp, J. L., H. D. Holland, and H. L. Volchok (1952*a*) Scintillation alpha counting of rocks and minerals, *Trans. Am. Geophys. Union 33,* 101–113.

Kulp, J. L., H. L. Volchok, and H. D. Holland (1952*b*) Age from metamict minerals, *Am. Mineralogist 37,* 709–718.

Kulp, J. L., L. E. Tryon, and H. W. Feely (1952*c*) Techniques of natural carbon^{14} determination, *Trans. Am. Geophys. Union 33,* 183–192.

Kulp, J. L., L. E. Tryon, W. R. Eckelmann, and W. A. Snell (1952*d*) Lamont natural radiocarbon measurements, II, *Science 116,* 409–414.

Kulp, J. L., W. S. Broecker, and W. R. Eckelmann (1953) Age determination of uranium minerals by the lead^{210} method, *Nucleonics 11,* no. 8, 19–21.

Kulp, J. L., G. L. Bate, and W. S. Broecker (1954) Present status of the lead method of age determination, *Am. J. Sci. 252,* 346–365.

Ladenburg, R. (1952) The absorption rate of cosmic-ray neutrons producing C^{14} in the atmosphere, *Phys. Rev. 86,* 128.

Lallemant, C. (1953) Prospection radioactive des minerais uranifères [Radiometric prospecting for uranium minerals], *Onde électrique 33,* 547–552.

Lane, A. C., and W. D. Urry (1935) Ages by the helium method, *Bull. Geol. Soc. Amer. 46,* 1101–1120.

Lane, D. A., B. B. Torchinsky, and J. W. T. Spinks (1953) Determining soil moisture and density by nuclear radiations, *Am. Soc. Testing Materials, Special Tech. Publ. 134,* 23–34.

Lang, A. H. (1952) Canadian deposits of uranium and thorium, *Geol. Survey Canada, Econ. Geol. Ser.*, no. 16, 173 pp.

Lapointe, C. (1950*a*) Analysis of uranium ores by Geiger methods, *Trans. Can. Inst. Mining Met. 8,* 324–327; also, *Can. Mining Met. Bull.*, August, 461–463.

Lapointe, C. (1950*b*) Equilibrium corrections in Geiger analysis, *Trans. Can. Inst. Mining Met. 8,* 328–331; also, *Can. Mining Met. Bull.*, August, 465–468.

Larsen, E. S., Jr., and N. B. Keevil (1942) The distribution of helium and radioactivity in rocks, III: Radioactivity and petrology of some California intrusives, *Am. J. Sci. 240,* 204–215.

Larsen, E. S., Jr., and N. B. Keevil (1947) Radioactivity of the rocks of the batholith of Southern California, *Bull. Geol. Soc. Amer. 58,* 483–493.

Larsen, E. S., Jr., N. B. Keevil, and H. C. Harrison (1952) Method for determining the age of igneous rocks, using the accessory minerals, *Bull. Geol. Soc. Amer. 63,* 1045–1052.

Larsen, E. S., Jr., C. L. Waring, and J. Berman (1953) Zoned zircon from Oklahoma, *Am. Mineralogist 38,* 1118–1125.

Lattes, C. M. G., P. H. Fowler, and P. Cuer (1947) Range-energy relation for protons and alpha particles in the new Ilford nuclear research emulsions, *Nature 159,* 301–302.

Lauda, J. (1936) Über das Abklingen des latenten Bildes auf der photographischen Platte [Fading of the latent image on the photographic plate], *Sitzber. Akad. Wiss. Wien, math.-naturw. Kl., Abt. IIa, 145,* 707–723.

Leith, T. H. (1952) Heat flow at Kirkland Lake, *Trans. Am. Geophys. Union 33,* 435–443.

Lerner, J. L., and D. F. Uecker (1951) An automatic plate counter, *Rev. Sci. Instr. 22,* 575–578.

Lester, J. G. (1950) The Geiger-Müller counter in geologic work, *Georgia Dept. Mines, Mining and Geol., Geol. Survey Bull. 56,* 112–117.

Leverenz, H. W. (1950) *Introduction to the Luminescence of Solids,* John Wiley & Sons, New York, 569 pp.

Levine, C. A., and G. T. Seaborg (1951) The occurrence of plutonium in nature, *J. Am. Chem. Soc. 73,* 3278–3283.

Libby, W. F. (1939) Stability of uranium and thorium for natural fission, *Phys. Rev. 55,* 1269.

Libby, W. F. (1946) Atmospheric helium^3 and radiocarbon from cosmic radiation, *Phys. Rev. 69,* 671–672.

Libby, W. F. (1952) *Radiocarbon Dating,* University of Chicago Press, 124 pp.

Liebson, S. H., and H. Friedman (1948) Self-quenching halogen-filled counters, *Rev. Sci. Instr. 19,* 303–307.

Lietz, J. (1937–1938) Beitrag zur Frage der Zirkone niedriger Dichte [Zircons of low density], *Z. Krist. 98,* 201–211.

Lind, S. C. (1911) Ozonization of oxygen by alpha particles, *Sitzber. Akad. Wiss. Wien, math.-naturw. Kl., Abt. IIa, 120,* 1709–1724.

Lind, S. C. (1919) Radium emanation, I: The combination of hydrogen and oxygen, *J. Am. Chem. Soc. 41,* 531–551.

Lind, S. C., and D. C. Bardwell (1926) Chemical action of gaseous ions produced by alpha particles, IX, *J. Am. Chem. Soc. 48,* 1556, 2335–2351.

Lind, S. C. (1928*a*) *Chemical Effects of Alpha Particles and Electrons,* Chemical Catalog Company, New York.

Lind, S. C. (1928*b*) On the origin of petroleum, *The Science of Petroleum, 1,* 39–41, Oxford University Press.

Linden, B. R. (1953) Five new photomultipliers for scintillation counting, *Nucleonics 11,* no. 9, 30–33.

Linden, B. R. (1954) New photomultipliers and operating data, *Nucleonics 12,* no. 3, 20–23.

Lindgren, Waldemar (1933) Differentiation and ore deposition, Cordilleran region of the United States *in Ore Deposits of the Western States* (*Lindgren volume*), 350–385, American Institute of Mining and Metallurgical Engineers, New York.

Loevinger, R., and M. Berman (1951) Efficiency criteria in radioactivity counting, *Nucleonics 9,* no. 1, 26–39.

Lo Surdo, A. (1921) Elio e neon "sintectici" ["Synthetic" helium and neon], *Atti accad. nazl. Lincei, Rend., Classe sci. fis. mat. e nat., Ser. 5ª, 30(i),* 85–88.

Lotze, F. (1928) Bemerkungen zu [Remarks on] J. Joly's "Theory of thermal cycles," *Gerlands Beitr. Geophys. 20,* 77–84.

Love, J. D. (1952) Preliminary report on uranium deposits in the Pumpkin Buttes area, Powder River Basin, Wyoming, *U. S. Geol. Survey Circ. 176.*

Lovering, T. S., and E. N. Goddard (1950) Geology and ore deposits of the Front Range, Colorado, *U. S. Geol. Survey Prof. Paper 223,* 319 pp.

Lundberg, H. (1952) An attempt to interpret radioactive patterns obtained from airborne recordings, *Proc. Geol. Assoc. Can. 5,* 117–125.

Lundberg, H., K. I. Roulston, R. W. Pringle, and G. W. Brownell (1952) Oil exploration with airborne scintillation counters, *Oil in Canada,* June 16.

Lundberg, H., and G. Isford (1953) Oil prospecting with the radioactive method, *World Petroleum 24,* no. 7, 40–42.

Macnamara, J., and H. G. Thode (1950) The isotopes of xenon and krypton in pitchblende and the spontaneous fission of U^{238}, *Phys. Rev. 80,* 471–472.

Mader, M. (1934) Die Eigenschaften der Samarium-Strahlung [Properties of the radiation from samarium], *Z. Physik 88,* 601–612.

Marble, J. P. (1937) The analysis of allanite for age determination *in Nat. Research Council* (*U. S.*) *Rept. Comm. Geol. Time,* 65–77.

Mardock, E. S., and J. P. Myers (1951) Radioactivity logs define lithology in the Spraberry formation, *Oil Gas J. 50,* November 29, 96–102.

Martin, G. R. (1953) Recent studies on iron meteorites, IV: The origin of meteoritic helium and the age of meteorites, *Geochim. et Cosmochim. Acta 3,* 288–309.

Mattauch, J. (1937) Das Paar Rb^{87}-Sr^{87} und die Isobarenregel [The pair Rb^{87}-Sr^{87} and the isobar rule], *Naturwissenschaften 25,* 188–191.

Mattauch, J. (1947) Stabile Isotope, ihre Messung und ihre Verwendung [Stable isotopes, their measurement and use], *Angew. Chem. A,* no. 2, 37–42.

McGregor, M. H., and M. L. Wiedenbeck (1952) The decay of Rb^{87}, *Phys. Rev. 86,* 420–421.

McKelvey, V. E., and J. M. Nelson (1950) Characteristics of marine uranium-bearing sedimentary rocks, *Econ. Geol. 45,* 35–53.

McKinney, C. R., J. M. McCrea, S. Epstein, H. A. Allen, and H. C. Urey (1950) Improvements in mass spectrometers for the measurement of small differences in isotope abundance ratios, *Rev. Sci. Instr. 21,* 724–730.

Meitner, L., and W. Orthmann (1930) Über eine absolute Bestimmung der Energie der primären Beta-Strahlen von Radium E [Absolute determination of the energy of the primary beta rays from radium E], *Z. Physik. 60,* 143–155.

Menaul, P. L. (1944) Corrosion in condensate fields, *Oil Gas J. 43,* no. 27, 80–81, November 11, 1944.

Meyer, S. (1950) Die Vorgeschichte der Gründung und das erste Jahrzehnt des Institutes für Radiumforschung [Events leading to the founding of the Institute for Radium Research and the first decade of its existence], *Österr. Akad. Wiss., math.-naturw. Kl., Sitzber, Abt. IIa, 159,* 1–26.

Minami, E. (1935) Gehalt an seltenen Erden in europäischen und japanischen Tonschiefern [Rare earth content of European and Japanese shales], *Nachr. Ges. Wiss. Göttingen, math.-physik Kl., Fachgruppen IV, 1,* 155–170.

Mining World (1953) Mozambique to have first uranium plant (short news item), *15,* no. 11, 85.

Misener, A. D., L. G. D. Thompson, and R. J. Uffen (1951) Terrestrial heat flow in Ontario and Quebec, *Trans. Am. Geophys. Union 32,* 729–738.

Morehead, F. F., Jr., and F. Daniels (1952) Storage of radiation energy in crystalline lithium fluoride and metamict minerals, *J. Phys. Chem. 56,* 546–548.

Morgan, J. V. (1952) Correlation of radioactivity logs of the Lansing and Kansas City groups in central Kansas, *J. Petroleum Technol. 4,* April; also, *Trans. Am. Inst. Mining Met. Engrs. 195,* 111–118.

Mossop, S. C., and G. Gafner (1951) The thermal constants of some rocks from the Orange Free State, *J. Chem. Met. Mining Soc. S. Africa 52,* 61–73.

Mott, N. F., and R. W. Gurney (1948) *Electronic Processes in Ionic Crystals,* 2nd ed., Oxford University Press, 275 pp.

Mousuf, A. K. (1952) K^{40} radioactive decay: Its branching ratio and its use in geological age determinations, *Phys. Rev. 88,* 150–151.

Mügge, O. (1909) Radioaktivität und pleochroitische Höfe, II: Eigenschaften und Vorkommen der natürlichen Höfe [Radioactivity and pleochroic halos, II: Properties and occurrence of natural halos], *Centr. Mineral. Geol. 71,* 113, 142.

Mühlhoff, W. (1930) Aktivität von Kalium und Rubidium gemessen mit dem Elektronenzählrohr [Radioactivity of potassium and rubidium measured with a counter], *Ann. Physik. 1,* 205–224.

National Bureau of Standards (U. S.) (1953) Mass spectroscopy in physics research (a symposium), *Circ. 522,* 273 pp.

National Research Council (U. S.) (annually, 1924 to date) *Report of the committee on the measurement of geologic time* (A. C. Lane, chairman, 1924–1946; J. P. Marble, Chairman, 1946 to date), Washington.

Nelson, J. M. (1953) Prospecting for uranium with car-mounted equipment, *U. S. Geol. Survey Bull. 988-I,* 211–221.

Neville, O. K. (1953) $Carbon^{14}$ sample preparation and counting techniques, I: Gas counting methods, *Atomics 3,* 88–90.

Ney, W. O., W. W. Crouch, C. E. Rannefeld, and H. L. Lochte (1943) Petroleum acids, VI: Napthenic acids from California petroleum, *J. Am. Chem. Soc. 65,* 770–777.

Nicolaysen, L. O., L. T. Aldrich, and J. B. Doak (1953) Age measurements on African micas by the strontium-rubidium method (abstract), *Trans. Am. Geophys. Union 34,* 342–343.

Nielsen, E. S. (1952) The use of radioactive carbon (C^{14}) for measuring organic production in the sea, *J. conseil permanent intern. exploration mer 18,* 117.

Niepce de Saint-Victor (1867) Sur une nouvelle action de la lumière [A new action of light], *Compt. rend. 60,* 505.

Nier, A. O. (1935) Evidence for the existence of an isotope of potassium of mass 40, *Phys. Rev. 48,* 283–284.

Nier, A. O. (1938) Variations in the relative abundances of the isotopes of common lead from various sources, *J. Am. Chem. Soc. 60,* 1571–1576.

Nier, A. O. (1939*a*) The isotopic constitution of uranium and the halflives of the uranium isotopes, *Phys. Rev. 55,* 150–153.

Nier, A. O. (1939*b*) The isotopic constitution of radiogenic leads and the measurement of geological time, II, *Phys. Rev. 55,* 153–163.

Nier, A. O. (1940) A mass spectrometer for routine isotope abundance measurements, *Rev. Sci. Instr. 11,* 212–216.

Nier, A. O., R. W. Thompson, and B. F. Murphey (1941) The isotopic constitution of lead and the measurement of geological time, III, *Phys. Rev. 60,* 112–116.

Nier, A. O. (1947) A mass spectrometer for isotope and gas analysis, *Rev. Sci. Instr. 18,* 398–411.

Nier, A. O., E. P. Ney, and M. G. Inghram (1947) A null method for the comparison of two ion currents in a mass spectrometer, *Rev. Sci. Instr. 18,* 294–297.

Nier, A. O. (1950) A redetermination of the relative abundances o fthe isotopes of carbon, nitrogen, oxygen, argon and potassium, *Phys. Rev. 77,* 789–793.

Nockolds, S. R., and R. L. Mitchell (1948) The geochemistry of some Caledonian plutonic rocks, etc., *Trans. Edinburgh Geol. Soc. 61,* 533–575.

Nockolds, S. R., and R. Allen (1953) The geochemistry of some igneous rock series, *Geochim. et Cosmochim. Acta 4,* 105–142.

Nogami, H. H., and P. M. Hurley (1948) The absorption factor in counting alpha rays from thick mineral sources, *Trans. Am. Geophys. Union 29,* 335–340.

Norinder, H., A. Metnieks, and R. Siksna (1952) Radon content of the air in the soil at Uppsala, *Arkiv Geofysik 1,* 571–579.

Occhialini, G. P. S., and C. F. Powell (1947) Nuclear disintegrations produced by slow charged particles of small mass, *Nature 159,* 186–190.

Officer, C. B., M. Ewing, and P. C. Wuenschel (1952) Seismic refraction measurements in the Atlantic Ocean, IV: Bermuda, Bermuda Rise, and Nares Basin, *Bull. Geol. Soc. Amer. 63,* 778–808.

Orbain, G. (1931) Untersuchungen über die Radioaktivität der Alkalimetalle mit der Nebelstrahlmethode [Studies of the radioactivity of alkalis by the cloud chamber method], *Sitzber. Akad. Wiss. Wien, math.-naturw. Kl., Abt. IIa, 140,* 121–139.

Orlov, N. A., and L. M. Kurbatov (1934–1936) K voprosu o radioaktivnosti goriuchikh slantsev [The radioactivity of bituminous shale], *Khim. Tverdogo Topliva 5,* 525–527; *6,* 278–291; *7,* 94–98.

Pabst, A. (1952) The metamict state, *Am. Mineralogist 37,* 137–157.

Palache, Charles, Harry Berman, and Clifford Frondel (1944, 1951) *Dana's System of Mineralogy, 1,* 834 pp., *2,* 1124 pp., John Wiley & Sons, New York.

Palevsky, H., R. K. Swank, and R. Grenchik (1947) Design of dynamic condenser electrometers, *Rev. Sci. Instr. 18,* 298–314.

Paneth, F., and K. Peters (1928) Heliumuntersuchungen, III [Helium investigations, III], *Z. physik. Chem. B, 1,* 253–269.

Paneth, F., H. Gehlen, and P. L. Gunther (1928) Heliumuntersuchungen, V [Helium investigations, V], *Z. Elektrochem. 34,* 645–652.

Paneth, F., and W. D. Urry (1930*a*) Heliumuntersuchungen, VIII [Helium investigations, VIII], *Z. physik. Chem. A, 152,* 110–126.

Paneth, F., and W. D. Urry (1930*b*) Heliumuntersuchungen, IX [Helium investigations, IX], *Z. physik. Chem. A, 152,* 127–149.

Paneth, F., W. D. Urry, and W. Koeck (1930) The age of iron meteorites, *Nature 125,* 490–491.

Paneth, F. (1948) Meteorites, *Encyclopaedia Britannica 15,* 340.

Paneth, F., P. Reasbeck, and K. I. Mayne (1952) Helium^3 content and age of meteorites, *Geochim. et Cosmochim. Acta 2,* 300–303.

Paneth, F. (1953) Recent studies on iron meteorites, I, *Geochim. et Cosmochim. Acta 3,* 257–260; see also: *ibid.,* p. 261 *et seq.;* Chackett et al., 1953; Dalton et al., 1953; Martin, 1953.

Paneth, F., P. Reasbeck, and K. I. Mayne (1953) Production by cosmic rays of helium^3 in meteorites, *Nature 172,* 200–201

Papish, J., and L. E. Hoag (1927) The detection of uranium by a photoluminescence test, *Proc. Nat. Acad. Sci. U. S. 13,* 726–728.

Patterson, C., H. Brown, G. Tilton, and M. Inghram (1953*a*) Concentration of uranium and lead and the isotopic composition of lead in meteoritic material, *Phys. Rev. 92,* 1234–1235.

Patterson, C., G. Tilton, and M. Inghram (1953*b*) Abundances of uranium and the isotopes of lead in the earth's crust and meteorites (abstract), *Bull. Geol. Soc. Amer. 64,* 1461.

Patterson, C., E. D. Goldberg, and M. Inghram (1953*c*) Isotopic compositions of Quaternary leads from the Pacific Ocean, *Bull. Geol. Soc. Amer. 64,* 1387–1388.

Peacock, W. C., and W. M. Good (1946) An automatic sample changer to be used for measuring radioactive samples, *Rev. Sci. Instr. 17,* 255–261.

Peirson, D. H. (1951*a*) A transportable radioactivity monitoring equipment used for geological surveying by car, *Ministry Supply (Brit.) Atomic Energy Research Estab. Rept. EL/R 750,* 7 pp.

Peirson, D. H. (1951*b*) The background counting rate in a Geiger-Müller counter, *Proc. Phys. Soc. (London) B64,* 427–428.

Peirson, D. H. (1951*c*) Alpha particle assay and the measurement of the thorium-uranium ratio in radioactive ores, *Proc. Phys. Soc. (London) B64,* 876–888.

Peirson, D. H. (1953) Some cold cathode valve circuits used in the measurement of radioactivity, *Ministry Supply (Brit.) Atomic Energy Research Estab. Rept. EL/R 1204.*

Peirson, D. H., and J. Pickup (1954) A scintillation counter for radioactivity prospecting, *J. Brit. Inst. Radio Engrs. 14,* 25–32.

Pelc, S. R. (1947) Autoradiograph technique, *Nature 160,* 749–750.

Pellas, Paul (1953) Sur l'établissement de l'état métamicte dans la gadolinite. Bilan énergétique de la recristallisation [Establishment of the metamict state in gadolinite. Energy balance of the recrystallization], *Compt. rend. 236,* 619–621.

Pettersson, H. (1930) *Teneur en radium des dépôts de mer profonde* [Radium content of deep sea deposits], Imp. de Monaco, 50 pp.

Pettersson, H. (1937) Das Verhältnis Thorium zu Uran in den Gesteinen und im Meer [The proportion of thorium to uranium in rocks and in the sea], *Anz. Akad. Wiss. Wien, math.-naturw. Kl.*, 127–128.

Pettersson, H. (1939) Die radioaktiven Elemente im Meere [Radioactive elements in the sea], *J. conseil permanent intern. exploration mer, Rap. Proc. Verb. 109,* 66–67.

Pettersson, H. (1943) Manganese nodules and the chronology of the ocean floor, *Göteborgs Kgl. Vetenskaps-Vitterhets-Samhäll. Handl. Ser. B, 2,* no. 8, 43 pp.

Pettersson, H. (1949) Exploring the bed of the ocean, *Nature 164,* 468–470.

Pettersson, H. (1951) Radium and deep-sea chronology, *Nature 167,* 942.

Phair, G., and K. O. Shimamoto (1952) Hydrothermal uranothorite in fluorite breccias from the Blue Jay Mine, Jamestown, Boulder County, Colorado, *Am. Mineralogist 37,* 659–666.

Phair, G., and H. Levine (1953) Notes on the differential leaching of uranium, radium and lead from pitchblende in H_2SO_4 solutions, *Econ. Geol. 48,* 358–369.

Picciotto, E. (1949) L'étude de la radioactivité des roches par la méthode photographique [Study of the radioactivity of rocks by the photographic method], *Bull. soc. belge géol. paléontol. et hydrol. 58,* 75–90.

Picciotto, E. (1950) Distribution de la radioactivité dans les roches éruptives [Distribution of radioactivity in igneous rocks], *Bull. soc. belge géol. paléontol. et hydrol. 59,* 170–198.

Picciotto, E., and S. Wilgain (1954) Thorium determination in deep-sea sediments *Nature 173,* 632–633.

Piggot, C. S. (1929) Radium in rocks, I: The radium content of some representative granites of the eastern seaboard of the U. S., *Am. J. Sci.* (*5*) *17,* 13–34.

Piggot, C. S. (1931) Radium in rocks, II: Granites of eastern North America from Georgia to Greenland, *Am. J. Sci.* (*5*) *21,* 28–36.

Piggot, C. S., and H. E. Merwin (1932) Location and association of radium in igneous rocks, *Am. J. Sci.* (*5*) *23,* 49–56.

Piggot, C. S. (1933) Radium content of ocean bottom sediments, *Am. J. Sci.* (*5*) *25,* 229–238.

Piggot, C. S. (1936) Apparatus to secure core samples from the ocean bottom, *Bull. Geol. Soc. Amer. 47,* 675–684.

Piggot, C. S. (1938) Radium in rocks, V: The radium content of the four groups of pre-Cambrian granites of Finland, *Am. J. Sci.* (*5*) *35A,* 227–229.

Piggot, C. S., and W. D. Urry (1939) The radium content of an ocean-bottom core, *J. Wash. Acad. Sci. 29,* 405–415.

Piggot, C. S., and W. D. Urry (1941) Radioactivity of ocean sediments, III: Radioactive relations in ocean water and bottom sediment, *Am. J. Sci. 239,* 81–91.

Piggot, C. S., and W. D. Urry (1942) Time relations in ocean sediments, *Bull. Geol. Soc. Amer. 53,* 1187–1210.

Piggot, C. S. (1944) II: Radium content of ocean bottom sediments, *Carnegie Inst. Wash. Publ. 556,* 183–193.

Poole, J. H. J. (1915) The average thorium content of the Earth's crust, *Phil. Mag.* (*6*) *29,* 483–489.

Poole, J. H. J., and J. Joly (1924) The radioactivity of basalts and other rocks, *Phil. Mag.* (*6*) *48,* 819–832.

Poole, J. H. J., and J. W. Bremner (1948) The emission of alpha particles from the different faces of a radiactive crystal, *Phys. Rev. 74,* 836.

Poole, J. H. J., and J. W. Bremner (1949) Investigation of the distribution of the radioactive elements in rocks by the photographic method, *Nature 163,* 130–131.

Poole, J. H. J., and C. M. Matthews (1951) The theory of the use of alpha ray ranges in nuclear emulsions for the determination of the radioactive contents of materials, *Sci. Proc. Roy. Dublin Soc. 25,* 305–316.

Pose, H. (1943) Spotane Neutronenemission von Uran und Thorium [Spontaneous neutron emission of uranium and thorium], *Z. Physik. 121,* 293–297.

Pratt, W. E. (1934) Hydrogenation and the origin of oil, *Problems of Petroleum Geology,* 234–245, American Association of Petroleum Geologists.

Present, R. D. (1947) On self-quenching halogen counters, *Phys. Rev. 72,* 243–244.

Pringsheim, P. (1949) *Fluorescence and Phosphorescence,* Interscience, New York, 794 pp.

Puckle, O. S. (1951) *Time Bases,* John Wiley & Sons, New York, 387 pp.

Rabe, Eugene (1950) Derivation of fundamental astronomical constants from the observations of Eros during 1926–1945, *Astron. J. 55,* 112–126.

Raitt, R. W. (1949) Studies of ocean-bottom structure of Southern California with explosive waves (abstract), *Bull. Geol. Soc. Amer. 60,* 1915.

Rajewsky, B. (1943) Das Geiger-Müller Zählrohr im Dienste des Bergbaues [The Geiger-Müller counter applied to mining], *Z. Physik 120,* 627–638.

Ramsay, W., and W. M. Travers (1897) Gaseous constituents of certain mineral substances and natural waters, *Proc. Roy. Soc. (London) A60,* 442–448.

Ramsay, W., and F. Soddy (1903) The production of helium from radium, *Proc. Roy. Soc. (London) A72,* 204–207.

Rankama, Kalervo (1946) On the geochemical differentiation in the earth's crust, *Bull. comm. géol. Finlande,* no. 137, 1–21.

Rankama, Kalervo, and T. G. Sahama (1950) *Geochemistry,* University of Chicago Press, 911 pp.

Rankama, Kalervo (in press) *Isotope Geology,* Pergamon Press, London.

Reines, F., and C. L. Cowan, Jr. (1953*a*) Proposed experiment to detect the free neutrino, *Phys. Rev. 90,* 492(L)–493.

Reines, F., and C. L. Cowan, Jr. (1953*b*) Detection of the free neutrino, *Phys. Rev. 92,* 830(L)–831.

Reinganum, M. (1911) Streuung und photographische Wirkung der Alpha-Strahlen [Scattering and photographic effect of alpha particles], *Physik Z. 12,* 1076–1077.

Revelle, R. R., and A. E. Maxwell (1952) Heat flow through the floor of the eastern North Pacific Ocean, *Nature 170,* 199–200.

Reynolds, G. T. (1952) Solid and liquid scintillation counters, *Nucleonics 10,* no. 7, 46–53.

Richards, T. W., and M. E. Lembert (1914) Atomic weight of lead of radioactive origin, *J. Am. Chem. Soc. 36,* 1329–1344.

Richards, T. W. (1926) Note on the effect of alpha particles on paraffin, *Proc. Cambridge Phil. Soc. 23,* 516–522.

Ridland, G. C. (1945) Use of the Geiger-Müller counter in the search for pitchblende-bearing veins at Great Bear Lake, Canada, *Trans. Am. Inst. Mining Met. Engrs. 164,* 117–124.

Roberts, Arthur (1949) Portable Geiger counter for drill holes, *Radio and Television News 42,* no. 3, 16–28.

Roberts, F. H. H., Jr. (1952) The carbon^{14} method of age determination, *Smithsonian Inst. Publ. 4078, Rept. for 1951,* 335–350.

Rodden, C. J. (1949) Determination of naturally occurring radioactive elements, *Anal. Chem. 21,* 327–335.

Rodgers, John (1952) Absolute ages of radioactive minerals from the Appalachian region, *Am. J. Sci. 250,* 411–427.

Rona, E. (1943) Radioactivity of sea water, *Am. Phil. Soc. Yearbook,* 136–138.

Rona, E., and W. D. Urry (1952) Radioactivity of ocean sediments, VIII: Radium and uranium content of ocean and river waters, *Am. J. Sci. 250,* 241–262.

Rosenblum, Ch. (1937) Production de benzène dans la polymerisation radiochimique de l'acetylène [Production of benzene in the radiochemical polymerization of acetylene], *Bull. soc. chim. Belg. 46,* 503–518.

Rosholt, J. N., Jr. (in press) A quantitative radiochemical method for the determination of major sources of natural radioactivity in ores and minerals, *Anal. Chem.*

Ross, V. F. (1952) Autoradiographic study of marine shales, *Econ. Geol. 47,* 783–793.

Rossi, B. B., and H. H. Staub (1949) *Ionization Chambers and Counters. Experimental Techniques,* McGraw-Hill Book Co., New York, 243 pp.

Rubey, W. W. (1951) Geologic history of sea water, *Bull. Geol. Soc. Amer. 62,* 1138–1139.

Russell, H. N., and D. H. Menzel (1933) The terrestrial abundance of the permanent gases, *Proc. Nat. Acad. Sci. U. S. 19,* 997–1001.

Russell, H. N., R. S. Dugan, and J. Q. Stewart (1945) *Astronomy, 1 (The solar system),* rev. ed., Ginn and Company, New York, 470 pp.

Russell, R. D., H. A. Shillibeer, R. M. Farquhar, and A. K. Mousuf (1953) Branching ratio of K^{40}, *Phys. Rev. 91,* 1223–1224.

Russell, R. D., R. M. Farquhar, G. L. Cumming, and J. T. Wilson (1954) Dating galenas by means of their isotopic constitutions, *Trans. Am. Geophys. Union. 35,* 301–309.

Russell, W. L. (1944) The total gamma ray activity of sedimentary rocks as indicated by Geiger counter determinations, *Geophysics 9,* 180–216.

Russell, W. L., and S. A. Scherbatskoy (1951) The use of sensitive gamma ray detectors in prospecting, *Econ. Geol. 46,* 427–446.

Russell, W. L. (1952) Interpretation of neutron well logs, *Bull. Am. Assoc. Petroleum Geol. 36,* 312–341.

Rutherford, E., and R. K. McClung (1900) Energy of Röntgen and Becquerel rays and the energy required to produce an ion in gases, *Phil. Trans. Roy. Soc. (London) A196,* 25–59.

Rutherford, E., and F. Soddy (1902) The cause and nature of radioactivity, *Phil. Mag. (6) 4,* 569–585.

Rutherford, E. (1906) The mass and velocity of the alpha particles expelled from radium and actinium, *Phil. Mag. (6) 12,* 348–371, see p. 368.

Sahama, Th. G. (1946) On the chemistry of the East Fennoscandian Rapakivi granites, *Bull. comm. géol. Finlande,* no. 136, 15–67.

Sanderman, L. A., and C. L. Utterback (1941) Radium content of ocean bottom sediments from the Arctic Ocean, Bering Sea, Alaska Peninsula and the coasts of southern Alaska and western Canada, *J. Marine Research 4,* 132–141.

Satterly, John, and J. C. McLennan (1918) The radioactivity of the natural gases of Canada, *Trans. Roy. Soc. Can., Sec. III, 12,* 153–160.

Sawyer, G. A., and M. L. Wiedenbeck (1950) Decay constants of K^{40}, *Phys. Rev. 79,* 490–494.

Saxon, D. (1949) The neutrinos from the sun and the source of the earth's heat, *Phys. Rev. 76,* 986(L).

Scharff-Goldhaber, G., and G. S. Klaiber (1946) Spontaneous emission of neutrons from uranium, *Phys. Rev. 70,* 229.

Schenck, J. (1952) Neutron-detecting phosphors, *Nucleonics 10,* no. 8, 54–56.

Scherbatskoy, S. A., T. H. Gilmartin, and G. Swift (1947) The capacitative commutator, *Rev. Sci. Instr. 18,* 415–421.

Schmitt, O. H. (1938) Thermionic trigger, *J. Sci. Instr. 15,* 24–26.

Scotty, C. B., and E. F. Egan (1952) Neutron derived porosity-influence of bore hole diameter, *J. Petroleum Technol. 4,* August; also, *Trans. Am. Inst. Mining Met. Engrs. 195,* 203–206.

Scotty, C. B., and E. F. Egan (1953) Hole diameter influences neutron derived porosity, *World Oil 136,* 172–178.

Scrivenor, J. B. (1928) *Geology of Malayan Ore Deposits,* MacMillan and Company, London, 109 pp.

Seaborg, G. T. (1945) The chemical and radioactive properties of the heavy elements, *Chem. Eng. News 23,* 2190–2193.

Segrè, E., and C. E. Wiegand (1949) Experiments on the effect of atomic electrons on the decay constant of Be^7, *Phys. Rev. 75,* 39–43; erratum, *Phys. Rev. 81* (1951), 284.

Segrè, E. (1952) Spontaneous fission, *Phys. Rev. 86,* 21–28.

Segrè, E. (ed.) (1953) *Experimental Nuclear Physics,* John Wiley & Sons, Sons, New York, 3 vols.: *1,* 789 pp.; *2,* 600 pp.; *3,* in press.

Seitz, F. (1949) On the disordering of solids by action of fast massive particles, *Discussions Faraday Soc.,* no. 5, 271–282.

Seitz, F. (1952) Imperfections in nearly perfect crystals, a synthesis *in* W. Shockley (ed.), *Committee on Solids Symposium, Nat. Research Council (U. S.),* John Wiley & Sons, New York.

Senftle, F. E., and N. B. Keevil (1947) Thorium-uranium ratios in the theory of genesis of lead ores, *Trans. Am. Geophys. Union 28,* 732–738.

Senftle, F. E. (1948) The effect of potassium in prospecting for radioactive ores, *Can. Mining J. 69,* no. 11, 55–57.

Senftle, F. E., T. A. Farley, and L. R. Stieff (in press) Theoretical alpha star population in loaded nuclear emulsions, *Geochim. Cosmochim. Acta.*

Sheppard, C. W. (1944) Radioactivity and petroleum genesis, *Bull. Am. Assoc. Petroleum Geol. 28,* 924–952.

Sheppard, C. W., and V. L. Burton (1946) The effects of radioactivity on fatty acids, *J. Am. Chem. Soc. 68,* 1636–1639.

Sheppard, C. W., and W. L. Whitehead (1946) Formation of hydrocarbons from fatty acids by alpha particle bombardment, *Bull. Am. Assoc. Petroleum Geol. 30,* 32–51.

Sherwin, C. W. (1948) The neutrino, *Nucleonics 2,* no. 5, 16–24.

Siegel, S. (1949) Effect of neutron bombardment on order in the alloy Cu_3AU, *Phys. Rev. 75,* 1823–1824.

Simpson, D. J. (1953) Correlation of the sediments of the Witwatersrand system in the West Witwatersrand, Klerksdorp and Orange Free State areas by radioactivity borehole logging, *Trans. Geol. Soc. S. Africa 55,* 133–152.

Singer, S. F. (1952) Meteorites and cosmic rays, *Nature 170,* 728–729.

Singer, S. F. (1953) Meteorites and cosmic rays, *Mém. soc. roy. sci. Liège (4) 13,* 339–349.

Slack, H. A. (1949) Radioactivity measurements in the Kirkland Lake area, northern Ontario, *Trans. Am. Geophys. Union 30,* 867–874.

Slack, H. A., and K. Whitham (1951) A further investigation of the radioactivity of the Round Lake and Elzevir batholiths, *Trans. Am. Geophys. Union 32,* 44–48.

Slack, H. A. (1952) The application of recent counting techniques to geophysical research, I: Field measurement of the radioactivity of rocks, *Trans. Am. Geophys. Union 33,* 897–901.

Slater, J. C. (1951) The effects of radiation on materials, *J. Appl. Phys. 22,* 237–256.

Slichter, L. B. (1941) Cooling of the Earth, *Bull. Geol. Soc. Amer. 52,* 561–600.

Slichter, L. B. (1950) Rancho Santa Fé conference concerning the evolution of the earth, *Proc. Nat. Acad. Sci. (U. S.) 36,* 511–514.

Smeeth, W. F., and H. E. Watson (1918) The radioactivity of Archaean rocks from the Mysore State, South India, *Phil. Mag. (6) 35,* 206–209.

Smits, F., and W. Gentner (1950) Argonbestimmungen an Kalium-Mineralien, I: Bestimmungen an tertiären Kalisalzen [Determinations of argon in potassium minerals, I: Determinations in tertiary potassium salts], *Geochim. et Cosmochim. Acta 1,* 22–27.

Soddy, Frederick (1908) Attempts to detect the production of helium from the primary radio-elements, *Phil. Mag. (6) 16,* 513–530.

Soddy, Frederick (1914) *The Chemistry of the Radio-elements, Part II,* Longmans, Green, London, 46 pp.

Sommer, A., and W. E. Turk (1950) New multiplier phototubes of high sensitivity, *J. Sci. Instr. 27,* 113–117.

Spicer, H. C. (1946) Gamma-ray studies of potassium salts and associated geologic formations, *U. S. Geol. Survey Bull. 950,* 143–161.

Spinks, J. W. T., D. A. Lane, and B. B. Torchinsky (1951) A new method for moisture determination in soil, *Can. J. Technol. 29,* 371–374.

Stackelberg, M. von, and K. Chudoba (1937) Dichte und Struktur des Zirkons, II [Density and structure of zircon, II], *Z. Krist. 97,* 252–262.

Stackelberg, M. von, and E. Rottenbach (1939–1940*a*) Dichte und Struktur des Zirkons, III [Density and structure of zircon, III], *Z. Krist. 102,* 173–182.

Stackelberg, M. von and E. Rottenbach (1939–1940*b*) Dichte und Struktur des Zirkons, IV [Density and structure of zircon, IV], *Z. Krist. 102,* 207–209.

Stead, F. W. (1950) Airborne radioactivity surveying speeds uranium prospecting, *Eng. Mining J. 151,* no. 9, 74–77.

Stěp, J., and F. Becke (1904) Das Vorkommen des Uranpecherzes zu St. Joachimstahl [Pitchblende ore occurrence at Joachimsthal], *Sitzber. Akad. Wiss. Wien, math.-naturw. Kl., Abt. I, 113,* 585–618.

Stern, M. O. (1949) The masses of the heavy isotopes, *Revs. Mod. Phys. 21,* 316–321.

Stevens, R. E., and R. C. Wells (1934) Determination of the common and rare alkalies in mineral analyses, *Ind. Eng. Chem. Anal. Ed. 6,* 439–444.

Stevens, R. E. (1938) New analyses of lepidolite and their interpretation, *Am. Mineralogist 23,* 607–628.

Stieff, L. R., and T. W. Stern (1952) Preparation of nuclear-track plates and stripping films for the study of radioactive minerals, *Am. Mineralogist 37,* 184–196.

Stieff, L. R., T. W. Stern, and R. G. Milkey (1953) A preliminary determination of the age of some uranium ores of the Colorado Plateaus by the lead-uranium method, *U. S. Geol. Survey Circ. 271,* 19 pp.

Stothart, R. A. (1950) Reef surveying with radioactivity, *World Oil,* January, 61–63.

Strassmann, F., and E. Walling (1938) Abscheidung des reinen Strontium Isotops 87, etc. [Separation of pure strontium^{87}, *etc.*], *Ber. deut. chem. Ges. Abt. B, 71,* 1–9.

Strøm, K. M. (1939) Land-locked waters and the deposition of black muds *in* P. D. Trask (ed.), *Recent Marine Sediments,* 356–372, American Institute of Petroleum Engineers.

Strøm, K. M. (1948) A concentration of uranium in black muds, *Nature 162,* 922.

Strutt, J. W. (1896) On some physical properties of argon and helium, *Proc. Roy. Soc. (London) A59,* 198–208.

Strutt, J. W. (1897) On the amount of argon and helium contained in the gas from the Bath Springs, *Proc. Roy. Soc. (London) A60,* 56–57.

Strutt, R. J. (1906) On the distribution of radium in the Earth's crust, and on the Earth's internal heat, *ibid. A77,* 472–488.

Strutt, R. J. (1908*a*) Helium and radioactivity in rare and common minerals, *ibid. A80,* 572–594.

Strutt, R. J. (1908*b*) The accumulation of helium in geological time, I, *ibid. A81,* 272–277.

Strutt, R. J. (1909) The leakage of helium from radioactive minerals, *ibid. A82,* 166–169.

Strutt, R. J. (1910*a*) The accumulation of helium in geological time, II, *ibid. A83,* 96–99.

Strutt, R. J. (1910*b*) The accumulation of helium in geological time, III, *ibid.,* 298-301.

Strutt, R. J. (1911) The accumulation of helium in geological time, IV, *ibid. A84,* 194–196.

Suess, H. E. (in press) Nuclear shell structure and the cosmic abundance of nuclear species, *Nat. Research Council (U. S.), Nuclear Sci. Ser., Prelim. rept.*

Suess, H., H. Craig, and H. C. Urey *The Geochemistry of Nuclear Species,* to be published by John Wiley & Sons, New York.

Swift, Gilbert (1952) Simultaneous gamma ray and neutron well logging, *Geophysics 17,* 387–394.

Symposium on radiation chemistry and photochemistry (1948), *J. Phys. & Colloid Chem. 52,* 437–611.

Szalay, A. (1948*a*) Investigations into the thorium and uranium contents of the eruptive rocks in Hungary by means of Geiger-Müller counter tubes, *A Magyar*

Állami Földtani Intézet, Müködési Jelentések [*Hung. Geol. Inst. Yearly Rept., Rept. of Discussion*] *10,* 23–34.

Szalay, A. (1948*b*) Thorium and uranium content of the Velence Mountains, Hungary, *Nature 162,* 454–455.

Szalay, A., and E. Csongor (1949) Determination of radioactive content of rocks by means of Geiger-Müller counters, *Science 109,* 146–147.

Taylor, Denis (1950) British radio-activity-measuring apparatus, *Brit. Sci. News 3,* 117–122.

Taylor, Denis (1953) Recent instrument developments in England, *Nucleonics 11,* no. 3, 40–43.

Taylor, H. J. (1935) The tracks of alpha-particles and protons in photographic emulsions, *Proc. Roy. Soc.* (*London*) *A150,* 382–394.

Thayer, L. A. (1931) Bacterial genesis of hydrocarbons from fatty acids, *Bull. Am. Assoc. Petroleum Geol. 15,* 441–453.

Thode, H. G. (1951) Fission product yields and shell structure in atomic nuclei, *Trans. Roy. Soc. Can. 45,* 1–17.

Thode, H. G., J. Macnamara, and W. H. Fleming (1953) Sulphur isotope fractionation in nature and geological and biological time scales, *Geochim. et Cosmochim. Acta 3,* 235–243.

Thommeret, J. (1949) Evaluation de la teneur en uranium des minerais par la mesure des rayonnements nucléaires [Uranium assaying of ores by nuclear radiation measurement], *J. phys. radium* (*8*) *10,* 249–252.

Thomson, J. J. (1905) Emission of negative corpuscles by alkali metals, *Phil. Mag.* (*6*) *10,* 584–590.

Thoreau, J., and R. DuTrieu de Terdonck (1933) Le gîte d'uranium de Shinkolobwe-Kasolo (Katanga) [The uranium deposit of Shinkolobwe-Kasolo (Katanga)], *Inst. roy. colonial belge, Sect. sci. nat. et méd., Mém. 1,* 46 pp.

Tilley, C. E. (1936) The paragenesis of kyanite-eclogites, *Mineralog. Mag. 24,* 422–432.

Tilton, G. R., C. C. Patterson, and M. G. Inghram (1952) Mass spectrometric determination of thorium (abstract), *Bull. Geol. Soc. Amer. 63,* 1305.

Tilton, G. R., C. C. Patterson, H. Brown, M. Inghram, R. Hayden, D. Hess, and E. S. Larsen, Jr. (in press) The isotopic composition and distribution of lead, uranium and thorium in a pre-Cambrian granite, *Bull. Geol. Soc. Amer.*

Tiratsoo, E. N. (1941) Radioactivity and petroleum, *Petroleum* (*London*) *4,* 58–63.

Tittle, C. W., Henry Faul, and Clark Goodman (1951) Neutron logging of drill holes: The neutron-neutron method, *Geophysics 16,* 626–658.

Tolmachev, Yu. M. (1943) The adsorption of uranyl salts on solid adsorbents (in Russian, English summary), *Bull. acad. sci. U.R.S.S., Classe sci. chim.,* no. 1, 28–34.

Tomlinson, R. H., and A. K. Das Gupta (1953) The use of isotope dilution in determination of geologic age of minerals, *Can. J. Chem. 31,* 909–914.

Trask, P. D. (1932) *Origin and Environment of Source Sediments of Petroleum,* Gulf Publishing Company, 323 pp.

Tripper, G. H. (1914) The monazite sands of Travancore, *Records Geol. Survey India 44,* 186–196.

Tschitschibabin, A. E., F. W. Tschirikow, M. M. Katznelsson, S. M. Korjagin, and G. W. Tschelingew (1933) Über die Fettsäuren des kaukasischen Erdöles [Fatty acids in Caucasian crude oil], *Chem. Zentr. 104,* I, 3389.

Twenhofel, W. H. (1939) Principles of Sedimentation, 472–479, McGraw-Hill Book Co., New York.

United States Bureau of Mines (1906) Mineral resources of the U. S. in 1905, *Minerals Yearbook,* 1180–1223.

Urey, H. C. (1952) *The Planets,* Yale University Press, 245 pp.

Urey, H. C. (1953) On the concentration of certain elements at the earth's surface, *Proc. Roy. Soc. (London) A219,* 281–292.

Urey, H. C. (in press) On the dissipation of gas and volatilized elements from protoplanets, *Astrophys. J.*

Urry, W. D. (1932) Further studies in the rare gases, I: Permeability of various glasses to helium, *J. Am. Chem. Soc. 54,* 3887–3901.

Urry, W. D. (1933) Further studies in the rare gases, II: Diffusion of helium through crystalline substances and the molecular flow through rock masses, *J. Am. Chem. Soc. 55,* 3242–3249.

Urry, W. D. (1936*a*) Determination of the radium content of rocks, *J. Chem. Phys. 4,* 40–48.

Urry, W. D. (1936*b*) Ages by the helium method, II: Post Keweenawan, *Bull. Geol. Soc. Amer. 47,* 1217–1233.

Urry, W. D. (1941*a*) The radio-elements in the water and sediments of the ocean (abstract), *Phys. Rev. 59,* 479.

Urry, W. D. (1941*b*) Heat energy from radioactive sources in the earth, *J. Wash. Acad. Sci. 31,* 273–284.

Urry, W. D., and C. S. Piggot (1942) Radioactivity of ocean sediments, V: Concentration of the radio-elements and their significance in red clay, *Am. J. Sci. 240,* 93–103.

Urry, W. D. (1949*a*) Significance of radioactivity in geophysics. Thermal history of the earth, *Trans. Am. Geophys. Union 30,* 171–179.

Urry, W. D. (1949*b*) Radioactivity of ocean sediments, VI: Concentration of the radioelements in marine sediments of the southern hemisphere, *Am. J. Sci. 247,* 257–275.

Utterback, C. L., and L. A. Sanderman (1948) Radium analyses of mineral sediments in northern Pacific and adjacent waters, *J. Marine Research 7,* 635–643.

Vening Meinesz, F. A. (1950) A remarkable feature of the earth's topography, *Proc. Koninkl. Ned. Akad. Wetenschap. 53,* 973–974.

Vening Meinesz, F. A. (1951) A remarkable feature of the earth's topography, origin of continents and oceans, *ibid. 54,* 212–228.

Vening Meinesz, F. A. (1952) Convection currents in the earth and the origin of the continents, *ibid. 55,* 527–553.

Verhoogen, J. (1946) Volcanic heat, *Am. J. Sci. 244,* 745–771.

Victoreen, J. A. (1949) Ionization chambers, *Proc. Inst. Radio Engrs. 37,* 189–199.

Vinogradov, A. P., I. K. Zadorozhnyi, and S. I. Zykov (1952) Izotopnyi sostav svintsov i vozrast zemli [The isotopic composition of leads and the age of the earth], *Doklady Akad. Nauk S.S.S.R. 87,* 1107–1110.

Wack, Monique (1952) Dosage du potassium à l'aide de son rayonnement beta dans les sels naturels de potasse [Potassium analysis of natural salts of potassium by beta radiation], *Ann. géophys. 8,* 337–341.

Walton, G. N. (1952) The efficiency of an immersion counter for measuring beta and gamma emitters in solution, *Physica 18,* 1280–1286.

Waring, C. L., and Helen Worthing (1953) A spectrographic method for determining trace amounts of lead in zircon and other minerals, *Am. Mineralogist 38,* 827.

Wasserburg, G. J., and R. J. Hayden (1954) The branching ratio of K^{40}, *Phys. Rev. 93,* 645.

Waters, A. C., and H. C. Granger (1953) Volcanic debris in uraniferous sandstones and its possible bearing on the origin and precipitation of uranium, *U. S. Geol. Survey Circ. 224,* 26 pp.

Watson, J. H. L. (1947) Electron microscope observations of the morphology of several gases polymerized by charged particle bombardment, *J. Phys. & Colloid Chem. 51,* 654–661.

Westergård, A. H. (1944) Borrningar genom alunskifferlagret på Öland och i Östergotland, 1943 [Borings through the alum shale deposits on Öland and in Östergotland, 1943], *Sveriges Geol. Undersökn., Ser. C. Avhandl. och Uppsat. no. 463; Årsbok 38,* 18 pp.

Wetherill, G. W. (1953) Spontaneous fission yields from uranium and thorium, *Phys. Rev. 92,* 907–912.

Wheeler, H. P., Jr., and L. B. Swenarton (1952) Helium, bibliography of technical and scientific literature from its discovery (1868) to January 1, 1947, *U. S. Bur. Mines Bull. 484,* 76 pp.

Whitehead, W. L., and I. A. Breger (1950) The origin of petroleum: Effects of low temperature pyrolysis on the organic extracts of a recent marine sediment, *Science 111,* 335–337.

Whitehead, W. L., Clark Goodman, and I. A. Breger (1951) The decomposition of fatty acids by alpha particles, *J. chim. phys. 48,* 184–189.

Whitham, K. (1952) The application of recent counting techniques to geophysical research, II: Laboratory scintillation counters applied to some geophysical problems, *Trans. Am. Geophys. Union 33,* 902–911.

Wickman, F. E. (1939) Some graphs on the calculation of geological age, *Sveriges Geol. Undersökn., Ser. C. Avhandl. och Uppsat. no. 427; Årsbok 33,* no. 7, 8 pp.

Wickman, F. E. (1942) On the emanating power and the measurement of geologic time, *Geol. Fören. i Stockholm Förh. 64,* 465–476.

Wiesner, R. (1939) Bestimmung des Radiumgehaltes von Algen [Determination of the radium content of algae], *Sitzber. Akad. Wiss. Wien, math.-naturw. Kl., Abt. IIa,* 147, 521–528.

Wiles, D. R., B. W. Smith, R. Horsley, and H. G. Thode (1953) Fission yields of the stable and long lived isotopes of Cs, Rb, and Sr and nuclear shell structure, *Can. J. Phys. 31,* 419–431.

Williams, G. A., and J. B. Ferguson (1922) The diffusion of hydrogen and helium through silica glass and other glasses, *J. Am. Chem. Soc. 44,* 2160–2167.

Williams, H. (1932) Geology of the Lassen Volcanic National Park, California, *Univ. Calif. (Berkeley), Bull. Dept. Geol. Sci. 21,* no. 8, 195–385.

Wilson, E. E., V. C. Rhoden, W. W. Vaughn, and H. Faul (in press) Portable scintillation counters for geologic use, *U. S. Geol. Survey Circular.*

Winn, E. B., and A. O. Nier (1949) Simplified emission regulator for mass-spectrometer ion sources, *Rev. Sci. Instr. 20,* 773–774.

Wood, D. O. (1911) Liberation of helium from minerals by the action of heat, *Proc. Roy. Soc. (London) A84,* 70–78.

Wyllie, M. R. J. (1952) Procedures for the direct employment of neutron log data in electric log interpretation, *Geophysics 17,* 790–805.

Yagoda, H. (1946*a*) The localization of uranium and thorium minerals in polished section, I: The alpha ray emission pattern, *Am. Mineralogist 31,* 87–124.

Yagoda, H. (1946*b*) Radiocolloid aggregates in uranium minerals, *Am. Mineralogist 31,* 462–470.

Yagoda, H., and N. Kaplan (1947) Fading of latent alpha ray image in emulsions, *Phys. Rev. 71,* 910–911.

Yagoda, H. (1949) *Radioactive Measurements with Nuclear Emulsions,* John Wiley & Sons, New York, 356 pp.

Zeuner, F. E. (1950) Dating the past by radioactive carbon, *Nature 166,* 756–757.

Zeuner, F. E. (1951) Archaeological dating by radioactive carbon, *Science Prog. 39,* no. 154, 225–238.

Zeuner, F. E. (1952) *Dating the Past,* Methuen, London, 495 pp.

Zobell, C. E. (1947) Microbial transformation of molecular hydrogen in marine sediments, with particular reference to petroleum, *Bull. Am. Assoc. Petroleum Geol. 31,* 1709–1751.

INDEX*

* Abbreviations: r = radioactive, R = radioactivity. Principal references to any subject are in *italics*.

Abbreviations: *r* = radioactive, *R* = radioactivity. Principal references to any subject are in *italics*.

Abbreviations: *r* = radioactive, *R* = radioactivity. Principal references to any subject are in *italics*.

Abbreviations: *r* = radioactive, *R* = radioactivity. Principal references to any subject are in *italics*.

Abbreviations: *r* = radioactive, *R* = radioactivity. Principal references to any subject are in *italics*.